PLASTICS-IN-BUILDING HANDBOOK

Plastics-in-Building Handbook

Compiled by

W. S. Penn, B.Sc.

MACLAREN & SONS, LTD.
LONDON

©

1964, W. S. Penn

Made and printed in the Republic of Ireland by Hely Thom Limited.

691.175 P

MACLAREN & SONS, LTD.
LONDON

CONTENTS

		Page
	PREFACE	vii
	ACKNOWLEDGMENTS	ix
Part 1	OUTLINE OF PLASTICS	1
Part 2	ROADS AND FLOORING	19
Part 3	WALLS	73
Part 4	ROOFS AND CEILINGS	109
Part 5	PLUMBING	137
Part 6	INTERIOR FITTINGS	227
Part 7	PLASTICS ON BUILDING SITES	241
Part 8	PLASTIC FINISHES	248
Part 9	STRUCTURAL WORK	283
	ADVERTISERS' ANNOUNCEMENTS	299
	DIRECTORY OF MANUFACTURERS AND SUPPLIERS	311
	GENERAL INDEX	323

PREFACE

Much interest has arisen recently in the use of plastics in the building industry, which is, of course, a desirable trend. The more prefabrication the better.

At the same time only the more obvious and spectacular uses come to general notice such as flooring, pipes, foams (for insulation) and the occasional polyester spire or tank. Plastics have much more to offer than this. There are hundreds of applications and the list grows daily.

Unfortunately the average user can only become aware of this through journals which he perhaps does not retain; through manufacturers' literature and the visits of manufacturers' representatives. The amount of literature is great and naturally biased, which is perhaps rather confusing. Moreover, users have no yardstick with which to compare.

This handbook is designed to overcome these difficulties. In the first place and for the first time a systematic classification of products into groups and sub-groups has been made. Thus a user, if he so desires, need only concern himself with the products he wishes to use. In the second place the technical advantages of using plastics instead of other materials are given, which provides one yardstick. Another yardstick is detailed technical descriptions of several manufacturers' products (for each object) so that a comparison can be made.

The book is meant for all those concerned with the building industry. This includes architects, builders, surveyors, builders merchants, plumbers, designers, etc. There are technical articles on all subjects; there are lists of suppliers of products and services; there is a detailed description of some manufacturers products within each group and there are practical details on laying pipes and floors, methods of jointing, welding, etc.

Although an architect or user may at this moment be interested in specific products only, a persual of the book will unquestionably suggest other applications to him. The plastics industry has much to offer and it is hoped that this handbook will channel information in a compact form from the plastics industry to the building industry. It should, of course, be stressed that the plastics industry is changing rapidly and sometimes, therefore, certain information may already be out of date. This will be corrected with each new edition, but in the meantime, once a user has made a choice, he should write to one or two selected manufacturers for confirmation of details given.

IMPORTANT NOTE

The names of many manufacturers are given in this book but it is not claimed that any list is complete. The exclusion of any names does not imply any reflection on the companies concerned but is merely due to the fact that their names have not been drawn to our attention. Any such companies are invited to send details of their products for the next edition.

Although every effort has been made to be accurate there will inevitably be changes between the receipt of information and publication. Where changes have occurred the companies concerned are invited to send us regular details of changes so that they may be incorporated in the next edition.

Under each heading it has only been possible to give details of the products of some of the companies due to lack of space. There is no implication in this that the products of one company are superior to those of any other company. It may be possible to include further details in the next edition and all companies are invited to send details.

Although to the best of our knowledge there are few products whose use is restricted by patents we cannot guarantee this, and if there is any doubt at all the companies concerned should be contacted.

Many details of products and techniques are given in the book. The information is given without engagement and we cannot vouch for the claims of the contributing companies.

ACKNOWLEDGEMENTS

I would first of all like to thank the hundreds of companies concerned for their co-operation in the production of this book. In many cases their literature has been directly included in the text. It would serve no useful purpose to include their names in this general acknowledgement, but in every case their products are described under their own company product names which is my acknowledgement to them.

There are two general publications from which I have gleaned much useful information although none of the actual text has been used. These are the "Plastics in Building" brochures produced by Imperial Chemical Industries Ltd., and the excellent catalogues produced for the "Building Exhibition" (1961 and 1963) by The Building Trades Exhibition Ltd.

I am very much indebted to the editors and proprietors of various journals for readily agreeing to the reprinting of parts of many of my articles which first appeared in their journals. I must thank in particular Mr. H. Ryland of the *Plumbing Trade Journal,* Mr. Leo Newbold of *Industrial Architecture* and Mr. Roy Pearl of *Flooring and Finishes News* (Roy Pearl Ltd.).

Finally, I should like to thank the editorial staff of Maclaren and Sons Ltd. for editing the book, and my wife Kathleen for the excellent way in which she sorted and typed a complex manuscript.

March, 1964   W. S. PENN

Part 1

OUTLINE OF PLASTICS

CONTENTS

1.1 Introduction

1.2 Outline of Handbook

1.3 The Different Plastics

1.3.1 PVC

1.3.2 "Perspex"

1.3.3 Polythene

1.3.4 Phenolic and Similar Plastics

1.3.5 Polystyrene

1.3.6 Epoxy Resins

1.3.7 Polyesters

1.3.8 Plastic Foams

1.3.9 Nylon

1.3.10 PTFE

1.3.11 Silicones

1.3.12 Natural and Synthetic Rubbers

1.3.13 Plastic-coated Metals

Part 1

OUTLINE OF PLASTICS

1.1 Introduction

It is probably true to say that the building industry, with one major exception, is still largely employing conventional materials. At the same time it cannot but be aware of the impact that plastics are making in a number of departments. Some of these will be immediately obvious, but others are not so well known although they warrant careful consideration.

The main exception referred to is pvc flooring. Although it is not possible to give statistics there can be little doubt that a large proportion of houses, and public and industrial buildings being built today are provided with pvc floors of one type or another. Undoubtedly this development will continue to grow.

Some other developments which will also be fairly well known include pvc rainwater goods, polythene film for damp courses and other purposes, plastic pipes, plastic foams for insulation, various lavatory goods and so on. These are examples of a wide range which is continually increasing.

Amidst all this activity in these new materials, the architect and builder will no doubt be puzzled by the conflicting stories they hear about "plastics". In some cases claims are made that plastics will outlast conventional materials by many years or that they are unbreakable and, on the other hand, there will be many stories of plastic goods (particularly lavatory seats) breaking very quickly. Both accounts are true which is brought about by two main reasons. In the first place there is a general lack of knowledge about plastics since there are many kinds and each one must be employed for its correct sphere of duty or trouble may be experienced. The second reason is that many plastics were developed rapidly in the immediate post-war years and some of the materials and products made at that time undoubtedly gave trouble. There has, however, been considerable development over the years and, although it cannot be claimed that there are no troubles, it can be said that in many cases the products will give trouble-free service for the life of the building.

The object of this book is to give an outline of the plastics industry and to indicate where the materials should be used in the building industry.

1.2 Outline of Handbook

The main purpose of the book, however, is to bring plastics to the notice of the building trade. It is proposed to cover all aspects of the industry, ranging from the architect designing buildings to the builder on the site and the builders' merchants from whom the various products are obtained.

The book covers the following general subjects:—

Part 1. Outline of Plastics. (This gives an indication of the nature of each type of material and where it is used).

Part 2. Roads and Flooring. (Apart from pvc floors, this section deals with continuous epoxy resin floors and similar types).

Part 3. Walls. (The application of cladding products and plastic finishes for walls).

Part 4. Roofs and Ceilings. (In this section such products as roof-lights, foam insulation for roofs, ceiling coverings and acoustic tiles are dealt with).

Part 5. Plumbing. (Rainwater goods, plastic pipes, lavatory goods, foams for lagging and bathroom fittings are covered in this section).

Part 6. Interior Fittings. (Dealing with small moulded accessories, such as electrical fittings, door handles and the like).

Part 7. Plastics on Building Sites. (This part is mainly concerned with the use of polythene sheeting as working canopies, underlays, damp courses, temporary glazing and so on).

Part 8. Plastic Finishes. (Protective finishes for walls, sealing compounds and various adhesives are dealt with).

Part 9. Structural Work. (This deals with the application of plastics for structural work, particularly the use of laminated plastics in timber engineering and polyester/glass-fibre products).

Each part provides a general introduction to the subject saying why and where the materials are used. Detailed advice on the correct use of products and detailed methods of installation are also given. Finally, the names of suppliers of the products referred to are given in the appropriate sections, whilst an alphabetical list of suppliers with addresses is given at the end of the book.

It may well be that the architect or builder may have in mind using only a limited number of plastic products. However, following a study of the general information given in each of the sections, there is no doubt that ideas will be gleaned as to where plastics may be used more extensively to advantage over conventional materials.

1.3　The Different Plastics

Plastics may be divided into two main types. This division is very important since it affects the conditions under which certain of the plastics may be employed.

There are thermosetting plastics and thermoplastics. A thermoplastic, when heated, will soften and sometimes melt but on returning to the original temperature it will harden again. This process may be repeated any number of times provided the decomposition point of the plastic is not exceeded. On the other hand, thermosetting plastics do not soften when heat is applied and they retain their form.

To appreciate the importance of these different qualities it means, for example, that if a hot iron be placed on a pvc floor, then the floor will be seriously damaged. The same iron on a "Formica" laminated plastic floor will not, generally speaking, cause damage. The following lists give the two types of plastics, according to the above division, which are mentioned in this handbook:—

Thermosetting Plastics	*Thermoplastics*
Epoxy resins	PVC
Polyester resins	Polystyrene
Synthetic rubbers	"Perspex"
Silicones	Polythene
Polyurethanes	Polypropylene
Phenolics (often referred to as	Nylon
"Bakelite")	PTFE
Urea and Melamine plastics	
Laminated plastics	

Because the thermoplastics soften at elevated temperatures, each one of them has a maximum temperature above which it must not be used. This temperature is given in the appropriate section but, as an example, it may be stated that plastic pipes for hot-water systems have not yet been seriously developed because of the thermoplastic nature of the materials employed. Even thermosetting plastics have temperatures above which they must not be used, but this is not because they soften but because, in time, they will chemically decompose. Their maximum working temperatures, however, are usually considerably higher than those of thermoplastics.

Apart from the chemical aspect, most plastics may readily be recognized by their appearance, physical characteristics or uses, and they will therefore be normally described from these points of view.

1.3.1 PVC (*Polyvinyl chloride*)

This is perhaps the best known of the plastics used in the building industry and it is also sometimes known under the name of "vinyl". The material is employed in two main forms—flexible and rigid types. The latter is based on the same basic chemical as the former but has no plasticizer (i.e. softener) in it. Because of this composition difference, the rigid type is often known as "unplasticized pvc" and the flexible type as "plasticized pvc".

The flexible variety will be recognized as that used for raincoats, hose and the like, whilst the latter is employed for rainwater goods and pipes for cold-water systems.

The density of pvc is approximately 1·4, which means that it is relatively light compared with many other building materials. Rigid pvc pipes and the like are therefore easy to carry. All forms of pvc are highly resistant to a variety of solvents, they are normally non-inflammable, can be highly coloured and are weather resistant. Abrasion resistance is also good so that the material can be expected to have a long life even when used out-of-doors.

Whether rigid or flexible, the material is a thermoplastic and details of its limiting temperature are given in the section on pvc pipes. A word of explanation is also required regarding flame resistance. When this term is applied to plastics, it usually means that a product will burn while in a flame but extinguish itself when it is removed from the flame.

The material is used in the building industry for such products as floor tiles, continuous floors, wall tiles, plastic sheet wall coverings, plastic covered hardboards, profile sections for wall cladding, extrusions for the protection of window frames, films for the protection of fencing and gates, rainwater goods, plastic pipes and a variety of other minor products.

Manufacturers

The primary manufacturers of the basic pvc in the United Kingdom are:— Bakelite Ltd.; British Geon Ltd.; I.C.I. Ltd.; Shell Chemical Co. Ltd. These suppliers are usually prepared to give full details of their products.

1.3.2 "Perspex"

This material is best known in the form of transparent corrugated sheet for roof and wall cladding. Actually, "Perspex" is the trade name of I.C.I. Ltd., so that the chemical term "acrylics" is sometimes used to describe the material.

Another well known use for acrylics is for the manufacture of bathroom fittings, particularly baths themselves and wash basins. These applications give a clue to their properties.

The products are weather resistant and reasonably abrasion resistant, although the material does scratch fairly readily but this cannot always be seen. It can be transparent (92% transmission) which makes it ideally suitable for cladding applications, but it can be given opaque, transparent or translucent colours to give it the highly attractive finish so well known with baths.

The acrylics must be used in their proper context since they tend to have poor impact strength. The softening point is also relatively low and boiling water could cause damage. The solvent resistance is moderate although the water resistance is excellent. The action of some solvents can be an advantage since the material is readily machined and the parts can be cemented together to form a wide range of products. In this connection, the material is similar to rigid pvc, both of which can be cut up and fabricated "on site" where necessary.

Manufacturers

The only manufacturer of acrylics in the U.K. is I.C.I. Ltd. The American equivalent—Oroglas—is marketed in the U.K. by Charles Lennig and Co. (G.B.) Ltd.

1.3.3 Polythene

The next best known material is polythene, often referred to by its chemical name of polyethylene. The normal material has a density of about 0·92 which makes it extremely light. It is one of the most highly resistant of the plastics to chemicals and water which gives a clue to its use. It is accordingly popular for use as pipes for cold-water plumbing and as film for damp courses. Since it is relatively cheap and can be calendered into thin films of about 0·001 in. thick, the film made from it is widely employed as canopies and the like on building sites. Film of this thickness is not very strong but thicker and stronger films are available if required.

In recent years a product known as high-density (H.D.) polythene has become available. Consequently, the normal polythene is often referred to as low-density material. The main difference between the two is that the high-density variety can be used at rather higher temperatures. It has found its main use in moulded products such as bowls and buckets as well as pipes through which hot water can be carried, but not under pressure.

Yet another material which looks very much like polythene is polypropylene. This has similar properties except that it can be used at much higher temperatures, probably up to 130–140°C. (80–90°C. for low-density polythene and 110°C. for high-density polythene). At the moment, the use of the material is confined to moulded products but it is hoped that it may ultimately be employed for hot-water pipe installations. For chemical reasons this cannot be done at the moment but the idea should be carefully watched.

Manufacturers

The principal manufacturers of these products in the United Kingdom are:—I.C.I. Ltd.; Bakelite Ltd.; Shell Chemical Co. Ltd.; Monsanto Chemical Co. Ltd.; Distillers Co. Ltd. (British Resin Products Ltd.).

1.3.4 Phenolic and Similar Plastics

Phenolic resins are thermosetting and are frequently referred to under the trade name "Bakelite". The materials are best known as mouldings, particularly for switches and other electrical fittings.

A much more valuable form of the products for building purposes is when they are combined with paper and other fillers. If certain varieties of paper are impregnated with phenolic resins, a number of sheets can be plied together and heat and pressure applied to form a "laminate". This is a strong board-like product which, in a corrugated form, is used for wall cladding. Similar materials are used for partitioning.

The phenolic and similar resins are restricted to dark colours. Because of this, the urea and melamine types of plastics were developed and have similar properties except that they can be transparent, or given a wide range of colours. When combined with cloth or paper bearing designs, then they give the well-known decorative laminaess. All of these have excellent resistance to domestic fluids, cigarette burns and the like.

Manufacturers

Some of the principal firms manufacturing these products are:—Bakelite Ltd.; I.C.I. Ltd.; British Resin Products Ltd.; Birkbys Ltd.; James Ferguson Ltd.; B.I.P. Chemicals Ltd.; Sterling Moulding Materials Ltd.

1.3.5 Polystyrene

This material is not so readily recognized but it is very light and available in a number of forms. For example, as a moulding it is used as light trays inside refrigerators and cupboards. However, it is fairly brittle, although this can be improved by various modifications, and should not normally be used where impact strength is likely to be required.

The most important form in which it will be encountered is as polystyrene

2

foam. This has a low density (down to about 1 lb./cu. ft.) and the rigid product in block or sheet form is used extensively for thermal insulation. This application will be described in detail in other sections.

Manufacturers

The principal manufacturers of polystyrene are:—Monsanto Chemicals Ltd.; Shell Chemical Co. Ltd.; Sterling Moulding Materials Ltd.; Mobil Chemicals Ltd.

1.3.6   Epoxy Resins

These materials are not at present well known to the architect and builder. Their two principal forms in building are for the manufacture of screeds for flooring and as highly resistant paints.

In flooring, a screed made from an epoxy resin and sand has a high resistance to the effects of vehicular traffic, a wide variety of chemicals and dampens noise. Much lesser thicknesses than with concrete can be employed, giving a big weight saving so that the products are likely to have extensive use in multi-story buildings.

Paints in which epoxy resins are used, although expensive, have a life of from 5 to 10 years on walls or floors.

Manufacturers

The principal suppliers of the products are:—Bakelite Ltd.; CIBA (A.R.L.), Ltd.; Leicester Lovell and Co. Ltd.; Shell Chemical Co. Ltd.; J. M. Steel & Co. Ltd.

1.3.7   Polyesters

These materials are well known under the name of glass-fibre products. The polyesters are the resins and various forms of glass fibres are combined with them to give a range of very strong products. Such products are also light, can be obtained in colours and are chemical and weather resistant. At the present time they are best known in corrugated form as roof and wall lights. They are sometimes employed for guttering and being so simple to form into complex shapes there is no reason why they should not be adopted extensively over a wide field. The strength of these materials would indicate their possibilities for structural purposes. They have already been employed for certain small buildings and this aspect is discussed in Part 9. There are firms who are prepared to consider the manufacture of tanks, stacks, guttering, roof lights, dustbins and many other products to customer's design. Details may be obtained from Wembley Fibreglass and Plastics Ltd.

Manufacturers

The principal suppliers of polyester resins are:—British Resin Products Ltd.; Bakelite Ltd.; Beck, Koller and Co. (England) Ltd.; Scott, Bader and Co. Ltd.; United Coke and Chemicals Co. Ltd.; J. M. Steel and Co. Ltd.; W. A. Mitchell and Smith Ltd.

1.3.8 *Plastic Foams*

Foams are of great value in the building industry, mainly for thermal insulation. Detailed uses are given in Sections 2.6.2 (floors), 3.7 (walls), 4.4 (roofs), and 5.6 (plumbing). Some general aspects of this important subject are considered below.

The earliest foam in use was, of course, the natural sponge. This was only used, however, for washing purposes, mainly because of its cost and its unsatisfactory technical properties. When chemists first learned to make plastics they soon appreciated that foams for sponges could be made artificially but their early efforts were only directed towards imitating the natural product for washing purposes.

In due course, it was realized that, since the chemical process could be closely controlled, the properties of the sponges could also be controlled within wide limits. After this realization, the development of foams (or expanded products as they are called in preference to "sponges") grew rapidly and today we have at our disposal a wide range of products.

The most common plastic foams are known as the polyurethanes and polystyrene. Others include expanded pvc, natural and synthetic rubbers, cellulose, phenolic and urea types, and many others. The first two mentioned are the most important and will be considered in some detail.

General Purposes and Uses

There are many foams available today which would be confusing to the user were it not possible to reduce them to a system. In the first place, there are the various chemical types mentioned above, the two most important being the polyurethane and polystyrene foams. The former is thermosetting (cannot be softened by heat) and the latter is thermoplastic, which means that it can be softened by heat and the cell structure will collapse. All foams can be divided into these two types.

The next main variable is the density of the foam. By varying the degree of expansion of the products, densities ranging from 2 lb./cu. ft. up to about 60 lb./cu. ft. can be made. The softer they are (or less dense) the less load they will bear and vice versa.

The foams can also be of the open cell type or the closed cell type. In the former case the cells are communicating, which means that the product acts as a sponge. In turn, this means that the products are not suitable for use in water unless, of course, used as a filter or a sponge. On the other hand, the foams with closed cells are suitable for use in water and pick up very little when immersed.

The uses of foams vary a great deal. The most important application is undoubtedly thermal insulation whether this be to retain heat or exclude heat. The "K" value or thermal conductivity of most of the products is very low indeed. This use is, of course, the one likely to be of greatest interest to the building trade but draught or odour exclusion are other interesting fields. Even filtration could possibly be of value as will be discussed later.

Polyurethane Foams

The flexible foams sold so widely in shops at the present time are likely to be the polyurethanes. Merely for purposes of definition it may be stated that all polyurethane foams are based on chemicals known as isocyanates which are reacted with other chemicals, usually polyesters or polyethers. Both types of sponges made are thermosetting.

Raw materials for making the foams are sold by:

> J. M. Steel and Co. Ltd.
> I.C.I. Ltd.
> Shell Chemical Co. Ltd.
> The Baxenden Chemical Co. Ltd.
> Guest Industrials Ltd.

One important point in the manufacture may be noted. The blowing agents employed are usually either carbon dioxide or fluorinated hydrocarbons (the Freons of Du Pont). The former gives higher "K" values than the latter, examples being 0.26 and 0.15 respectively (units in B.Th.U. in./ft.^{2}h. °F).

These foams are resistant to attack by fungi, moulds, termites and rodents. They are quite resistant to most chemicals, including petrol, diesel oil, alkalis and acids, and many organic solvents. Exceptions include ketones and chlorinated hydrocarbons.

These foams may be used up to temperatures of about 120°C. for prolonged periods, although the support of compressive loads should not be undertaken at temperatures in excess of 110°C. So far as fire-resistant characteristics are concerned, the foams burn in a flame but are self-extinguishing when the flame is removed.

The foams are odourless, hygienic, and resistant to detergents and dry cleaning. They are usually flexible (although they can be made rigid) so that if they are crushed by a load they will return to their original shape when the load is removed. Some properties of a typical polyurethane foam are given below.

Properties of Polyurethane (Clocel P.E.2) Foam

Density, lb. per cu. ft.	2·1
Tensile strength, psi	44·0
Elongation, %	3·8
Compressive yield strength (yield point at 9% deflection)	43·4
Closed cell content, %	90
Water absorption 6 in. cub.—4 ft. head for 14 days, % vol./vol.	1·0
K value (original) at 75°F.	0·11
K value (after ageing) at 75°F.	0·145

Polystyrene Foams

These foams are also widely used and are available from stockists. The differences between polystyrene and polyurethane which affect their performance must be stated at once. The main difference is that the polystyrene is thermoplastic. If excessive heat is applied to it, then the cell structure will permanently collapse. However, a safe maximum working temperature may be taken as about 175°F.

The other big difference is that the polytsyrene foams are normally rigid although a sheet will take a certain amount of bend. The rigidity also means that if the product is crushed it will not return to its original position. Where blows are to be expected, therefore, the material must be protected.

As far as other properties are concerned, one of the most important is that polystyrene is very resistant to water. It functions quite well as a water vapour barrier, even in the highest humidity. Simultaneously, the product is an excellent thermal insulant and is as good and in some cases better than polyurethane.

The material is highly resistant to many chemicals, including alkalis and acids (except concentrated nitric acid) sea water and alcohol. It is, nevertheless, badly affected by certain solvents, which include ketones, esters, chlorinated hydrocarbons, ethers and aromatic hydrocarbons (the most common being benzene and toluene).

The plastic is odourless and does not absorb odours. It is completely resistant to fungi and provides no sustenance for termites. Its weakness has already being mentioned, however, and it could be pecked by birds unless protection is afforded.

A defect of the normal grade is that it supports combustion. Special grades are produced, therefore, which are non-inflammable. Thermal properties are, of course, excellent and are discussed in detail later. Some properties of polystyrene foams are given below.

Properties of Polystyrene Foams (Baxenden Chemical Co. Ltd.)

Density, lb./cu. ft.	1·0	2·0
Compressive yield strength, psi	7·7	21·8
Impact strength, in. lb./in. unnotched	0·023	0·047
Tensile Strength, psi	21·3	53·0
Coefficient of linear thermal expansion °C.	$2·1 \times 10^{-5}$	
K value		
Water absorption, % (after 12 days immersion)	2·3	2·6

The most important application, although by no means the only one, is thermal insulation. The foams may be employed to keep products cool or to keep them hot, depending on the end use. Extremes of temperature which can be catered for are +250°F. (polyurethanes) or +175°F. (polystyrene) down to almost any temperature—minus 125°F. is possible.

Many of the plastic foams contain up to 98% still air. If the fact that the cells (pores) can be made non-communicating is realised, then it will be appreciated that the degree of thermal insulation is great. In the table below, a comparison is made between various foamed plastics and more conventional insulating materials.

The K value mentioned is the thermal conductivity expressed in B.Th.U. in./h./ft.² °F. It will be seen that expanded plastics are available which are far superior to any standard materials. It should be noted, however, that it is possible to obtain foams with widely varying K values and this point should be discussed with the suppliers of the materials. The nearest approach to foamed plastics from the insulating point of view is glass wool, but this is extremely costly as well as rather an undesirable material to handle. The plastic foams are making great headway against all materials.

Thermal Insulating Properties of Foams and Other Materials

Material	Density, lb./cu. ft.	K Value
Polyurethane foam (rigid)	4·0	0·22
Polyurethane foam (rigid)	10·0	0·24
Polyurethane foam (rigid)	24·0	0·33
Polyurethane foam (Clocel P.E.2)	2·1	0·11
Polystyrene foam (Poron P. 30)	2·0	0·2
Polystyrene foam (Poron P. 20)	1·25	0·22
Polystyrene foam (Poron P. 15)	1·0	0·23
Glass wool	5·0	0·23
Cork board	8·75	0·32
Hardboard	60·0	0·71
Plaster board	60·0	1·1
Asbestos cement sheeting	96·0	1·9
Roofing felt	50·0	4·0

An interesting point about the thermal insulation of plastic foams is that it actually improves as the temperature decreases. This is illustrated below.

Variation of Insulation Properties with Temperature (for "Styrocell")

Temperature, °F.	K Value
50	0·24
0	0·21
—27	0·19
—40	0·18
—126	0·14

One final advantage of plastic foams—in refrigeration—may be mentioned. Considerably less foam is required to insulate than conventional materials. This not only saves cost but space and gives more internal room for storage.

Suppliers

There is quite a large number of suppliers of plastic foams and their products are discussed in detail later. Most of them supply either polystyrene or polyurethane foam in a variety of forms. A list of suppliers is given below.

Company	Material	Application	Trade Name
The Baxenden Chemical Co. Ltd.	Polystyrene and polyurethane	Insulation and building, etc.	Spandoplast and Clocel
Bells Asbestos and Engineering Ltd.	Polyurethane	Pipe insulation	Raplag

Company	Material	Application	Trade Name
Coopers Plastic Foams Ltd.	Polyurethane (polyether and polyester)	Upholstery, washers, insulation and filtration	Coolag and Coofilt
Declon Foam Plastics Ltd.	Polyurethane	Filtration	Scott Industrial Foam
Expanded Rubber and Plastics Ltd.	Polystyrene	Insulation, packaging, buoyancy, and shuttering	Polyzote
Flamingo Foam Ltd. (Monsanto)	Polystyrene	Building (insulation)	Flamingo
Guest Industrials Ltd. (AB Bofors Nobelkrut)	Polyurethane	Sound and thermal insulation, upholstery, etc.	Lockfoam
I.C.I. Ltd.	Polyurethane	Chemicals for making foams *in situ*	Daltolac and Suprasec
Microcell Ltd. (BTR)	Polyurethane (polyether) and pvc	Insulation, buoyancy etc.	Plasticell and Crestafoam
Newalls Insulation Co. Ltd.	Polyurethane and polystyrene	Insulation	Newalls XPX
Poron Insulation Ltd.	Polystyrene	Thermal, packaging, etc.	Poron
Sealdraught Ltd.	Polyurethane	Self-adhesive dust excluder and anti-vibration mounting	Tesamoll
Semtex Ltd.	—	Pipe insulation	Foamflex
Shell Chemical Co. Ltd.	Polystyrene	Building, packaging and others	Styrocell
Venesta Manufacturing Ltd.	Polyurethane (raw materials only)		

Company	Material	Application	Trade Name
J. M. Steel & Co. Ltd.	Polyurethane	Building, upholstery, insulation, etc. (chemicals for producing foam *in situ*)	
Thermalon Ltd.	Urea-Formalde-hyde	Insulation	Thermalon
Ruberoid Ltd.	Polystyrene	Insulation, building	Ruberfoam
Robinson Bros. Cork Growers Ltd.	Polystyrene	Insulation, building	Superlite
Warmafoam Ltd.	Polystyrene	Insulation, building	Warmafoam
Jablo Group Sales Ltd.	Polystyrene	Insulation	Jablite
The Wall Paper Manufacturers Ltd.	Polystyrene	Insulation	Kotina

Forms Available

Some details of specific forms available are given later. It is useful, however, to have a general idea in which forms the foams are sold since this indicates not only where the foams can be used at present but where they may be used in the future. It is probably true to say that almost any required form or shape will be provided on request. Some general details are given below.

Polyurethanes
(1) As liquids for foaming *in situ*.
(2) Shaped cylindrical sections for fitting round pipes.
(3) As sheets, say $\frac{1}{12}$ in. up to 4 in. thick and 36 in. to 79 in. wide and varying lengths, often quite long (say, 250 yards).
(4) Strips with self-adhesive backing.
(5) Prefabricated shapes as cushions, mattresses, etc.
(6) Large blocks.
(7) Specially tailored products for fitting in standard filter fittings (for example).

Polystyrene
(1) Pellets for expansion during moulding by heat.
(2) Standard sheets in thicknesses from $\frac{1}{4}$ in. up to 12 in. and sizes of, say, 9 ft. × 4 ft.; 4 ft. × 4 ft.; 3 ft. × 2 ft.; 2 ft. × 1 ft. and many others.
(3) Expanded beads or pellets for mixing with concrete to make it light.
(4) Strips up to, say, 2 ft. wide and many lengths, mainly depending on transport considerations.
(5) Shaped sections for pipes.

(6) Panels for tanks.

(7) Moulded shapes, particularly for packaging articles.

PVC

(1) Flat sheets from $\frac{1}{16}$ in. up to $3\frac{1}{2}$ in. thick in widths from 12 in. up to 58 in.

(2) Strips up to 36 ft. long.

(3) Blocks $3\frac{3}{4}$ in. thick and sizes up to 6 ft. $\times$ 4 ft.

(4) Various shapes and sizes to order.

1.3.9 Nylon

This material is available in a wide variety of forms including the type used for stockings. However, in the industrial field it is best known for a number of mouldings and machined parts. In this connection its principal advantage is that it is extremely tough so that working parts of doors are made from it. These often last longer than steel and at the same time are silent in action.

Manufacturers

The principal manufacturer in the United Kingdom is I.C.I. Ltd. J. M. Steel and Co. Ltd. also sell nylon in the U.K. under the trade name "Durethan".

1.3.10 PTFE (Polytetrafluorethylene)

PTFE will not be well known to the building trade. It is highly resistant to chemicals but its principal use at the present time in the building industry is for pipe jointing. Its use eliminates the necessity for employing conventional jointing compounds and pipes can be tightened and sealed by finger pressure alone.

Manufacturers

The principal manufacturers of PTFE products in the United Kingdom are:—I.C.I. Ltd.; Du Pont (U.K.) Ltd.

1.3.11 Silicones

This material has become well known in its form of a fluid for conferring water repellency to surfaces. This aspect is considered in this handbook.

1.3.12 Natural and Synthetic Rubbers

The principal application of natural and synthetic rubbers in the building industry is as floor tiles. They have been used for many years and some attractive designs and colours are available. A synthetic rubber known as "Hypalon" can be made into tiles for use out-of-doors. Apart from possessing many similar properties to pvc tiles, floors employing such tiles are silent.

There are a number of minor applications of synthetic rubbers in the building industry, some of which will be considered. For example, butyl can be made into the form of a putty-like seal which is being adopted widely because of its excellent characteristics.

1.3.13   *Plastic-coated Metals*

A process of universal application to the building industry is that of coating metals with various plastics. More detailed technical aspects of the subject are given in Section 5.3.13 but here the examples of the type of application will help architects and builders in their thinking. Some of the products made by Plastic Coatings Ltd. are as follows:—

1. Fume Ducting—Mild steel fume ducting coated both inside and out in Vylastic RS.60 PVC. This coating is entirely corrosion resistant and will never need maintenance. With ducting above 12 in. diameter the problems of support associated with rigid pvc make the use of coated mild steel a cheaper alternative.

2. Fencing—Fencing or balustrading for use either indoors or out can be coated with pvc or nylon. Both are entirely resistant to the elements and sea water, as well as impact and abrasion. Nylon is the more decorative; pvc is preferred where resistance to acids is required in chemical plant and it is also the cheaper alternative where continuous lengths of over 7 ft. have to be coated in one piece.

3. Expanded Metal—Expanded metal can be coated in pvc or nylon and the choice of material depends upon the conditions which are to be encountered.

4. Cable Tray and Conduit—A permanent protective finish for cable tray is provided by pvc coating, which is particularly valuable wherever corrosive conditions are encountered. Coated conduit pipes and fittings are also available, and in each case pvc-coated steel combines a chemically resistant coating with the earth continuity of the substrate.

5. Welded Mesh—Welded mesh in a variety of meshes and gauges is available in pvc or nylon coating. Again, the choice of material depends on various factors, but it should be borne in mind that pvc is the thicker and more resilient of the two, whilst nylon is harder and generally more decorative— both are quite unaffected by sea water. The dipping technique ensures complete coverage.

6. Flooring—PVC-coated open-mesh flooring is becoming increasingly used in industry. Its permanent corrosion-resistant finish lasts for many years even under the most arduous conditions. The insulative nature of the coating prevents condensation in damp atmospheres and therefore eliminates the drips which are often found under overhead walkways. The non-slip finish can be impregnated with carborundum if required to provide additional safety.

7. Gutter Brackets—PVC is the coating normally applied to metal gutter brackets. This combines the corrosion resistance of pvc with the inherent strength of the metal substrate, thereby ensuring that the gutters are always firmly held even under the most severe condition of snow and ice. When used in conjunction with extruded pvc guttering the system is entirely permanent and maintenance free.

8. *Handles and Controls*—Nylon coatings are now available in a variety of bronze and silver finishes similar to conventional colours of door and window furnishings, in addition to the normal colour range. The coatings are permanent, never need polishing and will not chip. Furthermore, they are warm to the touch even in the coldest weather.

9. *Window Frames*—The introduction of nylon coating as a finishing medium on window frames means that regular repainting is eliminated, corrosion is positively prevented and overall costs reduced. The thermal barrier provided by the nylon coating prevents loss of heat through the window frame and it can be used in conjunction with double glazing.

10. *Domestic Taps*—Nylon coating is now available as a standard finish on domestic taps. A full range of colours is available to suit household decorations. The elimination of the high polishing costs associated with chromium plating makes nylon coating a most economic as well as attractive alternative.

Part 2

ROADS AND FLOORING

CONTENTS

2.1 Introduction

2.2 Vinyl Floor Tiles
    2.2.1 General Consideration
    2.2.2 Detailed Products of Some Manufacturers
    2.2.3 Laying Instructions
    2.2.4 Special Vinyl Floors
    2.2.5 Some Technical Aspects

2.3 Rubber Floor Tiles
    2.3.1 Rubber Floors, Manufacturers
    2.3.2 Special Synthetic Rubber Floors
    2.3.3 Special Floors

2.4 Epoxy (Jointless) Floors
    2.4.1 What are Epoxy Resins?
    2.4.2 Some Outstanding Properties
    2.4.3 Application Properties
    2.4.4 Some Typical Applications
    2.4.5 Materials Available
    2.4.6 Basic Flooring Components
    2.4.7 Some Practical Flooring Compositions
    2.4.8 Method of Application
    2.4.9 Suppliers of Flooring Compositions
    2.4.10 Paint Finishes

2.5 Polyester (Jointless) Floors
    2.5.1 The Resins
    2.5.2 Spraying Techniques
    2.5.3 A Typical Example ("Terrazzite")
    2.5.4 Indentation Resistance
    2.5.5 Hardness
    2.5.6 Abrasion
    2.5.7 Wear Resistance

2.6 Electric Floor Heating
    2.6.1 Methods
    2.6.2 Thermal Insulation with Foam

Part 2

ROADS AND FLOORING

2.1 Introduction

Plastics are today entering nearly all domestic and industrial fields on an increasing scale. One of the most active of these is flooring in buildings of all kinds. It would be a virtually impossible exercise to estimate how many vinyl tiles have been used in the building trade, but it must now be many millions.

The following are the types of floors, described in the Sections indicated:—

    2.2   Vinyl Floor Tiles
    2.3   Rubber Floor Tiles
    2.4   Epoxy (jointless) Floors
    2.5   Polyester (jointless) Floors
    2.6   Electric Floor Heating:
          (a) Methods
          (b) Thermal Insulation with Foam

Perhaps one of the most interesting developments in the field of plastic flooring is the use of polyester resins and epoxy resins in concrete flooring. This technique is being adopted rapidly and gives excellent results.

An indication of the extensive use of plastics in flooring was given by the Timber Development Association Ltd. This organization, and its members, must view with increasing concern the adoption of plastics in flooring, particularly on top of cement bases. They have, however, adopted the sensible view about the situation. The Association has worked on the development of a satisfactory method of laying plastic tiles, etc, on a timber subfloor. Actually this is of considerable value, since wood enables very good bonds to be achieved.

Vinyl tiles are the most important products in the laying of floors, certainly in the application of plastic and rubber fields, if not in the flooring field as a whole.

The most obvious feature of the tiles, apart from technical properties, is the extensive colour range now available. All manufacturers have taken considerable trouble in this respect, employing industrial designers to produce a modern range of colours and patterns.

Most of the companies producing vinyl tiles, also offer similar products in sheet form. Marley, for example, offer "Marleyflor" and "Marleytred", the latter with felt backing.

"Semflex" is also available in long lengths 4 ft. wide in the usual range of colours. Armstrong have their "Corlon" sheet to give a minimum of seams, as in fact do all the sheet products.

Although plastic flooring now takes first place, the merits of rubber flooring should not be forgotten. This particularly applies to some of the new synthetic materials which can give attractive, hard-wearing flooring. There are a number of possible combinations of various materials.

British Technical Cork Products illustrate an example of this combination of materials with their "Britcork", available in seven colours. It is a cork and synthetic rubber combination giving the warmth of cork and the resilience of rubber. The Bulgomme-Silence flooring gives a combination in a different way, utilizing a hard-wearing rubber surface with a fabric inter-liner and a cellular rubber backing. The flooring, of course, has great resilience and cushioning powers.

A wide range of colours can be achieved with rubber as well as pvc, some plain and some marbled. Rubber, unlike pvc, lends itself to reinforcement with suitable fillers, and high strength can be achieved. In addition, the synthetic rubber provides resistance to domestic cooking fats (and other chemicals) and the marbling goes right through the thickness of the tile. Hypalon synthetic rubber, in particular, offers considerable advantages in chemical resistance.

In terms of plastics, seamless flooring may be taken to mean compositions including resins which are laid as one whole. These usually employ polyester and epoxy resins mixed with more conventional materials, particularly asbestos. A good example of the type is the "Plastik" plastic flooring (of undisclosed composition) of Vigers Bros., Ltd. The floor is laid by them, without seams (except for expansion joints), to give a non-slip, oil- and water-resistant surface. It is trowelled on to cement, terrazzo, granolithic and other surfaces where it sets to a hard finish.

Epoxy resins are very popular for this type of flooring. A good example is that of Tretol Ltd. with their "Epiflor" which will adhere strongly to concrete and cement giving a hard surface with exceptional chemical resistance. In the case of "Epiflor" the composition is supplied to contractors for laying. Evode Ltd. supply their "Evoscreed" for similar purposes. It may be laid on to almost any type of flooring, including concrete, timber, mature asphalt floors, metal and the like to a minimum thickness of $\frac{3}{16}$ in.

Cementex (U.K.), Co. offer a remarkable range of products for preparing and repairing concrete structures. Their "Epoweld" can be used for applying to floors followed by sprinkling on silicon carbide or sand to give a hard wearing surface. "Epoxicrete" is a sand-loaded epoxy alloy which is mechanically stronger then cement and yet is "elastic". All the epoxy products contain 100% solids, an important feature, since it means that there is no loss of volume or shrinkage on setting. This company also makes "Brobond", a non-shrinking, elastic levelling agent based on Neoprene synthetic rubber.

Although many companies use epoxy resins, Plastics and Resins Ltd. use polyester resins in similar flooring compositions. The final properties of the two types of resin have much in common and both set in a short time to hard, tough products. "Certite" (Stuart B. Dickens Ltd.) resins are for jointing present concrete units. They give excellent adhesion, there is no cracking due to shrinkage and they provide thin, non-corrosive, waterproof joints.

Roads are, of course, a specialized form of "flooring". The main interest from the rubber and plastics point of view is electric heating and the use of epoxy resins. The latter is particularly prominent in giving hard wearing surfaces.

2.2 Vinyl Floor Tiles

These tiles are by far the best known and widely used. It is therefore proposed to consider them in some detail, as follows:—

2.2.1 General Considerations
2.2.2 Detailed Products of Some Manufacturers
2.2.3 Laying Instructions
2.2.4 Special Vinyl Tiles (vinyl cork, sheeting, textile backed and others)
2.2.5 Some Technical Considerations

2.2.1 General Considerations

It is probably true to say that the majority of floors laid today in offices, laboratories, schools and similar buildings are made of rubber or plastic. All architects must be aware of the revolution in flooring materials which has taken place during the past few years, particularly with plastics. An indication of this is given by the search which was made for a suitable vinyl flooring for the NATO Headquarters building in Paris. Over 200 types of floor covering manufactured by 15 NATO countries were examined before a choice was made, and this fell on "Pegulan", sold by Redfern's Rubber Works. More than 33,000 sq. yd. of this flooring were laid.

Marley thermoplastic tiles (*The Marley Tile Co Ltd*)

Why has such a change come about? There is no doubt that parquet and stone flooring are very attractive and reasonably durable. They are expensive, however, and the former in particular, needs polishing regularly to maintain the attractive finish. Plastic floors, on the other hand, need little polishing; cleaning with soap and water is often sufficient. They are also relatively cheap,

3

just as durable, considerably more so in laboratories, and available in a variety of colours and designs which cannot be approached in natural materials.

These and other properties have assured the ready acceptance of plastic and, to a lesser extent, rubber floors.

Virtually all so-called plastic tiles are based on pvc. This material is blended with a variety of fillers, mainly a special grade of asbestos, which give greater rigidity and increases resistance to damage. Many of these tiles are made in accordance with B.S.3260: 1960.

One of the advantages of these tiles is that they have great resistance to fire. They will not burn at all unless held continuously in a naked flame, and when the flame is removed they extinguish immediately. At the same time, the floors should not have very hot objects (above about 80–90°C.) placed on them, or they will be damaged.

Two other properties of these tiles are exemplified in the "Houseproud" vinyl tiles of Nairn-Williamson Ltd. As far as flexibility is concerned, the $1 \cdot 6$ mm. tiles can be bent round a 2 in.-diameter mandrel at 25°C. In the case of resistance to indentation, a force of about 3,000 p.s.i. is applied to the tiles in the form of a load of 80 lb. for 10 minutes by means of a $0 \cdot 178$ in.-diameter rod. After the load has been removed for an hour the indentation does not exceed $0 \cdot 010$ in. This is obviously very good and demonstrates resistance to loads greater than those normally to be expected.

The chemical resistance of the tiles is very good. The following materials after 24 hours on the floors have a negligible effect on them: water, soap and detergents, paraffin, petrol, white spirit, methylated spirit, washing soda, bleaching powders, hydrogen peroxide, concentrated ammonia, caustic soda, beer, milk, cooking fats, oils, blood, fruit juices and vinegar. Dilute acids will cause slight surface marking but serious damage is caused by concentrated acids and such solvents as ketones and chlorinated types.

Other interesting properties may be mentioned. Although pvc floors will not resist high temperatures, the action of a cigarette on such floors is very small. Electrical properties of such floors are good and this makes them suitable in electrical installations. Scratching resistance is also good.

There are several types of flooring available. The most common is perhaps relatively thin vinyl tiles of varying area and thickness. Usually they are square but some companies additionally manufacture various matching shapes. They are secured by adhesives.

To avoid the labour of laying so many tiles, continuous lengths of pvc flooring are available. The joints can be welded in certain cases to produce seamless flooring. Similar designs are available but obviously they must be continuous.

Similar products are available in rubber and are described later. They include tiles in much the same sizes and thicknesses and continuous flooring. Rubber floors can be very attractive and are more resilient than vinyl floors, but require more attention to keep them in first-class condition.

In addition to these standard floors, there are other types. The most common are hessian-backed flexible vinyl flooring which gives a feeling of great resilience, something like a deep-pile carpet. Foamed products are also used in sandwich constructions to give exceptional resilience. One of the most attractive features about vinyl floors is the tremendous range of colours and designs available. A word of caution is required in choosing colours from catalogues. Printed patterns cannot well match tiles, and colours should, therefore, be chosen from tile samples. In addition, it is not easy during manufacture to guarantee exact colour matching from one batch to another so care must be exercised in making a choice and, as far as possible, one consignment should be used for one room.

2.2.2 Detailed Products of Some Manufacturers

The following is a list of some pvc tile manufacturers:Nairn-Williamson Ltd. ("Houseproud"); Armstrong Cork Co. Ltd. ("Accotile", "Corlon" and others); Semtex Ltd. ("Semflex", etc.); Redfern's Rubber Works Ltd. ("Pegulan"); Humasco Ltd. ("Amtico" Vinyl); Marley Tile Co. Ltd. (Various names); Adamite Co. Ltd.; Bulgomme-Silence; Armoride Ltd. ("Kumfy-Lay"); Phoenix Rubber Co. Ltd.; James Williamson and Sons Ltd.; Holm-sund Flooring Ltd.; Robbins Linoleum Ltd. (also coved skirting); The Limmer and Trinidad Group of Companies; Goodyear Tyre and Rubber Co. (G.B.) Ltd.; Thomas Witter and Co. Ltd.; Hordern Richmond Ltd.; Gerland Ltd. (products include antistatic and high vinyl content tile); J. H. Bennett (Flooring) Ltd. (includes high vinyl and coved based skirting in 120-ft. lengths).

Details of some of the foregoing materials mentioned are as follows:—

Nairn-Williamson Ltd.

Composition:

The tiles are made from a thoroughly blended composition of resinous binder (polyvinyl chloride), special grade asbestos fibre, fine mineral fillers and pigments. They conform to the "British Standard for PVC (Vinyl) Asbestos Floor Tiles" (B.S. 3260:1960.).

They are $1 \cdot 6$ mm. ($\frac{1}{16}$ in.) thick, 9 in. square and weigh 6 lb. 8 oz. per sq. yd.

Colour Range:

The pattern numbers and names of the colours comprising the range of tiles are as follows:—

Pattern Nos. and Colours		Feature Strip Pattern Colours and Nos.	
117/01	Fawn	117 S.02	Red
117/02	Red	117 S.03	Turquoise
117/03	Turquoise	117 S.04	Blue
117/04	Blue	117 S.05	Light grey
117/05	Light grey	117 S.10	Yellow
117/06	Mid grey	117 S.11	White
117/07	Charcoal multi	117 S.12	Black
117/08	Beige		
117/09	Pink		
117/10	Yellow		
117/11	White		
117/12	Black		

"Crestaflex" is a new flexible vinyl flooring, manufactured in a gauge of 2.0 mm. It is made in tiles 9 in. × 9 in. and 12 in. × 12 in., and it is also available in sheet form 5 ft. wide. It is available in 12 colours.

The company also manufactures "Crestalux" with a high pvc content and vinyl on cork flooring, a tough flexible pvc flooring with a cork underlay. It is made in 51-in. wide sheets.

Armstrong Cork Co. Ltd.

Accoflex

Size:	9 in. × 9 in.
Gauge:	$\frac{1}{16}$ in. thick for normal wear; $\frac{1}{8}$ in. thick for heavy traffic.
Colours:	28.
Feature strip:	Available in six plain colours, $\frac{1}{2}$ in. to 6 in. wide.
Maintenance:	Normal sweeping and washing are sufficient to maintain a fresh appearance, with occasional application of a plastic emulsion such as Armstrong Accogloss satin seal floor polish.

These are vinyl asbestos tiles.

Accotile

Size:	9 in. × 9 in.
Gauge:	$\frac{1}{8}$ in. thick for normal wear; $\frac{3}{16}$ in. thick for heavy traffic.
Colours:	25.
Feature strip:	Available in six plain colours, 1 in. to 6 in. wide.

A thermoplastic tile.

Also "Arlon" flexible vinyl tiles in 12 colours; "Tessera" vinyl Corlon with vinyl blocks and a Hydrocord backing in rolls; "Patrician" vinyl Corlon sheet with Hydrocord backing with vinyl chips in five colours and "Montina" vinyl Corlon in five colours.

Semtex Ltd.

Vinylex Floor Tiles

Vinylex flooring is made of extra-durable pvc resins, reinforced with asbestos fibres. These high-grade materials retain their lovely clear colour and give excellent service under varied traffic conditions.

Tiles are available in standard 9 in. × 9 in. size and in $\frac{1}{10}$ in., $\frac{1}{8}$ in. and 0·080 in. thicknesses. There are 24 attractive colours. Tiles of $\frac{3}{16}$ in. thickness are also available in a limited number of colours.

Decorative border strip is supplied in an attractive colour range, in widths of 1 in. to 6 in. in 1 in. multiples. Coved skirting "sit-on" type is available in plain colours, in 3 in. and 4 in. heights.

Semflex Flexible
Tile size 12 in. × 12 in.
Thickness is 2 mm. (3 mm. supplied to special order).
Semflex 2 mm. long-length sheeting, 4 ft. wide is available in colours SF81, SF82, SF85, SF86, SF87 and SF96. The Semflex range is now offered in 16 colours. Border strips are available in all the Semflex colours, widths 1 in. to 6 in. in 1 in. multiples. The material has exceptional resistance to stiletto heels.

Other Semtex Products
A new development is the *Vinazzo* range of high vinyl tiles in the style of terrazzo. The high vinyl content gives exceptional resistance to stiletto heels. Tiles are 12-in. squares and are available in a variety of colours.
Semflor vinyl flooring has been developed to satisfy a special demand—for a semi-matt finish, homogenous and flexible tile of moderate cost which can be laid on undamp-coursed ground concrete. Hard wearing and comfortable to walk on. Semflor also has an impact sound reduction factor (on a concrete base) of 10 decibels (floor-covering only), thus making a real contribution to noise level reduction. It is available in a range of 12 colours.
The company also manufactures *Semastic* decorative tiles.

Humasco Ltd.

This company provides a wide range of pure vinyl tiles and only a brief indication of these can be given.
Amtico Plain Colours.
Amtico Marbleized (a broad range of colours).
Amtico Terrazzo (co-ordinated over three popular designs).
Amtico Renaissance, Onyx, Roman, Promenade, and Travertine (almost identical in appearance to genuine marble—in a wide range of colours).
Amtico Carefree.
Amtico Celestial.
Amtico Stardust.
Amtico Pebble.
Amtico Wood.
Amtico Flagstone.

Marley Tile Co. Ltd.

Standard Marley Tiles. These standard thermoplastic tiles are available in 28 colours and are extremely durable, rot-proof and fire resistant. They come in one size of 9 in. × 9 in., and thicknesses of $\frac{1}{10}$ in. and $\frac{1}{8}$ in.
Marleyflex, flexible and greaseproof, can be laid over wood or concrete and are immune from rot and damp. In kitchens, and wherever there is a risk of contamination from grease and oil, they are particularly suitable.
The Marleyflex vinyl asbestos tile is made in standard size 9 in. × 9 in., and in the following thicknesses: $\frac{1}{8}$ in., $\frac{1}{10}$ in. and 0·080 in.
A new addition to this range of tiles is the "Arcadia" tile which incorporates a metallic mottling. It comes in a variety of colours—coral, almond green, pale blue, light brown and black—with mottling of gold and white.
In addition to the "marbled" colours characteristic of Marleyflex tiles, there are the "Broadloom" and "Harlequin" series. The Broadloom, in 9 in. × 9 in. tiles, $\frac{1}{10}$ in. thick, give an "all-over" dappled effect whilst the floor retains the quality associated with tiles. Colours are of delicate pastel tones growing progressively

bolder for those who wish to make the floor the colour key-note. The Harlequin series (0·080 in., 9 in. × 9 in. tiles) in gaily splashed patterns, is another variation on the "all-over" theme. Both these series retain the qualities associated with Marleyflex tiles.

Marley De Luxe, high vinyl tiles come in a distinctive 12 in. × 12 in. size. They are fully flexible, rotproof, greaseproof, resistant to household chemicals, and quiet to the tread. A luxury tile suitable for rooms where a distinctive note is needed, and only the best will do. There is a full range of colours.

Marley Plaza 12 in. × 12 in. tiles are the newest addition to the De Luxe range and come in a unique "kaleidoscope"-type of patterning in various colours. Gold or silver glitter tiles are also available in the series.

In addition to the range of tiles so far mentioned, there is a variety of "cut-out" designs—9 in. × 9 in. tiles available in most types—with such decoration as a rabbit, a teapot or a bird incorporated in them in a separate colour. They are particularly pleasing for use in a children's nursery or bedroom.

Marleyflor Consort makes an attractive and hard-wearing floor covering for this bathroom (*The Marley Tile Co Ltd*)

For those who wish to "do-it-themselves", there are Marley Homelay tiles which include Harlequin and Broadloom, which may be laid by the amateur. There is a wide choice of colours.

Another product is the Marleyflor Consort 9 in. × 9 in. and 12 in. × 12 in. tile. It is flexible being made of similar material to that used in the "Marleyflor" sheet covering range. The material has a clear vinyl surface which gives perfect protection and wipes clean with a damp cloth. There are 18 colour styles with a transparent vinyl layer to protect the pattern.

Goodyear Tyre and Rubber Co. (G.B.) Ltd.

This company manufactures a true vinyl tile in two grades—De Luxe ($\frac{1}{8}$ in. thick and patterned all through) for the heaviest conditions and Custom ($\frac{1}{16}$ in. thick) for normal wear. They are available as 9 in. × 9 in. tiles in a number of marbled patterns.

2.2.3 Laying Instructions

The laying of vinyl floors is a specialist's job, but for those who wish to do it themselves, the following are the methods recommended by Nairn-Williamson Ltd., for their "Houseproud" tiles.

New Concrete Floors

The cement screed should consist of a 3:1 sand/Portland cement mixture trowelled to a smooth level finish.

It is recommended that the screed should not be given a glazed finish as this may delay the setting of the adhesive. Time should be allowed for constructional moisture to dry out of the floor before tiles are laid. If the floor is constructed of light-weight cellular concrete which contains a high proportion of water, extra drying time must be allowed. When the dryness of a new concrete floor is in doubt, a dampness test should be carried out.

Old Concrete Floors

Worn or broken surfaces should be patched or levelled. If the floor is in direct contact with the ground, no dampness test will be necessary if previous floor-coverings have shown no signs of dampness or condensation. Where the history or construction of such a floor is not known, a dampness test should be made. These comments do not, of course, apply to suspended concrete floors.

Quarry Tiles or Flagstone Floors

These are invariably constructed without a damp-proof course. Before laying a floor-covering, quarry tiles are usually lifted and the floor laid with concrete. Flagstones, on the other hand, are usually covered over with concrete to give a level surface. Neither of these treatments, however, provides immunity against rising dampness and again a dampness test should be carried out.

Damp Floors

Where floors are found to be damp, the only certain cure is to cover the surface with ½ in. of a flooring grade of asphalt before laying "Houseproud" tiles.

Wood Floors

Wood floors should be level and have good underfloor ventilation. They should also be rigid, otherwise repeated vertical movement may in time cause cracking of the tiles and failure of the adhesive. Wood floors which have an irregular surface may be levelled by one of the following methods:—

    (a) By means of a sanding machine to produce a smooth and level finish (the quickest method, but one which involves equipment and labour from a joine or flooring contractor). The fresh wood surface should be primed and a bitumen-impregnated paper-felt underlay bonded to the wood, and the tiles, in turn, laid on the underlay.

(b) By nailing the boards firmly to supporting timbers and screeding over with a levelling composition of rubber-latex-ciment fondu. Very effective provided no vertical movement of the boards is possible to produce break-up of the levelling cement.

(c) By laying sheets of hardboard or plywood over the floor and nailing every 6 in. across the sheets and every 4 in. along the edges of the sheets. Hardboard, which is the cheaper of the two materials, should first be wetted according to the manufacturer's instructions and then laid with the polished side uppermost. Flat-headed hammer-drive screw nails should be used and the sheet joints should be staggered as the jointing of bricks on a brick wall.

Composition Floors

Mastic asphalt or pitch mastic flooring makes a good foundation for "Houseproud" tiles, provided it is smooth and level. Composition floors of magnesite vary considerably in quality and at ground level frequently contain no damp-proof course. Floors of this type, which are damp and of a crumbling texture, are unsuitable for "Houseproud" tiles.

Heated Subfloors

"Houseproud" tiles can be laid on a heated floor provided the surface temperature of the floor does not exceed 80–85°F. It is important that all residual moisture be allowed to dry out of the concrete before tiles are laid. As a precautionary measure, heating should be turned on for approximately a week before the tiles are laid. The heat should be turned off when the laying of tiles is in progress.

Primers

All porous or dusting floor surfaces should be primed. A suitable primer can be made by diluting Nairn P.12 adhesive with an equal volume of water. The mixture should be stirred vigorously and used as quickly as possible. It should not be allowed to stand overnight as it will coagulate and become useless. The primer should be scrubbed into the floor in order to obtain good penetration. It is important that the primer should be thoroughly dry before the adhesive is spread for tile laying.

Adhesive

The adhesive recommended for use with "Houseproud" vinyl tiles is Nairn P.12. This adhesive can be used on any of the following types of floors:—Concrete; heated concrete; mastic-asphalt; pitch-mastic; cement-latex; magnesite; and wood.

Adhesives containing coal-tar derivatives of the Synthaprufe-type are, it is considered, unsuitable for laying "Houseproud" tiles.

On impervious surfaces, such as asphalt, extra time should be allowed for the adhesive to become tacky before tile-laying is begun.

Cleaning and Maintenance

Nairn P.12 adhesive when still wet can be removed from the surface of a newly-laid floor by rubbing with a damp cloth. The dry adhesive can be removed with a cloth moistened with white spirit. Care should be taken to prevent the white spirit from seeping between the tiles as it softens the adhesive and could thereby affect the adhesive bond. The floor should then be washed with warm water and soap or a household detergent. During the first week, when the adhesive bond is maturing, washing should be restricted. When the floor is clean and dry, two coats of Nairn vinyl polish should be applied. This polish dries quickly and the first coat should be allowed to dry thoroughly before the second coat is applied.

Other detailed laying instructions are given in Section 2.3.2 and this includes a moisture test.

The laying of rubber and plastic floors is a specialist business. In particular, very close consideration must be given to whether or not damp-proof barriers are required. The concensus of opinion is that all rubber floors require moisture barriers, vinyl floors are best with them although vinyl/asbestos do not need them.

Suitable barriers are:
(a) A sandwich-type membrane to BS 743 or rock asphalte to BS 1418 in contact with the damp-proof course in the wall;
(b) asphalte with a minimum thickness of $\frac{1}{2}$ in. to BS 1410;
(c) "Structoplast" at $\frac{1}{8}$ in. thick;
(d) sometimes 500 or 1000 gauge polythene;
(e) one or two special adhesives may be satisfactory but claims in this direction must be treated with the greatest caution. A possibility is an epoxy adhesive such as "Aquabar" sold by James Williamson and Son Ltd.

For further details users should apply to the Building Research Station at Watford. This organisation has produced their Building Research Station Digest No. 86 "Damp-proof Treatments for Solid Floors". An excellent booklet has also been produced by Marley entitled "The Laying of Thermoplastic Floor Tiles and Vinyl Flooring".

2.2.4 Special Vinyl Floors
Vinyl Cork

Nairn-Williamson Ltd. manufacture a vinyl cork floor in sheet form.

Vinyl Sheeting

There are two main advantages in laying vinyl floors as sheeting (in roll form) rather than as tiles. First, it is quicker, and secondly the number of joints is considerably reduced and in some cases even those can be welded. This is often important for hygienic reasons, particularly in hospitals. Such examples are as follows:—

Marley Tile Co. Ltd.

Marleyflor is a long-wearing sheet-flooring with properties only vinyl offers. It will not crack or buckle, is flexible and resists oils, grease and household chemicals. A wide colour range is offered in rolls 48 in. wide, and in four thicknesses: standard $\frac{1}{16}$ in., 0·080 in. and $\frac{1}{10}$ in.

Marleyflor Consort is one of the latest additions to the Marley range of floor coverings. The basic difference between this and the standard Marleyflor is a clear top coat of vinyl that protects the pattern.

It also produces a stain-free and greaseproof surface that is easy to clean. "Marleyflor Consort" is safe to use in those places where one usually hesitates when installing a flooring such as in entrances, hallways, kitchens and bathrooms. It is easily installed, and is available in 48 in.-wide rolls.

Redfern's Rubber Works Ltd.

Pegufelt comes in 150 cm. (59 in.) wide sheets, 60 cm., 75 cm. and 90 cm. (23½ in., 29½ in. and 35 in.) wide runners, and as adhesive tiles. There are 20 modern, marbled colours to meet every taste and also printed designs.

An interesting development in sheet flooring is the gravure or flexographic printed vinyl sheet with a clear pvc upper layer. This is not only attractive but the pure vinyl film has the same attractions as those described for tiles.

Manufacturers of Sheet Flooring

The following firms manufacture flooring in sheet form:—Dermide Ltd.; Marley Tile Co. Ltd.; Nairn-Williamson Ltd.; North British Rubber Co. Ltd.; Petmar Industries Ltd.; Phoenix Rubber Co. Ltd.; Redfern's Rubber Works Ltd.; S. and J. Walsh (Plastics) Ltd.; Welwyn Plastics (1955), Ltd.; James Williamson and Son Ltd.; Greengate and Irwell Rubber Co. Ltd.; Gerland Ltd.; James Halstead Ltd. (Poly-Flor); J. and H. Bennett (Flooring) Ltd.

Textile Backed

There are a number of specialized vinyl floor materials which are felt or fabric backed. These have a cushioning effect and, in general, are softer and quieter to walk on. Some details are as follows:—

Bulgomme-Silence

Plastylon—Top grade pvc flooring, fabric backing. 2 mm. thickness, sheets 4 ft. 10 in. wide, 100 ft. long; seams welded by hot-air process giving complete film of flooring, no joins being visible. This material has a polyvinyl-chloride content of 82% which gives it high wearing properties, flexibility, impeccably smooth appearance, comfortable tread, and ease of maintenance.

Plastylon-Jet is a lightweight economy alternative to Plastylon. It can be laid with and without impact adhesive and can be welded by means of Thermoweld Strip which can be applied with only the aid of a domestic iron.

Foam-Plastylon

Plastylon pvc floor covering with fabric interliner and cellular-rubber base. Thickness 3 mm. *Foam-Plastylon* floor covering, but, with its cellular-rubber base, has the additional advantage of sound-absorption—which has become a necessity in this modern age—as well as extra comfort underfoot.

Both materials are supplied in the following colour range: comblanchien; marron marble; red marble; yellow marble; green marble; black marble; blue marble; grey marble.

Marley Tile Co. Ltd.

Marleytred is a felt-backed sheet vinyl floor covering. It is suitable for virtually any room in the house, and its outstanding quality is that it combines the comfort and quietness of carpeting with the long life of a vinyl surface. It comes in rolls 48 in. wide, in a wide choice of colours. The material is made in five designs, each in a variety of colour combinations. There is now an extra top coat of clear vinyl.

The Adamite Co. Ltd.

The coating consists of 85% (average) plasticized pvc on (1) hessian backing (trade name: *Altro*), and (2) needle loom pure jute felt (trade name: *Vynoleum*). The percentage pvc content of "Altro" safety flooring is slightly reduced due to the abrasive grain content.

"Altro" floorings and "Vynoleum", with the exception of the cord and basket weave embossed ranges, have smooth low-gloss slightly etched surfaces. This new finish has been standardized in place of the original smooth gloss finish as it tends to break up light reflection and to prevent scuffing. These finishes can be polished to provide a gloss finish. An extensive colour and pattern range is available. "Altro Safety" flooring, containing abrasive grain, has a semi-matt finish.

Owing to the tough flexible nature of the pvc, these floor coverings will withstand extremely hard wear. Their wear resistance is greater than that of pressed granite paving flags. "Altro" (hessian backed) flooring can be laid for use under heavily loaded steel wheel trucks. PVC floor coverings have a high recovery characteristic from indentations due to point loading and they have been used with great success under conditions where many harder floorings, with little recovery, have failed. For areas under factory trucking, where uneven compression may take place, "Altro" flooring, not "Vynoleum", should be used.

The soft toughness of pure pvc floorings not only acts as an insulator against the penetration of impact noises through the subfloor, but also cuts down sound reverberation in the room where it is laid. It is quiet to walk on. Where sound insulation is of prime importance, "Vynoleum" with its felt backing has a distinct advantage.

"Altro" and "Vynoleum" floor coverings, because of their resilience, are soft to walk on and at the same time minimize the danger of slipping. The use of "Altro" Safety flooring naturally reduces this danger still further, but where the floor is likely to be covered with a thick coating of grease, "Altro" nonslip Prestile or Safety Treads should be used.

"Altro" and "Vynoleum" floor coverings are supplied in long rolls 72 in. wide, thereby insuring a minimum number of joints. If desired, these joints can be welded, thus providing a finish suitable for use where the floors are frequently under water, even with a chemical content.

	Average Overall Thickness	Average Weight per sq. yd.	Total
"Altro" Heavy Duty	0·1 in. (2·54 mm.)*	Hessian 7 oz. pvc 4 lb. 9 oz.	5 lb.
"Altro" Safety	0·1 in. (2·54 mm.)	Hessian 7 oz. pvc + Abrasive Grain 5 lb. 5 oz.	5 lb. 12 oz.
"Altro" Safety	0·15 in. (3·81 mm.)	Hessian 7 oz. pvc + Abrasive Grain 8 lb. 9 oz.	9 lb.
"Vynoleum"	0·14 in. (3·5 mm.)	Felt 1 lb. pvc 3 lb.	4 lb.

"Vynoleum"   0·1 in. (2·54 mm.)—after compression of the felt in laying.

*"Altro" heavy-duty material can be supplied in 0·15 in. (3·81 mm.) thickness for special orders.

Other Manufacturers

Other manufacturers of these specialized vinyl floor materials include:— Dermide Ltd.; Armoride Ltd.; Armstrong Cork Co. Ltd.; J. and H. Bennett (Flooring) Ltd.

Special Floors

One special type of flooring is anti-static and is intended for use in hospital wards, ordnance factories and explosives laboratories. Resistance, in the electrical sense, of pvc floors is usually quite high but the anti-static types are semi-conducting. They are made by the Marley Tile Co. Ltd.

The Marley Tile Company have the following to say on the subject:—

In the endeavour to evade the high resistance problem, thermoplastic tiles have been offered in which, by the incorporation of graphite or other forms of carbon filler, the electrical conductivity of the flooring has been increased. Tiles modified in this way have not been offered by the Marley Tile Company because such additions have unfavourably affected the wear resistance of the flooring and have limited the colour to black.

Research has shown that to dissipate static charges on a tile, the surface conductivity is all important. It has now been found possible to produce a tile, the surface conductivity of which is such that the accumulation of static charges is prevented. The resistivity to mains supply voltages is still, however, of the order of 10^{10} ohms, ensuring safety from accidental short circuits.

These anti-static tiles are a special grade of the "Marleyflex" range and are available in the wide range of colours characteristic of this flooring.

Where maintenance by waxing is desired, as will usually be the case, it is important to use the special grade of anti-static wax polish which has been developed for this purpose. Normal wax polishes can give a non-conductive film which would impair the anti-static nature of the floor. A colourful attractive floor can now, therefore, be maintained in hygienic condition without impairing the anti-static characteristic.

The anti-static properties of such floors do not depend upon the use of conductive grids beneath the surface which have to be specially earthed. Installation is by the ordinary methods over concrete, wood or other bases and is simple, straightforward and clean.

Another type of special flooring is the safety type mainly associated with the avoidance of slip. This is manufactured by the **Adamite Co. Ltd.; Bulgomme-Silence** and the **Marley Tile Co. Ltd.**

Special parts for flooring include stair-tread and riser covering, and stair nosing.

The Marley organization produces both of these. Their hard wearing, resilient vinyl stair-tread and riser coverings are easily installed, either to cover staircases completely or to leave margins at the sides. The front edges of the bull-nose and angle-nose treads have a serrated, non-slip strip for added security. Stairtreads and risers come in matched all-through colours of red, white, black, green and grey and are available in 9 ft. lengths. The stairtreads are 14 in. deep, adequate for cutting to suit any depth of tread, and the risers are $7\frac{1}{2}$ in. high.

Interesting decorative effects can be achieved using treads and risers of different colours. The stair covering should be cleaned with soap and water, and is unharmed by vigorous scrubbing. Extremely stubborn marks can be removed with a small knot of 00 gauge steel wool. However, because they are made of vinyl, the treads are dirt and stain resistant, and regular dry mopping keeps them clean between washings. If desired, the stair-tread may be treated with an emulsion polish, such as "Marley Superwax". Marley stair-tread can, if desired, be supplied and fixed by the Marley organization.

Marley Rigid Stair Nosing is for concrete or wooden stairs. Made in 3 ft. and 6 ft. lengths, the nosing has a special serrated, non-slip tread, and comes in four colours—bronze, deep bronze, pewter, and black. The nosing may be drilled and countersunk, and fixed with screws in conjunction with Marley adhesive. It is $1\frac{1}{2}$ in. wide.

Marley Flexible Stair Nosing is easily and quickly fixed. Available in a bull-nosed, and three different angle-nosed sections, the nosing is available in standard 9 in. lengths and stock colours of black, brown and white. Other lengths and colours may be made to special order. Flexible stair nosing is $\frac{1}{8}$ in. thick (it can be used with $\frac{1}{8}$ in. thick tiles) and is fixed with Marley M21 adhesive. Angle-nosed treads, for concrete stairs (FSN 1 90°, FSN 2 80°, FSN 3 70°), are $2\frac{1}{2}$ in. wide. Bull-nosed treads (FSN 4) are $1\frac{3}{4}$ in. wide.

2.2.5 Some Technical Aspects

There is little doubt that vinyl flooring is becoming established as the major flooring material for domestic dwellings. It is also widely used in commercial buildings and factories although in the latter situation not so much as the former. It is quite certain that this tendency will continue at a rapid rate so that vinyl flooring will become one of the biggest sections of the building industry.

Considerable attention has been paid to the aesthetic requirements of the flooring in a number of ways. The principal suppliers offer up to 30 colours in any one range and many also offer a variety of shapes to give special effects. Thus, the appearance of vinyl floors is well catered for. On the technical side, however, the picture is not so satisfactory. Many manufacturers' leaflets describing their products will call their tiles "durable" and "chemical resistant". These claims are undoubtedly true but they have the widest possible meaning and all tiles will certainly not be satisfactory in all situations. This is realized to a certain extent since speciality flooring for hospitals, car showrooms and the like are offered.

It is clear, therefore, that the technical aspects of vinyl flooring should be examined. Is sufficient information given to the customer? Is sufficient, in fact, known about the properties of the material itself? Should there not be a wider variety of products for special purposes and more technical data given to customers?

Properties to Consider

The great majority of companies offering vinyl flooring merely make a general reference to chemical resistance. This, therefore, is one property which needs to be considered in detail. Occasionally, also, some reference will be made to the abrasion resistance and, coupled with this, may be resistance to indentation, particularly from stiletto heels.

Apart from the properties mentioned, there are a number of others which can sometimes be of great importance. A good example is electrical conductivity, particularly significant in operating rooms. Thermal conductivity can also be improved, the same applying to the low-temperature characteristics.

Fire resistance, usually associated with cigarette burns, is worthy of investigation since there are some rather doubtful claims made about this subject. Other properties which may be considered are colour fastness, sound insulation and staining characteristics. These properties will be considered from the points of view of the type of pvc itself and of the end usage.

Composition of PVC

A pvc compound used for the manufacture of vinyl floor tiles contains a number of ingredients. It is important to know a little about these to understand the variations which can be made to affect the properties that have been described.

A pvc compound consists essentially of the pure pvc resin itself which is an extremely hard material with plasticizer, stabilizer, filler, lubricant and pigment. The lubrication is purely for processing purposes and need not be considered further.

The plasticizer modifies the properties of the hard resin to give it the typical flexibility of pvc compounds. In flexible vinyl toys there may be 30–50% of plasticizer for high flexibility but in vinyl tiles the proportion is usually very low, perhaps less than 5%. Thus pvc tiles are not very flexible.

The filler is one of the most important ingredients of the mix and large quantities are added to give a suitable product. The filler reduces cost but also confers stiffness. One of the most common fillers is asbestos and this type of composition is covered in B.S.3260:1960.

Another ingredient, the stabilizer, is not of such great concern as it is mainly required for processing. However, if the correct stabilizer is not chosen it is liable to react with impurities in the asbestos to cause discoloration. A choice of a suitable stabilizer is therefore important.

The only other ingredient is the colour. Suitable pigments must, of course, be chosen to give colour fastness and, where resistance to chemicals is involved, there should be no attack on the colours by the chemicals. A typical mix used for tiles is as follows:—

Ingredient	Parts by Weight
Vinyl resin (pvc)	100
DIOP (plasticizer)	15
Lankroflex ED.3 (stabilizer)	12
Lankro Mark 225 (stabilizer)	6
Asbestos (filler)	100
Calcium carbonate (cheap filler)	150

There are, of course, many variations on this theme but this may be taken as an example. A wax may also be added to supply bloom to the surface and give the tiles a high polish.

Electrical Conductivity

A consideration of the electrical conductivity of pvc is a good point at which to start a study of technical characteristics. This is because a direct relationship between the composition of the mix and conductivity properties can be established.

Normally, pvc compounds are reasonably good electrical insulators and are used as such. Asbestos is not a good filler from the electrical point of view as it tends to lower conductivity on any floor tiles. This, of course, is of no importance. In general, the idea is to reduce conductivity so as to avoid the accumulation of static charges. Such an accumulation usually occurs at relative humidities below 80% and where some type of rubbing of the surface occurs.

The elimination of static electricity can frequently be of importance. Obviously, in hospitals, or rooms where inflammable solvents are kept, a discharge causing a spark could have disastrous results. Special flooring should therefore be used in such circumstances. Another point is that a static charge will attract dust and cause an unsightly appearance or the need for cleaning far more frequently than should be necessary.

The conventional way in industry of reducing the electrical conductivity of pvc rubber is to add a conducting carbon black such as Shawinigan Acetylene Black or Kosmos BB Voltex. Unfortunately, the use of 10 to 30 parts to 100 of resin is necessary and this is not desirable in vinyl flooring and in any case it restricts the colour.

Fortunately, some new anti-static compounds have been developed. One of these is manufactured by A. Boake Roberts and Co. Ltd. and is called Antistat A. Another is manufactured by I.C.I. Ltd. and is known as Negomel AL 5. It is normally required to use only 5 to 7·5 parts of these ingredients to produce a reasonable conductivity.

To be anti-static, a compound must have a volume resistivity (specific resistance) of less than 10^{10} ohm. cm., or preferably less than 10^8 ohm. cm. (B.S.2050:1953). The change in volume resistivity achieved by the use of Negomel AL.5 as here shown illustrates how the compounds may be used.

Percentage Negomel AL.5	Volume Resistivity (ohm.cm.)
0	$3 \cdot 0 \times 10^{14}$
1·25	$1 \cdot 03 \times 10^{11}$
2·5	$3 \cdot 3 \times 10^{10}$
5·0	8×10^9

The reduction in resistance is obvious and it may be further reduced by increasing the plasticizer content of the mix.

Fire and Heat Resistance

These properties which are often confused, are of importance in a number of instances. Fire resistance is primarily concerned with safety but in the case of heat it is the resistance to hot objects placed on the floors or incorporated floor heating.

Fire resistance is the ability to resist a flame. PVC compounds, quite rightly, are normally claimed to be flame resistant. However, the term is only relative and calls for further comment.

If a pvc compound be placed in a flame it will begin to burn. Once the flame is withdrawn, however, it should quickly extinguish itself. By compounding fillers it is possible to make the pvc extinguish itself immediately upon removal of the flame and this is most desirable. As it happens, most vinyl flooring compounds contain a large proportion of asbestos and this, coupled with the inherent fire resistance of pvc itself, makes the tiles fire resistant in the sense already described.

Heat resistance is rather a different matter. PVC is a thermoplastic which means that it softens when warmed and returns to its original state when cooled. Any hot object placed on it, therefore, depending on its weight, will tend to mark the pvc tiles. Up to temperatures of about 70°C. and for relatively light loads, there will virtually be no marking, but with increasing temperature and pressure the indentation is likely to become marked. Some manufacturers do take this into account and issue suitable warnings.

Although pvc compounds are thermoplastic, they may safely be employed with heated floors. Fortunately, the temperature of heating is usually quite low and well below the pvc danger point. In more specific terms, the heated floor should not reach a temperature greater than 80–85°F. although this does depend on the compound.

Associated with fire and heat resistance is the question of resistance to cigarette burns. Some manufacturers appear to make exaggerated claims in this connection to the effect that their tiles do, in fact, resist cigarette burns. Others, however, are practical about the matter and give a warning that a lighted cigarette applied to the surface will cause local softening and a scar. The severity of such burns will undoubtedly vary with the composition of the mix and may be less with higher filler content. Nevertheless, all vinyl floors will tend to suffer from this defect and a suitable warning should be given. If burning does occur, then the scar should be removed with some abrasive and re-polished. Although a householder could not achieve a repair by welding, a deep scar should be repaired by a contractor using a stick of pvc and a suitable ironing instrument.

Finally, the associated feature of thermal conductivity may be mentioned. In general terms, normal pvc compounds for floor purposes are poor conductors of heat. This, of course, is usually desirable. In specific terms, and the actual values will vary considerably according to the composition of the flooring, it is possible to give one or two figures in terms of B.Th.U. per sq. ft. per hr. for a 1 in. thickness of floor and a 1°F. difference in temperature. Such figures are likely to vary from about 0·6 up to 1·2.

Low-temperature Properties

In general terms, all pvc compounds gradually stiffen as the temperature is lowered. As the temperature approaches 0°C. they may become so brittle that they will shatter from a blow.

The low-temperature properties can be improved in a number of ways by compounding. However, this involves the use of special plasticizers which are usually required in greater quantities than normally employed in pvc flooring compounds. It is unusual, therefore, to cater for these properties but in really cold climates it would be advisable to devise a special compound.

Generally speaking, the main problem in the U.K. arises during laying. If a roll of pvc flooring be exposed at very low temperatures it may easily crack when unrolled. It is, therefore, advisable to allow such flooring to be at a moderate temperature before attempting to lay. One of the few companies who mention the point in their literature suggest a temperature of 45°F., which is reasonable for most compounds.

Once the pvc is installed, the temperature which it will withstand is not quite so critical. However, in cold rooms and in exposed buildings during construction in the winter, the floors might well crack if heavy loads are dropped on them. The point is worth keeping in mind.

A number of tests can be carried out to determine low-temperature crack resistance and some of these are given in B.S.2571:1955. These normally involve the application of an impact load to a sample of given size at a given temperature. Figures are comparative and enable a special compound to be designed or specified.

There is one certain way of improving flex resistance which is to reduce the filler content considerably. This obviously is undesirable from the cost point of view so that the method can rarely be used. Nevertheless, there is a compromise solution which some manufacturers have adopted. This is to make a laminate flooring with a pure vinyl resin on the top. This excellent practice confers other advantages as will be indicated later.

Abrasion Resistance

It is difficult to be precise about abrasion resistance with regard to pvc. Few figures are available on the subject, one of the reasons being that the

4

tests to measure it are unsatisfactory. They do not necessarily correlate with what is obtained in practice.

In theory, the use of large quantities of filler in flooring should lower its resistance to abrasion. Unlike natural rubber, fillers, with minor exceptions, do not reinforce pvc in any way; they merely act as diluants. The abrasion resistance of pvc flooring should therefore be very low.

In practice this does not appear to be so. However low the resistance as shown in the laboratory, there is no doubt that pvc tiles have been in use for as long as 30 years and have withstood considerable usage with little difficulty. Nevertheless, an unfilled compound has high abrasion resistance when used under appropriate conditions. Such compounds are often used in conveyor belting on which many abrasion tests have been carried out. Once again, therefore, the use of a laminate may well help in giving a good life for a pvc flooring. One of the few tests published concerning abrasion resistance is from the Adamite Co. Ltd. In this test, samples are clamped to a table revolving at 16 r.p.m. Two 10 in. $\times$ $1\frac{3}{4}$ in. wide iron truck wheels are mounted at opposite ends of an arm revolving at 90 r.p.m. This assembly is lowered into contact at one side of the sample so that when the machine travels, a path 10 in. wide (10 in. wheel centres) is worn round the inside of the periphery of a circle 23 in. in diameter. The load on each wheel is about 2 cwt. and the idea is to simulate a loaded truck turning in a small radius. Comparative tests on concrete paving and "Altro" flooring were carried out. The loss of weight for the concrete was 5·94 lb. and for the pvc flooring $\frac{1}{2}$ oz. In the case of the concrete, the average depth of wear was $\frac{5}{32}$ in.; wear on the pvc floor was negligible.

It would appear, therefore, that no matter what is done to pvc in a compounding sense, the abrasion resistance is still very good.

An unusual condition sometimes arises when pvc tiles are scratched. White lines appear and look most unsightly. This is caused by the use of large-diameter fillers which are not dispersed and held by the vinyl matrix. The problem can be overcome by the use of fillers having particles of smaller size.

Deformation

One of the most difficult problems to solve with pvc floors is that of deformation under a load. The loads are usually industrial trucks and equipment or furniture and stiletto heels.

Fortunately, the deformation sustained by pvc is reduced with increasing filler content. The penetration can readily be measured in the laboratory by penetration tests. In one of these, a 5 mm. ball is pressed into a sample under a load of 2 kg. for one minute and the deformation measured. In the case of a filler called Omya BSH, the following results were obtained:—

Temperature of test, °C.	Parts of Omya BSH			
	0	10	30	60
30	86	83	72	67
40	97	100	87	78
50	122	119	108	93
60	148	141	132	120

It will be seen from these results that the deformation (in microns) is considerably reduced with increasing filler content. Considering that the pvc compound contained 250 parts of filler compared with the 60 above, the improvement expected will be obvious.

The results given in the table also show that the deformation increases at elevated temperatures. Even here, however, the deformation is reduced with increasing filler content.

Unfortunately, deformation as such is not the only consideration. Permanent set is also of vital importance and means the degree by which any deformation is retained after removal of the load. With minor exceptions, unfilled compounds have the best resistance to permanent set and this is rapidly lowered as filler content is increased. The minor exception is with the use of Omya BSH, where the addition of 10 parts of filler actually reduced permanent set. After the addition of this filler, however, the permanent set starts to rise rapidly as with other materials.

Once again, therefore, the use of an unfilled compound in a laminate may offer advantages. It is problematical, however, whether increased deformation with this type of material or the reduced permanent set will show up to most advantage. This can be determined only by experience and experiment.

Some manufacturers do refer to this point of deformation in their literature although, generally, in vague terms, such as the tiles concerned are "resistant to stiletto heels". Another company claims that its tiles are "capable of withstanding static loads of up to 200 p.s.i. without permanent indentation." And yet another employs a load of 3,000 p.s.i. on a tile for 60 minutes (through a flat ended rod 0·178 in. in diameter) after which the residual indentation does not exceed 0·010 in.

Chemical Resistance

The claims by manufacturers for chemical resistance are normally in general terms. One company claims, for example, that their tiles are "grease-proof, stain-proof, resistant to alcohol, detergents, soaps and most acids and solvents". Others talk of "grease and oil" and yet others of "general kitchen chemicals". PVC compounds are, in fact, highly resistant to chemicals but there are some which attack the material seriously. These include aliphatic and aromatic ketones, aromatic amino compounds, acetic anhydride, organic compounds containing nitro and chlorine groups and lacquer solvents. However, the compounds resist such materials as nitric, sulphuric, hydrofluoric and chromic acids and strong alkalis, all at reasonable concentrations.

It should be stressed that the resistance of pvc to chemicals varies with concentration and temperature. The only way to be really specific is for manufacturers to give a detailed list of chemicals and the concentrations and temperatures at which they are safe. Manufacturers of pvc should be consulted for these details. However, various tile companies have carried out tests on vinyl tiles by spilling liquids on them and leaving them there for 24 hours. Some common materials which did not attack the pvc in any way are given in Section 2.2.1.

One feature of the chemical resistance of pvc should be mentioned. PVC

is seriously attacked or stained by certain bitumen compounds. It is impossible to be specific about this since there are hundreds of types, some of which
are satisfactory and others not. For this reason, care should be taken when
laying pvc floors on freshly laid bitumen and a primer is advisable. Some adhesives are bitumen based and these are best avoided unless the supplier gives
specific information to the contrary.

The compounding of pvc does not affect the chemical resistance very
much. Certain changes can be effected, of course, but they are usually unnecessary. A special class of plasticizer (polymeric) when used, reduces the
extraction of plasticizer by chemicals and also reduces marring.

Another source of possible damage to vinyl floors are certain types of
cleaners. Manufacturers, again, must give instructions here so that cleaners
and polishes containing solvents which attack pvc may be avoided.

2.2.5.9 Other Features

It is often necessary to lay tiles in situations which are likely to be damp.
Such conditions are likely to allow the growth of various bacteria and moulds.
Generally, pvc compounds are highly resistant to such organisms but resistance can be improved by the addition of insecticides to the compounds. In
spite of statements to the contrary, pvc is attacked by termites and, in general,
there is little that can be done about it.

The resistance of pvc floors to marking by rubber is a formidable problem.
Many rubber compounds contain what are called "staining antioxidants".
The anti-oxidants will be absorbed by the vinyl floors and the action of light
will cause discoloration. If this is seen to occur, the only real remedy, unless
there is some control over the composition of the rubber, is to protect the
floor from contact with the rubber.

There are many other minor features which only manufacturers themselves will meet occasionally. It will be obvious, however, that the problems of
the manufacturer of colours for pvc are greater than would perhaps at first be
thought. There is little doubt that insufficient information is passed on to
customers and serious consideration should be given to doing this in a simplified form. One or two manufacturers do this admirably but they are in the
minority. The manufacturers have a duty to users to explain what to do and
what not to do with floors if the best results are to be obtained.

2.3 Rubber Floor Tiles

Rubber flooring as such has been used for so long and is so well known,
that it warrants little description. Rubber flooring, available in a range of
attractive colours, has been known to last for 20 or 30 years and there is much
to recommend it.

There is probably little or no true natural rubber flooring today. It is all at
least blends with general-purpose synthetic rubbers, the properties of which
are much the same.

2.3.1 Rubber Floors, Manufacturers

Among the manufacturers of rubber floors are the following companies:

Robbins Linoleum Ltd.
Harefield Rubber Co. Ltd.
Greengate and Irwell Rubber Co. Ltd.
Morris Rubber Industries Ltd.
St. Albans Rubber Co. Ltd.
Leyland and Birmingham Rubber Co. Ltd.
Runnymede Rubber Co. Ltd.

2.3.2 Special Synthetic Rubber Floors

A synthetic rubber/cork combination, using nitrile rubber which, among other properties, is oil resistant, is made by British Technical Cork Products Ltd. Another synthetic rubber floor using "Hypalon" is of interest and is discussed in detail.

Synthetic Rubber/Cork Floors

British Technical Cork Products, Ltd.

The mixture of cork and rubber gives the warmth always associated with cork, together with the resilience of rubber, and is produced in seven colours:—Red, grey, mustard, green, black, tan, blue.

As well as these decorative tiles, the company also manufactures an industrial grade in a standard shade which, whilst having the same high quality, can be offered at a lower price.

The properties claimed are: Good resistance to stiletto heels; resistance to slip—even when wet; resistance to petrol and oils; sound absorbence; warmth and resilience; flexibility; ease of maintenance; special back to assist adhesion; hard wearing.

Specification

Standard size 12 in. × 12 in.; thickness ⅛ in.; density 55 lb./cu. ft. minimum; Colour fastness equal to B.S.5 (very good).

Indentation: After subjection to a half-ton per sq. in. load on a ½ in. diam. indentor the residual indentation after 10 minutes recovery was only 0·001 in./0·002 carried out in accordance with B.S.810 1957, which gives a permitted indentation of 0·010 in.

Coefficient of friction: Comparative tests were carried out using a rubber tile as a control, and in every case it was found that the "Decor" tile has a higher coefficient of friction.

The test results :
Untreated cork and rubber tile   0·603
Treated cork and rubber tile   0·530
Wet untreated cork and rubber tile   0·500
Rubber tile   0·466

The coefficient of friction was found by mounting the specimen on a weighted block and measuring the horizontal force required to move the block on a horizontal plane.

"Hypalon" Floors

The outstanding success and ready acceptance of vinyl floors has been so overwhelming that the consideration of yet another flooring material may seem to be superfluous. This position, however, should not prevent the flooring industry from examining other products since vinyl floors are certainly not perfect and have limitations in certain applications.

Two of the inherent defects of pvc are its thermoplasticity and the relatively high permanent set which it takes. Both of these limitations can be offset to a certain extent but they cannot be eliminated.

"Hypalon" is superior to pvc in both the properties mentioned and must clearly be considered as an alternative in certain cases. It is highly unlikely that it will ever become a serious competitor of pvc for general purposes because of cost consideration alone, but for specialist applications it might well find a useful place in the field.

"Hypalon" is a synthetic rubber which is flame and weather resistant, and highly resistant to a large variety of chemicals. It thus has a number of valuable characteristics so vital in a material to be used for flooring.

Chemically, "Hypalon" is a chlorosulphonated polyethylene made by reacting polyethylene (the plastic polythene) with chlorine and sulphur which converts the thermoplastic into a synthetic rubber. This means that in vulcanization it becomes a thermosetting material which cannot be softened by heat. Similarly, it acquires a good resiliency (i.e. low permanent set) so that the material at once has two advantages over vinyl flooring. These properties are considered in detail later.

"Hypalon" is manufactured by E.I. du Pont de Nemours and Co., Inc., of the U.S.A. and is sold in the U.K. by Du Pont Co. (United Kingdom), Ltd. who give a complete technical service from their laboratories at Hemel Hempstead. Du Pont are also the manufacturers of the well-known neoprene frequently used (among many other products) as the basis of adhesives for bonding "Hypalon" and other tiles to subfloors. "Hypalon" is the registered trade mark of the Du Pont Co.

Summary of Properties

The claimed properties of "Hypalon" floors may be summarized as follows:—

Super abrasion resistance;
Easy to clean;
Available in a wide range of stable colours;
Extreme resistance to ageing and can be used for outdoor applications;
Does not shrink or spread during service;
Resistant to indentation;
Deadens sound;
Will not burn and is not damaged by burning cigarette ends;
Resistant to chemicals; animal, vegetable and mineral oils and greases;
Resistant to heat;
Resilient and flexible.

These properties are not just a list designed for publicity purposes, but genuinely represent the characteristics of the material. They indicate without doubt, how valuable "Hypalon" can be under certain conditions. They might even be a good reason for using the tiles everywhere, a practice largely prevented by the relatively high cost.

Mechanical Properties

One of the most important properties of "Hypalon" is its resistance to indentation with subsequent high recovery. The indentation resistance is several times greater than any similar floor covering in use at the present time. Tests conducted by Du Pont indicate that "Hypalon" has residual indentation six times lower than vinyl, eight times lower than asphalt, 14 times lower than rubber, and 16 times lower than linoleum. Field trials and installations have confirmed these tests.

As far as abrasion resistance is concerned, "Hypalon" tiles compare very favourably with vinyl and rubber tiles and linoleum. This again has been confirmed in installations. For scratching and scuff resistance, "Hypalon" appears to be superior to vinyl and equal to rubber and other resilient floor coverings. The hardness is Shore 92°–95°.

One difficulty with vinyl flooring is the reduced flexibility at low temperatures. At very low temperatures brittleness is likely to be encountered. Asphalt behaves in a similar way. In the case of "Hypalon", however, the resilience remains constant at lowered temperatures.

The material also has good dimensional stability. The rubber is compounded with fillers and other ingredients to resist shrinkage or extension during service on the floor.

Traditionally, rubber and cork have been the better types of floor coverings to reduce the noise of foot traffic. "Hypalon" tiles have even greater sound-deadening characteristics.

Other Properties Affecting Use

Quite apart from actual chemical resistance, to be discussed in detail later, a desirable characteristic of any flooring material is to resist staining from foods, inks, cleaning agents and a number of common solvents. The way of achieving this resistance is to have a completely non-porous surface. This, "Hypalon" possesses, and it thus has excellent staining resistance.

A corollary of this property is the ease with which the floors may be cleaned. The smooth, hard surface and the resiliency prevent impregnation of dirt which facilitates cleaning. At the same time, a fine lustre may be obtained with a minimum amount of wax.

In certain applications, the weathering resistance can not only be important but extend the fields of application. In weathering resistance may be included resistance to oxygen, ozone and water. "Hypalon" is excellent in this respect, so much so, that it may safely be employed out-of-doors. Terraces and patios are obvious instances where this property will be of use.

This durability is irrespective of the colour. In this connection, the range of colours which may be obtained is virtually unlimited. Light pastel shades resistant to sunlight and discoloration are obtainable without difficulty.

Some figures for tests carried out in a weatherometer, simulating many months of exposure and water resistance, may be quoted:

Weather-O-Meter Discoloration

After:	1 day	none
	2 days	none
	4 days	none
	8 days	faded

Water absorption (70 hours at 70°C.)

Volume increase	2·3%
Weight increase	1·1%

A further important feature of "Hypalon" floors is their flame resistance. This is achieved, not just by the addition of flame resistant fillers, but by the inherent characteristics of the material. In this respect, it is similar to vinyl floors but considerably superior to rubber floors.

Chemical Properties of "Hypalon"

Although the chemical resistance can vary according to the compounding ingredients used in the tiles, the resultant products all have basic chemical resistance. It should always be stressed, however, that the results given are for general guidance, and if any doubt exists then the manufacturers should be consulted.

Some time ago, various interesting tests were undertaken by the University of Ottawa on "Hypalon" tiles made by Canadian General-Tower, Ltd. In these tests, a comparison was made between resilient vinyl, vinyl-asbestos and "Hypalon" tiles by subjecting them all to the following chemicals for 5 minutes and 20 minutes:

Concentrated sulphuric, hydrochloric, nitric, hydrofluoric and acetic acids, concentrated sodium hydroxide, acetone, xylene, chloroform, carbon tetrachloride, ethyl acetate, benzene.

The "Hypalon" tiles withstood the effects of all these chemicals, whereas the vinyl tiles were affected by some of them. Some of the chemicals removed the original gloss off the "Hypalon" tiles but this was restored by polishing with steel wool and no visible mark was left after the test. The worst offender of these chemicals was chloroform, but even in this case the original gloss could be restored by polishing.

The chemicals stated were chosen as being those most commonly used in the laboratories of the University. As a result of the tests, Dr. Pierre R. Gendon, Dean of the Faculty of Pure and Applied Science, thought that the tiles would be ideal for their building.

This is clearly a case of the specific application of "Hypalon" because of its superior properties to other materials.

In view of the possible importance of the use of "Hypalon" tiles in special applications, it has been thought useful to give detailed chemical resistance properties of the material (see tables).

Chemicals having little or no effect upon "Hypalon"

Chemical	Concentration by weight, %	Temperature, °F.
Ammonia	Liquid anhydrous	R.T.
Chlorine dioxide	14	150
Chrome plating sol		158
Chromic acid	50	200
Chromic acid	Concentrated	R.T.
Cottonseed oil		R.T.
Diethyl sebacate		R.T.
Dimethyl ether		R.T.
Ethylene glycol		158
Ferric chloride	15	200
Ferric chloride	Saturated	R.T.
Formaldehyde	37	R.T.
"Freon-12"		R.T.
Hydrochloric acid	37	122
Hydrofluoric acid	48	158
Hydrogen peroxide	50	212
Hydrogen peroxide	88·5	R.T.
Methyl alcohol		R.T.
Mineral oil		R.T.
Motor oil (SAE 10)		R.T.
Nitric acid	Up to 20	158
Nitric acid	70	R.T.
Phosphoric acid	85	200
Pickling solution	20% Nitric, 4 HF%	158
Potassium hydroxide	Concentrated	R.T.
Sodium dichromate	20	R.T.
Sodium hydroxide	20	200
Sodium hydroxide	50	158
Sodium hypochlorite	20	200
Stannous chloride	15	200
Sulphur dioxide	Liquid	R.T.
Sulphuric acid	Up to 50	200
Sulphuric acid	Up to 80	158
Sulphuric acid	Up to 95·5	R.T.
Tetrabutyl titanate		R.T.
Tributyl phosphate		R.T.
Water		200

Chemicals having a moderate effect upon "Hypalon"

Chemical	Concentration by weight, %	Temperature, °F.
Acetic acid	Glacial	R.T.
Acetone		R.T.
Aniline		R.T.
Chlorine (dry)	Liquid	R.T.
Cottonseed oil		158
Diethyl ether		R.T.
Hydrochloric acid	37	158
Mineral oil		212
Motor oil (SAW 10)		158

Chemical	Concentration by weight, %	Temperature, °F.
Nitric acid	70	122
Sulphuric acid	95·5	122
Turbo oil No. 15 (jet engine lub.)		R.T.

Chemicals having a severe effect upon "Hypalon"

Chemical	Concentration by weight, %	Temperature, °F.
Acetic acid	Glacial	158
Carbon tetrachloride		R.T.
Citrus oils		R.T.
Dichlorobutene		R.T.
Formaldehyde	37	158
Gasoline		R.T.
Hydrochloric acid	37	200
Jet engine fuel (JP-4)		R.T.
Nitric acid	30	158
Nitric acid	Fuming	R.T.
Nitrobenzene		R.T.
Perchlorethylene		R.T.
Turbo oil No. 15		350
Xylene		R.T.

As can be seen, extensive testing by Du Pont has shown that "Hypalon" possesses excellent resistence to most chemicals. In applications where contact with strong oxidizing chemicals is involved, the material has shown its superiority to all other elastomers, which means natural rubber, SBR, neoprene and so on.

The following is a list of chemical properties expressed in a different manner to the list given previously.

Key: A=little or no adverse effect; B=minor to moderate effect; C=severe effect.

	Rating	Temperature, °F.
Acetic acid, glacial	B	R.T.
Acetone	B	R.T.
Ammonium hydroxide	A	200
Amyl acetate	C	R.T.
Amyl alcohol	C	R.T.
Aniline	B	R.T.
Asphalt	C	
Beer	A	R.T.
Beet juice	A	R.T.
Benzene	C	R.T.
Butter and buttermilk	A	158 and 100
Calcium hydroxide (lime)	A	200
Calcium hypochlorite (bleach)	A	200
Carbolic acid (phenol)	B—C	R.T.
Carbon disulphide	C	R.T.
Carbon tetrachloride	C	R.T.
Castor oil	A	158
Chlorine water	B	R.T.
Chloroform	C	R.T.

	Rating	Temperature, °F.
Chrome plating solutions	C	158
Citric acid	A	R.T.
Copper plating solution	C	190
Creosote	B—C	R.T.
Cyclohexanone	C	R.T.
Diethyl ether	B	R.T.
Ethyl alcohol	A	200
Ethylene glycol	A	200
Ferric chloride	A	200
Formaldehyde	A	R.T.
Freon 12	A	R.T.
Fuel oil	B	158
Glycerin	A	200
Hydrochloric acid	A	R.T.
do.	C	158
Lubricating oil	B	158
Methyl ethyl ketone	C	R.T.
Milk	A	R.T.
Molasses	A	200
Nickel plating solution	A	140
Nitric acid (up to 30%)	A	R.T.
do.	B	122
do.	C	158
Olive oil	B	R.T.
Phosphoric acid	A	200
Potassium dichromate	A	200
Sea water (and sodium chloride solutions)	A	158
Soap solutions	A	200
Sodium hydroxide	A	200
Sulphuric acid—up to 50%	A	250
Tin salts	A	200
Toluene	C	R.T.
Tricresyl phosphate	B—C	R.T.
Turpentine	C	R.T.
Urine	A	R.T.
Wines and spirits	A	R.T.
Zinc salts	A	200

Applications of "Hypalon" Flooring

It is useful to consider some of the circumstances in which "Hypalon" tiles are used as it shows why the material was chosen for the application concerned.

As already indicated, one of the most important applications is in chemical and similar laboratories. The Du Pont laboratories at Hemel Hempstead have an area covered with "Hypalon" floor which is open to inspection at any time.

Another obvious application is in canteens and cafeterias. Reasons include ease of cleaning, resistance to food spillage and cigarette burns. Banks and similar buildings will also use "Hypalon" for long life, ease of cleaning, minimum maintenance and lasting attractive appearance. In addition, there is the usual reason of resistance to stiletto heels and furniture, and non-slip characteristics. The latter is also important on ships, and some of the crew's quarters of the S.S. "Oriana" have "Hypalon" floors. Sound deadening is also important here as it is in hospitals, churches and similar establishments.

An important area of activity is out-of-doors where resistance to weathering is important. Seaside hotels having patios and the like are obvious applications.

Church House, Westminster, used so extensively for conferences, has "Hypalon" floor tiling for its 48 ft.-long Council Room. It has replaced linoleum.

The tiles of "Hypalon" used at Church House are ⅛ in. thick, buffed on the back, with a high-gloss finish on the upper surface. They are 12 in. square and corn coloured. There is a surround border of brown tiles to blend in with the existing scheme of flooring in the building. The tiles are expected to last the lifetime of the building, whereas ordinary rubber tiles would probably not stand up for more than 10 years or so. The long-life property of "Hypalon" synthetic rubber, coupled with its minimum maintenance requirements, will prove it to be an economical material in the long run. The tiles are stuck to a substrate with a neoprene-based solvent adhesive.

The Council Room at Church House is the first in the building to be tiled with "Hypalon". Further floors will be similarly tiled as renewals of the existing flooring become necessary.

Some years ago, in the United States, a testing programme covering every feature important to quality tiling was carried out. The tests, conducted under extreme conditions not likely to apply in ordinary circumstances, were carried out on tiles of "Hypalon", pvc, pvc-asbestos, rubber, linoleum and asphalt floorings. The findings are of interest to those who may think that the claims for "Hypalon" tiles are excessive.

The tests showed that "Hypalon" synthetic rubber registered the highest percentage recovery from indentation, even after being subjected to the pressure of heavy library tables. It proved superior in resistance to scratching and abrasion, and showed excellent resistance to almost all of 40 different chemicals, foods and oils applied for periods of 48 hours. The tiles retained their original colour after one year of outside exposure to direct sunlight, and withstood the effects of the elements for one year without any sign of weather-cracking, chalking or discoloration. In addition, they compared favourably with other floor covering materials when tested for adhesion, ease of installation, and cleanability.

Some Commercial Considerations

It is difficult to make any cost comparisons with other tiles so that any figures given must be taken only as a guide. The prices here given were estimated by Du Pont.

The cost of pvc flooring ⅛ in. thick and depending on the quality, would be between 18s. and 32s. per yard. Equivalent prices for rubber is 18s. 6d. to 25s. per yard. In the case of "Hypalon", the prices would be 37s. 6d. to 42s. 6d. per yard. One manufacturer is charging rather more than this.

The initial cost is undoubtedly high, the main reason being the high volume cost of the raw material. In addition to this, because the materials are speciality types, prices are naturally higher than if the products were being made on a really large scale. There is one way of bringing down prices. Instead of the tile being made of all "Hypalon", a laminate construction can be employed. In this a, say, $\frac{1}{32}$ in.-thick "Hypalon" veneer is employed over a $\frac{3}{32}$ in. SBR substrate. This construction would achieve all the desirable properties of the "Hypalon" floor whilst bringing the selling price down to 26s. to 30s. per yd.

"Hypalon" tiles have been made by the Sussex Rubber Co. Ltd. and Rubberware Ltd.

A number of other firms have undertaken experimental work and have produced a limited number of tiles.

Rather more interest has been shown in the product in North America. Canadian General-Tower Ltd., of Galt, Ontario, have been particularly active and have produced a specification for their products of which the following are details.

Canadian General-Tower Ltd.

1. Material

Tower "Hypalon" tile shall be manufactured from a high-content "Hypalon" compound.

Tiles shall be homogeneous, properly vulcanized "Hypalon" tile compound containing thoroughly dispersed non-organic reinforcing materials, colour-fast pigments insoluble in water, highly resistant to light, detergents, and cleaning agents. The tile shall be free from objectional odours.

The tile shall present a smooth wearing surface, free from blisters, cracks, protruding particles and/or embedded foreign material. Mottling shall be homogeneous throughout the full thickness of the tile. The back shall present a roughened surface to ensure adequate bond.

2. Dimensional and Weight Tolerances

Tower "Hypalon" tiles shall be 9 in. $\times$ 9 in. $\times$ 0·125 in.
(a) Surface dimensions: 9 in. plus or minus 0·010 in. On tiles larger than 9 in. $\times$ 9 in., tolerance will be plus or minus 0·015 in. per linear ft.
(b) Thickness: 0·125 in. plus or minus 0·005 in.
(c) Weight: The weight shall be not less than 1·1 lb. per sq. ft. nor more than 1·4 lb. per sq. ft.

3. Physical Requirements

(a) *Hardness:* The Shore Durometer hardness shall not be less than 90 when tested according to Section 5·4 CSA specification No. A145-1959 for Rubber Tile.
(b) *Modulus:* The stress at 10% elongation shall be not less than 400 lb. per sq. in. when tested according to Section 5·3, CSA Specification No. A145-1959 for Rubber Tile.
(c) *Residual Indentation:* The residual indentation shall not be more than 2% when tested as follows:
The test shall be performed at 77°F.
The tile sample shall have the roughened back impression removed. The thickness shall be determined to the nearest 0·001 in. with a micrometer.

A sample 1·22 in. in diameter shall be placed on a flat plate and static pressure of 2,500 lb. per sq. in. applied through a steel cylinder 1·75 in. in diameter. The cylinder shall be centred over the sample.

The pressure shall be maintained for three minutes. The sample shall be permitted to condition at 77°F. for two hours, after which the thickness of the sample shall be determined.

The residual indentation shall be the average of three determinations and shall be expressed as a percentage of the original thickness.

Laying "Hypalon" Floors

All the subfloors must be smooth, dry and clean. This is important otherwise good adhesion will not be obtained.

In the case of wooden floors, spacing of joists shall be such that excessive spring of the floor is avoided. The air space for ventilation shall be at least 18 in., joints shall be filled with a plastic compound and the floor sealed with 1 coat of penetrating-type wood sealer such as 1 part of shellac and 4 or 5 of wood alcohol.

Concrete must be at least 3 months old before "Hypalon" tiles are laid on them. Tests must be made until no moisture is left in the floor and there is no alkalinity (test later). A moisture barrier is best incorporated and smoothness applies here also. There shall be no oil, grease, paint, varnish or wax on the concrete. Dust must be removed and cracks etc. filled up.

Adhesives should be applied by any of the usual means. Suppliers of suitable adhesives are:—Adhesive and Allied Products; Bostik Ltd.; Evode Ltd.; I.C.I. Ltd.; F. H. and H. S. Pechin Ltd.; Goodyear Tyre and Rubber Co. (G.B.) Ltd.; Surridges Patents Ltd.; Tretol Ltd.

Moisture Test for All Concrete Floors

Prior to laying floor tiles, the following procedure should be adopted to test for dampness:—

1. Drill $\frac{1}{2}$ in. hole, half the depth of the slab at each corner and in the centre of the room.
2. Form a ring of putty 6 in. in diameter and $\frac{1}{2}$ in. in height round each hole.
3. Place a level teaspoonful of granulated anhydrous calcium chloride in a watch glass within each ring.
4. Cover each ring with a clock glass, pressing the glass down into the putty so as to keep out all outside air.
5. If the floor is damp, beads of moisture will appear on the watch glass within 48 hours and the calcium chloride will be all or partially dissolved.

Tests should be repeated at weekly intervals until all traces of moisture are negative.

Alkalinity Test for Concrete

All concrete subfloors should also be tested for alkalinity as follows:—
1. Sweep floor clean of loose debris, and wet mop all over.

2. Leave for a few hours until partially dried.
3. Using neutral distilled water, dampen strips of red litmus paper and place at several points around the concrete subfloor. If the litmus paper changes to blue, floor is alkaline.
4. On the test providing positive alkalinity, floor area should be washed all over, using a 10% solution of hydrochloric acid; allow to soak for 30 minutes and follow with a warm-water washing, mopping dry. Allow 24 hours to dry out, then using a soft hair brush, remove all efflorescence and re-test floor.
5. Repeat hydrochloric acid treatment until floor shows neutral reaction.
6. Re-test for dryness and when all is satisfactory proceed to lay tiles.

2.3.3 Special Floors

The *Bulgomme-Silence Flooring* is sold by Bulgomme Silence Flooring. It has a hard rubber surface backed by a fabric interliner and a cellular rubber base. Such floors have exceptional wearing properties and good sound and vibration absorption qualities. It is available in 16 plain and marbled colours in tile form $\frac{3}{16}$ in. thick with a weight of 7 lb. per sq. yd.

Holoplast Ltd., manufacture *Chequerplast*, a laminated plastic with an embossed surface, which is used as a floor surfacing where acid and oil spillage is likely to be encountered.

Harelux is a rubber flooring with a sponge cushion underlay made by the Harefield Rubber Co. Ltd.

2.4 Epoxy (Jointless) Floors

Many materials have been used for floors, some of them with only mixed success. In the decorative field, parquet floors are very attractive but are expensive and require much attention to maintain their beautiful finish. Vinyl floors are much cheaper, are attractive and easy to maintain but are still not as resistant to stiletto heels as they might be.

In the industrial and utilitarian fields, asphalt and concrete are very common. The former is not particularly abrasion resistant and is restricted to dark colours. The latter soon sustains abrasive damage, forms a surface dust and is not particularly attractive.

It is clear, therefore, that there is still much room for new types of floors. These have become available in the last year or two in the form of compositions based on epoxy resins, members of the plastics family. These are about 10 times more resistant to abrasion than concrete, they can be laid as jointless floors, can be coloured in any way, are very light, resistant to chemicals and sustain no damage from stiletto heels. They can also be used for restoring concrete and as varnishes or paints for protecting woodwork and giving it a high gloss. Such finishes are discussed in detail in Section 2.4.10.

The epoxy resins are obviously of the greatest value and potential.

2.4.1 What are Epoxy Resins?

The epoxy resins are synthetic materials of the plastics family. They are also often called "epoxide" resins and chemically are usually glycidyl ethers of bisphenol-A. The chemical composition, however, need be of no concern.

As far as industry is concerned, the important point is the form in which the materials are available and the products which can be obtained from them. They are normally available as two liquids, the basic resin itself and the hardener. As long as these two are kept apart, they may be stored for long periods, but as soon as they are mixed they will set hard, at room temperature, in a matter of hours. They may thus be applied by all the conventional means and yet, without further treatment, give all the properties previously described.

Manufacturers

The four main producers of the basic resins are:—Bakelite Ltd., ("Bakelite Epoxide"); CIBA (A.R.L.) Ltd., ("Araldite"); Leicester, Lovell and Co. Ltd., ("Epophen"); Shell Chemical Co. Ltd., ("Epikote").

Manufacturers may either buy the resin and hardeners direct and make their own flooring compositions, or purchase ready-made products from a number of other firms. To cater for both requirements, details of compositions and names of firms producing proprietary compositions will be given.

If "Araldite" RY.152 is mixed with Hardener HY.152 and then further mixed with sand it forms a screed which can be laid as a first-class flooring composition. It is solvent free, which means that, virtually, it is shrink-free on setting, and when laid as a floor is hard enough in 24 hours for people to walk on it. A few days after this, the surface is strong enough to take vehicular traffic and after a month or so, it is much stronger than concrete. A further point is, that if the floor must be ready overnight to withstand people and vehicles, then this can be arranged by distributing a number of infra-red or other heaters over the floor. Heat greatly speeds up setting.

2.4.2 Some Outstanding Properties

The materials are resistant to a wide variety of chemicals which makes them suitable for many purposes. A typical range of chemicals is as follows:

Hydrochloric acid (below 36%)	Lactic acid (and milk and other fats)
Sulphuric acid (below 50%)	Sodium hydroxide
Nitric acid (below 10%)	Hydrocarbon solvents
Phosphoric acid	Sugar solutions
Acetic acid (and vinegar dilute)	Fruit juices
Citric acid	Ethyl alcohol
Tartaric acid	White spirit
Carbon tetrachloride	Calcium hypochlorite.

The floors are very resistant to the chemicals given, although the stronger acids will cause rapid deterioration. Ketones cause softening in about a week but the materials harden up on the removal of the solvent.

A number of colours are available with proprietary epoxy floors. For example, in the case of products of Evode Ltd. the standard colours are light grey, venetian red, pale green and light blue. There is obviously no limit here to colours and others will be made to special order.

The mechanical properties of such floors are very good. In general terms, the compressive, flexural, tensile and impact strengths are roughly double the value for the average concrete. Resistance to high pressure is good which means resistance to, for example, stiletto heels. The abrasion resistance is also good, which means the absence of dust which is a valuable characteristic in hospitals and kitchens.

In addition to the merits of epoxy floors, the snags must also be pointed out. The main one is the much higher cost as compared to concrete, so the materials may well be retained for topping, repairs and finishes. In addition, the materials can be damaged by excessive heat and flame and have poor resistance above about 110°C. They can be made relatively flame resistant, however. As compensation for this, the products are unaffected by the freeze-thaw cycle which is disastrous for concrete.

2.4.3   Application Properties

Some properties of the resins are particularly applicable to the installations where they are used. The first one of these is weight. The specific gravity is low but, in addition, only $\frac{1}{8}$ in. to $\frac{1}{4}$ in. of material need be applied to give floors equivalent to much thicker layers of other substances. Here are some examples:

Type of Floor	Weight (lb./sq. yd.)
$\frac{1}{2}$ in. Evoscreed G.P.	25
$\frac{1}{2}$ in. Evoscreed C.R.	27
1 in. Asphalt	110
$1\frac{1}{2}$ in. Concrete	170
1 in. Acid-resisting tiles	110

These low-weight floors are obviously of the greatest value. In particular, architects will be able to make considerable weight savings in multi-storey buildings. In this connection, most of the usual grades of epoxy flooring are rather more flexible than other in situ floors and are, therefore, invaluable for use on suspended steel floors. If architects are not satisfied with the normal degree of flexibility, then additional flexibility may be readily provided.

Another important point with the floors is that they can be applied to all existing floors whether they be concrete, metal or wood. It is only essential that the floors be clean and dry. Another valuable feature is that the slip properties of the floors can be controlled and any degree of non-slip characteristics imparted. Even when wet and with operators wearing rubber boots, there is no danger of slipping.

2.4.4   Some Typical Applications

The fact that epoxy floors are chemical resistant, hard wearing and non-slip has meant application in a number of specific fields such as in buildings that are likely to have chemicals spilt on the floor. Typical examples include laboratories, plating shops, battery rooms, photographic darkrooms, oil refineries, garage lubricating bays and chemical process areas in general.

Other normal applications are places where food is processed. Examples include hospitals, kitchens, sugar refineries, dairies, confectionery factories, bakeries, breweries and similar establishments.

5

The other important series of buildings are those which have to withstand much wear and tear. There are many of these, including warehouse gangways, factory gangways, blacksmiths shops, garage forecourts, loading bays and ramps and any industrial establishments where heavy wheeled trucks are employed.

It should not be thought that all applications are necessarily semi- or fully industrial. Many of the products are used in offices and the home. The epoxy paints are applied even to parquet flooring. This enhances the already high gloss and gives a really hard surface. Car showrooms have been treated in this way and the surfaces have been unaffected for years.

2.4.5   Materials Available

Two main types of products are available. First, there are the epoxy screeds which can be laid on subfloors to act as floors themselves in thicknesses of $\frac{1}{8}$ in. to $\frac{1}{4}$ in. Then there are compositions which are either applied as paint-like materials or thin coats to protect and strengthen existing floors of concrete, wood and the like. Both types will be described.

As far as availability of products is concerned, the user has two courses open to him. He can either make his own, and this is not particularly difficult, or he can obtain ready-to-use proprietary products from a number of suppliers. In the first case detailed compounding instructions will be provided and in the second case detailed lists of suppliers will be given, together with examples of how their products are used.

2.4.6   Basic Flooring Components

The essential ingredients required are the resin, the hardener and the filler.

The *resin* is, of course, the basic ingredient and may be obtained from any of the firms given previously. The resins are usually liquids so that other ingredients may be mixed in with them.

The *hardener* needs to be added to the resin before any reaction will take place. It is this which makes the composition go hard (often called setting or curing) and once it is added, the resultant composition will remain usable for only a limited period. The hardeners are also obtainable from the same firms as the resins.

The *filler* is added either to cheapen the mix (e.g. sand) or to give a non-slip surface (e.g. granite chippings).

A few suppliers are as follows:—

Hinkley's Silica Sand Ltd.—Congleton sand;
J. Arnold and Son—coarse silica sand and Leighton Buzzard No. 6;
H. A. Watson and Co. Ltd.—talc;
Barcoes Sales Ltd.—Asbestine.

Compositions using these ingredients are given later. Two other ingredients may be mentioned. These are flexibilizers added to increase the flexibility of the product (rarely necessary) and pigments. Materials such as red iron oxide may be added direct as colouring, but it is best to buy colour pastes which disperse more easily.

Suppliers are as follows:
Bakelite Ltd.—Flexibilizer DQ. 19116;
J. M. Steel and Co. Ltd.—Flexibilizer Thiokol LP-3;
CIBA (A.R.L.) Ltd.;
Ferro Enamels Ltd.;
Reeves and Sons Ltd.—Colour pastes.

2.4.7 Some Practical Flooring Compositions

The compositions to be described may be mixed by hand in large drums although really efficient agitation is required. It is preferable to use power-driven machines and many suitable industrial mixers are on the market. A cement mixer is ideal for screeds but it must be cleaned thoroughly after use (tumbling with pebbles will help) otherwise the machine may seize up due to the powerful bonding action of epoxy resins.

The method of laying the floor is given later, but in any case, the cleaned floor needs to be primed to give a good bond. The following are two priming compositions:—

(1)	Parts by weight
Bakelite Resin R. 18774	100
Bakelite Hardener DQ. 19159	25
Bakelite Hardener DQ. 19163	25

(2)	Parts by weight
CIBA "Araldite" RY. 152	100
CIBA Hardener HY. 152	50

These are compositions of low viscosity which can be painted on. A suitable chemical resistant flooring for application by trowelling and mixing by machine is:—

(3)	Parts by weight
Bakelite Resin R. 18774	100
Bakelite Hardener DQ. 19159	25
Bakelite Hardener DQ. 19163	25
Cellosolve Solvent	10
Talc (French Chalk)	50
Congleton Sand	1,200

A similar, but more expensive composition is suggested by CIBA:

(4)	Parts by weight
"Araldite" RY. 152	100
Hardener RY. 152	50
Sand	15—55

In the case of Mix (3), it should be noted that if hand mixing is to be employed the amount of sand should be reduced to 600 or 700 parts to allow easier handling. Not more than enough to last three-quarters of an hour should be mixed at a time otherwise it will start to harden and become very difficult if not impossible to lay. In the case of Mix (4), for the best chemical resistance the proportion of sand should be kept low (i.e. 15 parts) but for a flooring for vehicular traffic the higher amounts of sand should be used. However, it should be kept in mind that the higher the proportion of filler, the poorer the mechanical properties. About 1 lb. of Mix (3) at $\frac{1}{8}$ in. thickness covers one square yard.

One final example, a relatively low-cost non-skid flooring, may be given. In this particular case the granite chippings are omitted until the final operation, although a similar mix can be made by adding the chippings to the original mix if required:—

(5)	Parts by weight
Bakelite Resin R. 18774	100
Bakelite Hardener DQ. 19159	25
Bakelite Hardener DQ. 19163	25
Asbestine	70
$\frac{1}{16}$ in. granite chippings	30

The mix is made without the granite chippings and spread out on the floor. The chippings are then scattered over the screed and rolled in. This not only makes a non-skid floor but also gives a terrazzo effect, particularly attractive if it is recalled that the screed can be coloured.

2.4.8 Method of Application

The subfloor must first of all be prepared for the application of the top coat. Whatever procedure is adopted in detail, three important rules should be observed and these are, clean the floor, make it rough and dry it.

New concrete needs little treatment except to dry it out thoroughly. Old concrete, if free from oil and grease, only needs to be roughened by wire brushing, but if oil or grease are present then stronger measures should be taken. Usually cleaning and scrubbing with detergent solutions, followed by clean water, is satisfactory. In the case of particularly dirty floors more drastic treatment than this may be necessary. The best way is to treat with dilute hydrochloric acid followed by hosing with high-pressure water.

Other floors need to be treated in a similar way. Metal should be degreased and roughened and wooden floors should be cleaned and sanded. It should be noted that these treatments give an excellent bond and the subfloor and epoxy screed, in effect, become one.

After treatment as described, the floor must be allowed to dry thoroughly. Minor imperfections in the surface can be left but any serious cracks or holes must be filled up with a heavily filled epoxy screed. The final treatment before application of the top coat is priming with one of the compositions previously mentioned (1 and 2). This achieves an excellent bond between the epoxy screed and the subfloor and contributes to the general strength by the creation of a "laminated structure". It may be noted in this connection that epoxy resins are widely used in adhesive compositions and will virtually bond anything.

One of the advantages of epoxy screeds is that they can be laid by the methods normally employed by the builder. Small areas can be laid by means of a trowel or float without any difficulty. In the case of large areas, however, as in the case of concrete, it is best to employ a power-driven vibrating tamper although hand tamping can give satisfactory results.

It should be stressed that the foregoing methods can be used for both repairing old and damaged concrete and laying new floors. The main difference between the two is the amount of topping applied. By the use of a little imagination the scope of the technique can be greatly increased as a few examples will illustrate. Non-skid compositions can be widely used on a limited basis with great effect. For instance, on paths around swimming pools or thin strips on iron steps. The bonding properties can also be employed to apply a thin topping to an area likely to receive a considerable amount of wear. The best example of this is, perhaps, the stripes on zebra crossings which are often made from epoxy screeds. Ramps and gangways in factories are obvious examples of the technique.

It should be repeated that epoxy flooring compositions can be applied to all other floors including asphalt and stone. Another important point to remember is that the screeds can be made into other forms such as skirting, channels, steps and the like.

The products as described will be used as original floors in thicknesses of $\frac{1}{8}$ in.-$\frac{1}{4}$ in. or as topping compounds, merely to rejuvenate an existing floor. Here, a thickness of about $\frac{1}{16}$ in. will be employed. It should be noted that heavily loaded compounds may be used for the former application but only lightly loaded compositions for the latter application.

2.4.9 Suppliers of Flooring Compositions

Although epoxy resin flooring compounds are relatively simple to make, many users will prefer to purchase ready-made products. Quite a number of companies produce these as two-part compositions which merely have to be mixed before use. The following is a list of suppliers and trade names:—

Acalor (1948) Ltd. (*Acalor*)
British Bitumen Emulsions Ltd.
The Carborundum Co. Ltd.
Cementex (U.K.) Co. Ltd.
 (*Epoweld* and *Epoxicrete*)
Corrosion Technical Services Ltd.
 (*Corroproof*)
E. M. Cromwell and Co. Ltd.
 (*Ceemarcrete*, for repairing concrete; *Ceemarfloor*, high duty flooring; and *Ceemarcoat* anti-corrosive finish for metals)
Dussek Bitumen and Taroleum Ltd.
Evode Ltd. (*Evokote* and *Evoscreed*)
F. Haworth (A.R.C.) Ltd.
 (*Epilon*)

Industrial Flooring and Treatments Ltd. (*Cemaltex*)
Robert Jenkins Plastics Ltd.
Limmer and Trinidad Asphalt Co. Ltd.
Prodorite Ltd. (*Prodoflor*)
Semtex Ltd. (*Semtex*)
Structoplast Ltd. (*Structoplast*)
Surfex Ltd. (*Surclad*)
Technical Applications Ltd. (*Ceradek*)
Tretol Ltd. (*Tretol Epifloor*) (Also manufactures Chemiprufe Enamel M.90 for painting structural steelwork, etc.)

The following examples of the use of these materials are typical of the whole range.

Cementex (U.K.) Co. Ltd.

This company produces a range of products generally known as the *Epowelds* and *Epoxicretes*.

"*Epoweld*" *820*—This material is a liquid which may be applied by spray gun, brush or rubber squeegee. It is available in transparent gold brown, grey, green and other colours and in this form is used as a protective coating in water tanks, swimming pools and the like. On the other hand, when strewn with silicon carbide or other hard-grain material, it gives slip-free industrial flooring and gangways for use in the food and provision trades as well as in the heavy industries. It is hard wearing, has a dust repellant surface, full resistance against diluted inorganic or organic acids and alkalis as well as most solvents. Its pot life is 30-45 minutes and it is also used as a primer for *Epoxicrete 811*.

Epoweld 830—This can be applied in the same way as the *820* and has the same pot life. It can be used as a protective coating for asphalt surfaces in contact with petrol and oil spillage as in service stations and garages. If applied as two layers and strewn with sand, it can be used both as a traffic surface for concrete bridges and as a skid-free traffic surface on wooden bridges.

Traffic marks that last. A worker using yellow "Epoweld" to incorporate traffic markings into the actual road surface (*Cementex (U.K.) Co Ltd*)

Epoweld 812—This is quite a different type of material. It is the anchoring layer in the repair of old cement with new. The joint can take very high stresses and is stronger than the cement itself. If sand is added to the product, then it can be used for repairing cracks in cement. It is "cement" coloured, is applied by steel brush or spreader and has a pot life of 30-45 minutes.

Epoxicrete 811—This is used as a topping in thicknesses of $\frac{1}{8}$ in. to $\frac{1}{4}$ in. in places where there is extremely hard wear and where resistance to chemicals is also required. It has a certain amount of elasticity, can be used as a weatherproof joint-free surface, is available in green, grey, white, black and other colours and has a pot life of 60 to 90 minutes.

All the products described usually harden after 24 hours at a temperature of 77°F. They may, like all epoxy products, cause eczema on sensitive hands so that barrier creams should be used and protective gloves worn. Adequate ventilation should also be provided.

An interesting recent use of Cementex products was the repair of Stockholm's football stadium. The first stage of this work was to clean all surfaces by sand-blasting and to remove rubble from the expansion joints. The entire surface was then primed with dilute *Epoweld 812* and the surfaces levelled with *Epoxicrete*. Finally, vertical surfaces were waterproofed with two coats of *Epoweld* and horizontal surfaces were treated with undiluted *Epoweld* on which sand was sprinkled.

Evode Ltd.

The products of this company are known as *Evoscreed* and *Evokote*. They consist of an epoxy resin, a hardener in a separate container combined with accelerators, a flexibilizer and an aggregate. They have the usual chemical and abrasion resistance and may be applied to all types of floors. All of the ingredients are packaged in convenient sizes so that no weighing on site is necessary.

Evokote floor topping is supplied in six colours with slip resistant aggregate where required.

Evoscreed flooring provides a hard abrasion resistant floor and when applied ¼ in. thick is suitable for heavy industrial conditions where non-slip finish is essential. It is available in six colours and is suitable for breweries, bakeries, warehouses, workshops, etc.

2.4.10 Paint Finishes

As with screeds, paints can either be made up from basic ingredients by the user or purchased ready-made when only a hardener has to be added. It is useful to examine both methods.

A two-or three-coat system of this type has been used to coat concrete swimming pools, cold-storage room walls, asbestos-cement roofing, concrete buildings and the like. No elaborate surface pre-treatment is required but surfaces should be clean, dry and free from loose particles and grease.

Base paint	Parts by weight	Curing agent	Percentage weight
Epikote resin 1001	150	Versamid 115	50
Titanium dioxide (pigment)	200	Oxitol, etc.	20
Solvent mixture	200	Xylol, etc.	30
	550		100

"Epikote" is obtained from Shell Chemical Co. Ltd. and the "Versamid" from Cornelius Chemical Co. The titanium dioxide can be replaced by other pigments or even cheap white fillers (chalk or clay) if required. The solvent mixture will vary according to whether the paint is to be sprayed or brushed on. The brush mixture consists of:

per cent
by weight
MIBK   20–30
Oxitol   40–50
Octoro   30–40

The solvent mixture for spraying consists of 550 parts of the base solution mixed with 100 parts by weight of the curing agent. The mixture will have a pot life of up to 24 hours:

	per cent by weight
MEK	10–15
MIBK	10–15
IPA	10–15
Oxitol	20–30
Xylol	40–50

2.4.10.1   Commercial Paints

Most major paint companies make paints based on epoxy resins. A typical example is *Epigloss* line marking and floor paint made by Coates Brothers Paints Ltd., which is particularly suitable for factory floors of concrete or asphalt and dries to a hard gloss with the usual properties.

Coates Brothers Paints Ltd. (*Epigloss*)

Epigloss is supplied as a two-part paint in the usual way. When mixed it has a pot life of 2-3 days, is surface dry in 1-2 hours, hard dry in 16-24 hours and requires 7 days for maximum cure. The recoating times are 2-3 hours by spray and 3-4 hours by brush. The coats cover 30-35 sq. yd. to the gal.

International Paints Ltd. (*Episeal*)

This company manufactures *Episeal* as well as other epoxy products. It is a red-lead primer for iron and steel over which it is extremely effective and is much faster drying than the conventional primers. The material is recommended for superstructures and decks and has a spreading rate of 50-55 sq. yd. per gal.

Evode Ltd. (*Evoflor and Evokote*)

Evoflor floor paint can be applied to concrete, wood, or linoleum to give a hard wearing decorative protection. Available in six colours it is also used for painting lines on roads, etc. There is also a two-pack *Evokote Type 20* clear lacquer for application to wood surfaces.

These paints are only examples from a wide range. It should be stressed that all of them give a high gloss with exceptional abrasion resistance. The materials are well worth trying over existing floors.

2.5   Polyester (Jointless) Floors

In certain fields the conventional flooring materials are, at best, just good enough because it has been thought that no suitable alternatives were available. Obvious examples include any factory shops where corrosive chemicals are being used.

Again, for hygienic reasons, jointless floors may be necessary to prevent the trapping of dust and germs such as in hospitals and food manufacturing plants. In some cases exceptional abrasion resistance may be necessary, in areas where heavy trucks are moved about. It may, at the same time, be necessary to avoid the noise which would be expected should steel floors be employed.

All of these requirements can be satisfied with polyester resins. These are fully described in Section 5.7 where the principle of the products, methods of manufacture, suppliers and so on are given. Some details of the products as applied to flooring will be given in this section.

Some of the advantages of this type of flooring may be summarized as follows:

(1) They are self-coloured with the colour running right through the material.
(2) They are exceptionally resistant to chemicals and water. (See Section 5.7.12).
(3) Thermal insulation is good which means that heat will be saved compared with conventional floors.
(4) Abrasion resistance is exceptional.
(5) Mechanical properties are excellent.
(6) They are silent.
(7) Low specific gravity and they are therefore light in weight.

Other properties are given under a specific example of polyester flooring described later.

For floors, spraying with chopped glass strand is undoubtedly an important way of proceeding. It is also possible to make exceptionally strong laminates on site.

Some flooring manufacturers merely use the polyester resins with coloured chippings of wood or granite for example, to give a terrazzo-like effect. The ingredients are not fillers in the usual sense but the flooring material is merely bound by the resin. Such floors are very strong as an example given later will show.

2.5.1 The Resins

No specific references are made by suppliers to the types of resins to employ for flooring applications although details will be given on application. Some guidance on the subject can be given, however, since in many ways a flooring resin is similar to the gel coat used in moulding work. The gel coat is a pure resin (i.e. without reinforcement) painted on top of the moulding. It gives a high gloss surface free from glass-fibre pattern and possesses excellent chemical properties and chemical resistance; these properties deteriorate when reinforcing agents are added.

Unfortunately, pure resins are more liable to cracking than the reinforced types. Special grades must therefore be employed. British Resin Products recommend *Cellobond A2731*, a thixotropic type with a storage life of six months. Scott Bader suggest *Crystic 197*, preferably used with *Crystic 182* which is a plasticizing resin. Such resins as these need investigation for flooring purposes. Scott Bader sell a specially compounded resin for gel coats known as *Crystic Gelcoat 33*.

The gel coats may be applied by brush, roller or spray equipment. In the latter case, great care is necessary since one of the components (styrene) can evaporate quickly and cause undercure which results in a most unsatisfactory product. A very humid atmosphere can cause the same trouble as, in fact, can moisture of any nature. The presence of moisture will mean a longer curing time (which can be speeded up by the application of heat). In any case, the cure should be made as rapid as possible.

Various faults are possible in laying floors with any of the foregoing products. One of the most common of these will be crazing. This can be caused by a poor formulation, insufficient mixing, the addition of extra styrene (to make up losses) and the use of the wrong resin. The use of the plasticizing resin (*Crystic 182*) as well as attending to the matters mentioned, will help overcome the problem.

A suitable gel coat formulation is as follows:—

	Parts by weight
Resin	70
Plasticizing resin	30
Catalyst	4
Accelerator	4

It is essential to mix thoroughly as if this is not done, an inconsistent mix will result in which some sections will have gelled prematurely and other sections will be incompletely cured. Mechanical stirring is recommended for all production mixing. However, excessive stirring should be avoided otherwise air bubbles will be introduced and there will be loss of styrene.

Since the compounded mix has a short pot life, only sufficient should be mixed for the work in hand. The temperature of the mixing shop should be kept constant and as low as is consistent with comfortable working.

2.5.2 Spraying Techniques

Obviously, a convenient spray method can save much time and money and suitable equipment is now available, but the quality of the moulding can still rely on the skill of the operator.

The equipment consists basically of two components, the material containers and the spraying unit. Separate containers are, of course, required for the resin promoter and the resin catalyst mixtures. Where used, there must also be a container for the glass-fibre supplier.

There are two spraying nozzles to the equipment, one for each of the two liquids. This is clearly important since it is not required that the curing should begin until the promoter and catalyst come together. The guns are fed from pressurized tanks or by means of pumps, 60 p.s.i. being a suitable pressure. Some slight adjustment between the two nozzles is necessary to ensure a 50:50 ratio of catalyst and accelerated resin. If glass-fibre is used, a cutter is employed to chop it up as it is fed into the resin spray. It is essential that the correct viscosity resin be employed otherwise the spraying will not be successful. The types suggested have been *Cellobond Resins A.2652* and *A.2655*.

Suppliers

Some suppliers of polyester or similar floor-wall coverings are:—Plastics and Resins Ltd. (*Terrazzite*); The Limmer and Trinidad Group of Companies, and Liquid Metal Applicators Ltd.

2.5.3 A Typical Example ("Terrazzite")

A typical example of a flooring material based on polyester resins is *Terrazzite*. It is possible to recognize some of the properties already described in their claims for the material.

Terrazzite is a new, beautiful and durable flooring material that has recently been perfected. It consists of a special resin combination with hard and colourful aggregates mixed with various mineral fillers.

It resembles terrazzo in appearance but weighs only one fifth as much, whilst having many times its strength and wearing qualities. Unlike terrazzo, it does not craze, crack or dust. It will bond to concrete, brick, steel, wood and almost any surface that is clean, dry, free of contamination and, once laid, is virtually indestructible.

Having great density (in fact near that of plate glass) *Terrazzite* is non-absorbent, non-porous, water and grease proof and extremely acid and alkali resistant. It can be laid in any combination of colours, and in an endless variety of patterns. There is no limit to the area that can be laid, and dividing strips of ebonite, plastic or metal can be inserted as an architectural feature. Due to its plastic nature, an unlimited area can be laid without danger of cracking, and adjustments can be made for any reasonable amount of deflection such as would be the case with certain types of wood floors. It is ground and polished within a few hours of being laid, and is then ready for foot traffic. It reaches its full cured strength in only seven days. It is normally laid at a nominal thickness of $\frac{3}{16}$ in. Its dense surface cannot harbour bacteria, and it thus provides an extremely hygienic floor.

Skirtings, dados, treads and risers can, of course, be formed in the material.

An independent laboratory report has been made on the foregoing products and some of the results are interesting.

2.5.4 Indentation Resistance

Loads of 400 lb., 800 lb. and 1 ton were applied to the material surface through a cylindrical steel bar of 1 in. square section. The loads were each held for 5 minutes, then removed and the surface inspected. After subjection to these respective loads there was no detectable indentation of the surface.

2.5.5 Hardness

The impression made by a 1 in. diameter steel ball falling on to the surface from a height of 6 ft. was measured using the standard "carbon paper" method. Diameter of impression was 3·5 mm.

Corresponding figures for other materials were:—

Material	Diameter of Impression, mm.
Magnesite	3·5–6·8
Concrete	4·4
Quarry Tiles	4·0–4·5
Wood Blocks	8·9

2.5.6 Abrasion

A sample was scrubbed 100 times with an abrasive washing powder, and the effect on the surface noted. Small pinholes in the surface were rendered more easily visible, due to the accumulation of the white abrasive powder therein, and most of the surface was now matt. There was no real damage or colour change.

2.5.7 Wear Resistance

The specimens were dried to constant weight and then placed in a rectangular container with their wearing surfaces inwards. A thousand hard steel balls of $\frac{1}{2}$ in. diameter were placed in the container and the whole unit revolved along its horizontal axis at 60 r.p.m. for 22 hours. The specimens were removed for examination after 22 hours revolving in one direction only.

The dust was brushed off and the specimens reweighed with the following results:

Colour	Weight before test, lb.	Weight after test, lb.	Loss in weight, lb.
Black	42·47	42·44	0·03
Green	41·89	41·53	0·36
Red	41·31	41·06	0·25

2.6 Electric Floor Heating

2.6.1 Methods

This review is not meant to give detailed information on floor heating but only an indication of where rubber and plastics are employed in the various systems involved. Details of the floor heating systems themselves may be obtained from the following concerns:

Tyrad Electric Ltd.;
British Insulated Callender's
  Cables Ltd.;
H.V.E. (Electric) Ltd.;
Falks Ltd.;

Thermodare Ltd.;
Heating Investments Ltd.;
Crane Ltd. (skirting heating panels).

The main points to be considered are: (*a*) the type of insulation to use for the heating elements; (*b*) whether to bed direct into the screed or use a conduit; and (*c*) the permitted surface temperature of the floor.

The heating element is always a cable of some type, the most common being the conductor insulated with a high-temperature pvc. This is a satisfactory type and perhaps the safest if any wet conditions are likely to obtain.

It does, of course, suffer from the disadvantages of all thermoplastics and, in addition, if there is a fault followed by excessive increase in temperature, embrittlement of the pvc can occur followed by cracking and failure. On the whole, however, such failures are rare. Most trouble occurs at the joints (element to cold tails) a problem outside the scope of this book.

For those who prefer it, there are cables insulated with butyl rubber which does not embrittle. It is sheathed usually with neoprene or nitrile rubber. Whatever the material the end result is the same except that the butyl-neoprene or nitrile is perhaps more robust and suitable for roads, football fields and the like.

To place a cable in conduit appears to offer a big advantage. If a fault occurs it is a simple matter to withdraw the cable and replace it. Unfortunately, the air gap between cable and conduit (which can be metal but is often pvc) means that the cable has to be run at a higher temperature to give the same floor temperature and this causes many more faults to develop.

Most manufacturers of pvc floors recommend that the temperature of the floor should not exceed 80° to 85°F. Since most floor heating systems recommend these operating temperatures there should not be much trouble. Although pvc tiles and "Hypalon" tiles could operate at higher temperatures than this, the limiting factor may well be the adhesives used for bonding the tiles to the screeds.

If a higher temperature is required, then it is best to employ the jointless plastic floors. Epoxy and polyester floors could easily operate at 100°–120°F.

A development in floor heating is to underlay the screed (and elements) with polystyrene foam.

A typical set-up may be illustrated by an example from Heating Investments Ltd. What they claim is as follows:—

(1) Even heat distribution—no heat ridging or convected currents.
(2) Utilisation of the structure of the building.
(3) Fully automatic controls—no supervision required.
(4) Attendant labour costs completely eliminated.
(5) Completely free floor and wall areas.
(6) No heat flare or damage to furniture or decoration.
(7) Complies with smokeless zone air requirements.
(8) Architecturally is simply integrated.
(9) Low capital installation costs.

Running costs are extremely reasonable, being at least comparable with more conventional forms of central heating. In commercial and industrial premises of reasonable size, where adequate controls are used, running costs of under 1s. 6d. per sq. ft. per annum are common.

A competent design with full heat loss assessment is essential. Average loadings of 15 watts per sq. ft. can be misleading, particularly with the modern light forms of construction, if a full temperature rise is to be provided. In this respect Heating Investments Ltd. or any other member of the Electrical Floor Warming Association would be pleased to give advice.

As far as the element is concerned, development has taken place over many years and basically (for Heating Investments Ltd.) a medium voltage heating element is used with pvc insulation. Experience has proved that the best element is of stranded semi-high tensile steel. Each strand is of about 0·015 in. diameter. This is laid-up to provide an element giving a loading of between 4 and 5 watts per linear foot. The element is insulated with pvc.

The cable is made up into a range of sizes:

kW	Length, ft.	Colour Code
3·9	849	Dark green
3·3	720	Brown
3·0	660	Light Green
2·7	600	Orange
2·3	520	Yellow
1·75	400	Violet
1·4	300	White
1·1	250	Pink
0·9	200	Grey
0·7	150	Blue

Each made-up element is then fitted with copper conductor double insulated pvc cold tails, of the length to suit the requirements of the building (12 ft. minimum).

The joint between the cold tail and the element is manufactured with extreme care and rigidly tested to ensure that no consequential trouble arises after this has been buried in the floor. The joint is crimped and soldered for electrical continuity and mechanical strength, and a pvc sleeve is moulded overall for a completely waterproof joint.

From the above design, the elements are laid between specially extruded pvc fixing and spacing strip, which is pinned to the structural floor to provide a firm and accurate fixing. The spacing varies between 2·5 and 4-in. centres. The whole is then overscreeded with a calculated thickness of concrete to requirements.

The cold tails of each element are run back to a central position and connected to a suitable fuseboard, contactor and Thermotime regulator. The last item can have associated with it internal air thermostats, or these can be used as an alternative, according to circumstances. It is important that the controls should be adequate for the purpose to ensure that maximum economy is achieved in running costs. The sizes and ratings of the electrical equipment feeding the floor-warming system should be chosen with care as the resistance of the elements when cold (at switch-on) is higher than when the installation is at working temperature. Serious overloading (and a dangerous condition) can result.

2.6.2   Thermal Insulation with Foam

The loss of heat through floors, walls and roofs is accepted with resignation although the cost of this loss is incalculable and even now there is little thought of saving energy where heated floors are not to be employed.

Fortunately, the advent of floor heating has drawn our attention to the limitations of the existing systems and efforts are now being made to improve the situation. This development has been made possible, to a large degree, by the development of plastic foams. They have extremely low "K" and "U" values and are ideal for floor insulation.

Plastic foams and suppliers are dealt with in detail in Section 1.3.8. This section covers those aspects which particularly apply to flooring.

Commercial Information

It will be useful to know the forms in which the various foams are available. In the case of polyurethane, those which are likely to be of interest to the flooring industry include liquids for foaming on site, strips with self-adhesive backing (for sealing cracks), prefabricated shapes, sheets, say, $\frac{1}{12}$ in. up to 4 in. thick, and 36 in. to 79 in. wide in varying lengths (often up to 250 yards), and special tailored products for fitting into unusually shaped areas.

For floor heating purposes, the most usual form of polystyrene is in standard sheets. Thicknesses vary from $\frac{1}{4}$ in. up to 12 in. and sizes of, say, 9 ft. × 4 ft., 4 ft. × 4 ft., 3 ft. × 2 ft., 2 ft. × 1 ft. and many others. Moulded shapes can also be provided and the use of expanded beads or pellets for mixing with concrete will be mentioned later.

Floors in General

Slabs of polystyrene foam are laid on concrete floors to form an insulated foundation for flooring cements or composition floors. The thickness of the slabs usually varies between $\frac{1}{2}$ in. and 1 in. If the expanded slabs are laid before any part of the floor, then the ground should be covered with a layer of fine ashes. This is an advantage since it assists in excluding moisture.

On the other hand, an advantage of applying the polystyrene slabs over the concrete is that floors can be laid immediately as there is no seepage of moisture from the concrete. However, joints between slabs should be sealed with a filler or tape and covered with bitumen paper. It is also important that the cement or concrete foundation be even. Where joists are specified, the spaces between them can be filled with expanded beads or slabs.

In the case of wooden boards or parquet floors, these can be laid direct on the polystyrene slabs, using the normal techniques of bitumen under-felt and adhesive.

In the case of uneven concrete floors, these should be levelled with sand to avoid local overloading and consequent cracking of the cement screed.

Floors over basements, above archways and terraces, require a thicker layer of foam for perfect insulation. It is also advisable to use a layer of bitumen paper in such cases.

Polystyrene insulated floors have excellent sound and heat insulation properties. So far as heat is concerned, polystyrene is ideal for incorporation into floor heating systems where the cables, or conduits carrying them, are laid directly on the blocks. So far as sound insulation is concerned, by employing 1 in. of polystyrene over a bare concrete floor, the improvement is approximately 15 phons. To improve the elimination of sound transmission, polystyrene edge strips are laid along the wall corners before placing the main slabs into position and casting the cement floors.

Piggery Floor Insulation

As a specific example of the use of foam in floors, a piggery installation may be considered. A considerable increase in the food conversion factor is obtained when a piggery floor is properly insulated. This is quite well known but what is not so well known, however, is how to obtain proper insulation at a reasonable and economical cost.

Experiments with a number of trial floors under all kinds of conditions has shown that foamed polystyrene ("Poron" for example) used in the following form of floor construction gives first-class insulation properties, with a good hard wearing floor, resulting in a minimum loss of body heat by the pigs.

(1) The floor must be flat and of good surface (new construction should be

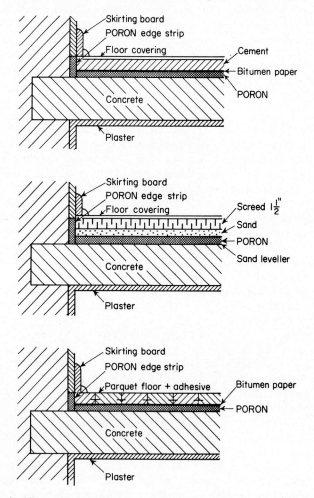

Various Poron foamed polystyrene perimeter insulation (*Poron Insulation Ltd*)

of well rammed hardfilling, say 3 in.–4 in. thick with 3 in.–4in. concrete of 6:3:1 mix with a screeded finish); existing floors should be broken up, rammed and surfaced with at least 2–3 in. of 3:1 cement-sand mix and screeded, or if otherwise mechanically sound, screeded to level with 3:1 mix of cement-sand—minimum 1 in. thick. It is recommended that the floor should be hacked to give a key for the screed or a coat of grout or slurry well brushed in and allowed to dry to form a key.

(2) This surface screed must then be coated with a bituminous solution at the rate of 15 to 20 yd. per gal. ("Synthaprufe" is one such suitable material). It is recommended that one coat be applied, allowed to dry, followed by a second coat.

(3) While the bituminous solution is still tacky, slide into place $\frac{3}{4}$ in. slabs of foam so that a small quantity of solution is forced up between the joints as a seal: it is recommended that "Poron" grade P.30 should be used as this has a higher compressive strength than the standard P.15 grade.

(4) A top screed of cement-sand in the ratio of 3:1, incorporating a wire-mesh or expanded metal reinforcement, should be laid over the "Poron" to a thickness of 2 in.

Use of Beads

The use of expanded polystyrene beads to "dilute" concrete is a valuable development in concrete flooring technology. A number of advantages result from this development. First, the "K" value of the concrete is considerably reduced. Secondly, moisture resistance and absorption (the cells for this purpose are non-communicating) are reduced and, finally, there is a considerable weight reduction. Expanded polystyrene beads at 2 lb. per cu. ft. may be compared with a stone aggregate at 140 to 150 lb. per cu. ft. The importance of this in structural steelwork and load-bearing wall considerations is obvious.

The following figures, based on information given by Dr. W. D. Brown of Monsanto Chemicals Ltd., illustrate the change in strength with varying polystyrene bead content.

Strength of Polystyrene-Concrete Mixtures

Parts by Volume			Bulk Density,	Crushing Strength,
Granules	Cement	Sand	lb./ft. cu.	lb./in. sq.
4	1	—	21	23
3	1	—	28	70
2	1	—	52	350
1	1	—	76	600
12	1	3	28	20
8	1	3	42	46
4	1	3	63	150
2	1	3	88	380
3	1	2	79	260

6

In mixing the screed, the water ratio should be sufficient only to give a workable mix as an excess of water will give a tendency for the granules to "float" to the surface. Concrete must be "placed" and not "dumped" into position. By the use of reinforcement, extremely lightweight slabs capable of high load bearing can be obtained.

Advantages of Foams

An outline of foam technology has been given to enable those concerned with floors to reconsider their designs and views thereon. The use of expanded plastics is not extensive at the moment, but there can be little doubt that their application will be extended when the properties and advantages of the materials have become better understood.

The biggest advantage of the use of foams is to improve heat insulation and the improvement is most marked. Sound insulation can also be improved and moisture ingress reduced. A weight reduction can also be obtained when expanded polystyrene is mixed with cement.

One or another of these advantages can be achieved in most installations. The cost, of course, is increased, at least as far as raw materials are concerned, but the saving, in terms of heat conservation, quickly offsets this. All flooring manufacturers would do well to consider these new materials.

Part 3

WALLS

CONTENTS

3.1 Introduction
    3.1.1 Rigid Plastic Laminates
    3.1.2 "Stick-on" Decorative Finishes
    3.1.3 Other PVC Finishes
    3.1.4 Sandwich Laminates
    3.1.5 Miscellaneous Applications

3.2 Continuous Plastic Wall Coverings
    3.2.1 Flexible PVC Coverings
    3.2.2 PVC-coated Fabrics
    3.2.3 Quilted PVC and Artificial Stone Wall Facings
    3.2.4 Rigid PVC Sheets
    3.2.5 Application of Plastic Coats
    3.2.6 PVC-coated Wallpaper
    3.2.7 Polystyrene Wallpaper Backings
    3.2.8 PVC Skirting

3.3 Wall Tiles
    3.3.1 PVC Wall Tiles
    3.3.2 Polystyrene Wall Tiles

3.4 Plastic Laminates and Boards
    3.4.1 Decorative Laminates
    3.4.2 Technical Properties and Machining
    3.4.3 Other Laminates and Suppliers
    3.4.4 Plastic-faced Boards

3.5 Plastics in Construction
    3.5.1 Sandwich Construction for Curtain Walling
    3.5.2 Cladding
    3.5.3 Doors
    3.5.4 Panels
    3.5.5 Miscellaneous

3.6 Plastic Glazing Products
    3.6.1 Properties of PVC
    3.6.2 Reasons for Using PVC
    3.6.3 PVC as a Complementary Material
    3.6.4 All-PVC Windows
    3.6.5 Manufacturers and Their Products

3.7 Insulation with Foam

3.8 Miscellaneous
    3.8.1 Plastic-covered Wire Fences
    3.8.2 Venetian Blinds

Part 3

WALLS

3.1 Introduction

Until quite recently, the usual conception of plastics for wall and similar finishes was simple. There were two principal subjects only, these being decorative laminates of one sort or another and paints. Many of the latter have "plastic" bases.

In the past few years the situation has changed considerably. There is now a wide variety of finishes which not only impart a pleasing appearance but also offer considerable protection to the underlying fabric and replace structural materials. In addition, many of the new sandwich laminates give a considerable amount of thermal and acoustic insulation. A summary of the applications of plastics to walls is as follows:

3.2 Continuous Plastic Wall Coverings
   (pvc and polyester resins)
3.3 Wall Tiles
   (pvc and polystyrene)
3.4 Plastic Laminates and Boards
3.5 Plastics in Construction
   (partition walls, cladding, doors, panelling)
3.6 Plastic Glazing Products
   (pvc-covered window frames)
3.7 Insulation with Foam
3.8 Miscellaneous
   (pvc-covered fences, venetian blinds)

Although decorative laminates are one of the oldest forms of plastics used in architectural design, their use is still growing rapidly. Moreover, most manufacturers are aware of the need to produce light-covered contemporary designs and a variety of these is now available.

The vinyl plastics (pvc) in one form or another are making a marked impression in the industry. Decorative sheets of thin pvc are available for sticking on to walls, and rigid pvc sheeting is available for applications where severe staining or attack by corrosive liquids is likely to occur. There are a number of pvc laminates, the best known being a pvc-surfaced hardboard, which gives the valuable properties of pvc to the older type material.

There are also a number of miscellaneous applications of great value and potential. For appearance and insulation purposes polystyrene wall tiles are becoming very popular. Attractive vinyl wall tiles are also being used on an increasing scale. "Perspex" in one of its many forms is used for internal partitions and facings to give unusual effects. There are also a number of plastic finishes which can be sprayed on to floors, ceilings or walls to give unusual and valuable properties and a pleasing appearance at the same time.

3.1.1   Rigid Plastic Laminates

Plastic laminates are being developed extensively, particularly from the point of view of providing contemporary as well as classical designs. Two of the best known names in this field are "Warerite" made by Bakelite Ltd., and "Formica" made by Formica Ltd. These laminates are made by impregnating paper or fabrics with various resins and bonding them under high pressure and heat. The top paper or fabric in the laminate can have any desired design.

A recent example of really attractive designs is provided by the s.s. "Oriana". "Warerite" murals were used extensively in the ship, notably in the ballrooms, restaurants and bars. An unusual feature was to employ "Warerite"-clad and coloured coded doors to indicate the function of the room behind. For example, a grey "Warerite" door indicates a shower room, fresco blue and terra-cotta doors indicate, respectively, ladies' and gentlemen's lavatories, whilst a black "Warerite" door indicates "For crew use only".

"Warerite", as with "Formica" and similar products, has the usual valuable properties of such materials. These include exceptional surface abrasion resistance and resistance to chemicals, non-stain characteristics and therefore easy cleaning properties. Usually, hot tea or coffee pots do not leave any marks but special cigarette-proof grades are available.

Several companies are concentrating on the production of new designs. Fablon Ltd. produce "Fablonite," a new decorative melamine plastic laminate. A recent introduction, the so-called Harmony range, has a two-in-one technique involving a cut-out shape superimposed on a contrasting effect. The idea of this Harmony range is to give the appearance of quality inlays and veneers.

Harrison and Sons Ltd. is another company that has developed a new range of contemporary plastics patterns in decorative laminates. The designs specially created include Tintagel, Samarkand, Promenade, Montmartre, Cheviot, etc. These have been developed in a variety of colours and shades and include a supplementary range of wood grains.

The well-known Swedish manufacturers Skanska Attikfabriken A.B. of Perstorp, represented in Britain by Perstorp Products (Great Britain) Ltd., have undertaken considerable work in developing suitable decorative laminates. The first textured decorative laminate has been produced by them and is called "Swedish Perstorp Relief". It has been designed for use on walls and other surfaces requiring particularly high aesthetic standards, and the light reflection, which cannot be avoided with normal laminates, is low and gives an impression of softness and warmth. One of the newer patterns in the standard range of Perstorp laminates is called "Doodles" and was designed by Count Sigvard Bernadotte, the internationally known designer and son of the King of Sweden.

3.1.2   "Stick-on" Decorative Finishes

One of the more recent developments in the plastics industry is the production of decorative sheets with a self-adhesive backing. Usually, these are made of pvc embossed with a special design on the paper surface and backed with adhesive on the lower surface, this in turn being protected with a paper which is peeled off before use.

Spicers Ltd. is one company that is producing a new material for interior decor called "Attracta". The material, once installed, is washable, resistant to grease, moisture and humidity as well as being extremely hard. It is available in many colourful patterns, and is highly flexible so that it can be bent, curved or angled round corners and the like. It is a triple laminate of pvc with the pattern protected by a top coat of transparent plastic.

A rather more unusual finish is provided by Cascelloid Ltd. They have produced an imitation stonework design employing a new moulding technique for pvc. Instead of the usual flat finish the stonework is reproduced in three dimensions. It can be painted any colour and really does look like a stone wall. It can be used either indoors or outdoors and is applied by using Bostik No. 1775 as the adhesive.

I.C.I. Ltd. are producing a number of pvc wall coverings of this type. One of their products is the well-known mural "Vynide" range which is available in 12 colours. They also produce "Vynalast" hard pvc foil which can be used for covering any surface such as hardboard, plywood, plaster board, chipboard and the like. It is available in roll form in 50-in. finished widths which therefore makes it suitable for covering the standard building board which is 48 in. wide, and to permit clean-edge trimming. The rolls are long enough to permit continuous lamination to boards. It is interesting to note that once "Vynalast" has been bonded to a non-metallic base material, the resulting laminates can be treated in exactly the same way as the base material. In other words, if the laminate produced is "Vynalast"-plywood it can be sawn by hand or mechanical means.

3.1.3 Other PVC Finishes

PVC is a versatile material and can be applied to walls in a number of ways. One of the most interesting is the use of vinyl-sprayed coatings which cover the surfaces with a continuous tough and flexible coating. It is considerably thicker than a conventional paint film and has a working life of at least 15 years without maintenance. The technique can be used internally and externally.

One firm which has developed a special system is R. A. Brand and Co. Ltd. who were the originators of the well-known "cocoon" sprayed skin technique for preserving equipment. Their new method of wall covering is called "Plastopak" and is an air-drying solution which is applied by spray gun. Flexible vinyl films from $0 \cdot 030$ in. to $0 \cdot 150$ in. thick are provided and form outstanding barriers to water, water vapour and dust. The solution is available in a range of colours which can be sprayed across gaps over which the vinyl film will form, thus giving a completely continuous film. This is obviously of great importance on walls having cracks, joins or other similar defects.

The technique developed by R. A. Brand and Co. can be extended to the use as a lightweight weatherproof roofing. Although this is more expensive than normal asphalt or multi-layer roofing felt, it can show a cost advantage where the roof is complicated by the presence of adjacent walls, parapets, roof lights and so on. In industrial finishes it is often necessary to provide exceptional protection to resist corrosive fluids. A recent example occurred at the Central Markets, Smithfield. The walls come into contact with the various juices from meat and the like and a hygienic and resistant finish was required. I.C.I.'s "Darvic" pvc sheet was chosen for the purpose by the Corporation of London for its good appearance and hard wearing and hygienic qualities.

PVC-surfaced hardboard has now become available and is manufactured by Plastics Marketing Co. Ltd. The material is made in a variety of plain colours, wood grains and patterns in sizes up to 12 ft. × 4 ft. The material has a hard surface which will not easily scratch and it can be cleaned with soap or mild detergents. The pvc component also imparts a high degree of flame resistance to the composite board. Some applications to date include ceiling panels, flush doors, shop window linings, bath panels and the like.

3.1.4   Sandwich Laminates

Ordinary laminates are well enough known but the sandwich laminates are now becoming more popular. They normally consist of an upper and lower face made of a plastic material separated by some type of honeycomb structure. The latter can be a foamed plastic product, glass-fibre or mineral wool. These materials have a number of valuable properties. Amongst these may be included thermal and acoustic insulating characteristics, coupled with light weight and good strength. They have good fire resistance apart from the normal surface properties of any other laminate. A good example of this type of material is "Holoplast" made by Holoplast Ltd.

It should be stressed that the sandwich technique is likely to develop extensively. The new polyurethane foams are easy to use, have valuable properties and are likely to be adopted extensively for sandwich laminates. The architect would therefore do well to follow developments closely in this important field.

3.1.5   Miscellaneous Applications

A few miscellaneous applications may be briefly described to indicate the wide scope of plastics in building. They indicate the versatility of plastics, the most attractive designs which can be obtained from them and the excellent protection against all sorts of deleterious influences which can be imparted.

A comparatively new development in plastics is the use of transparent or translucent materials in various colours to impart unusual optical effects. Polystyrene wall tiles applied by adhesives can fall into this category. The surface can be given a wide variety of designs and a most attractive finish results which can be washed down with water.

Other applications of plastics to walls (in the widest sense) may be mentioned. For example they are used in glazing, mainly for covering and protecting metal and wood parts. Walls are being insulated with foam, and even Venetian blinds are being made in plastics, particularly orientated polystyrene. The use of pvc for coating metals (sheets for panels or wire for fences) opens up new possibilities for structural materials and these are discussed in full. Many miscellaneous applications are also considered.

3.2 Continuous Plastic Wall Coverings

The use of the expression "continuous plastic wall coverings" is only relative in that it is meant to imply large sheets of material rather than tiles. At the same time, there are various resins which can be applied to walls to give a jointless surface and these are also included in the present section. The following are therefore the products dealt with:

3.2.1 Flexible PVC Coverings
3.2.2 PVC-coated Fabrics
3.2.3 Quilted PVC and Artificial Stone Wall Facings
3.2.4 Rigid PVC Sheets
3.2.5 Application of Plastic Coats
3.2.6 PVC-coated Wallpaper
3.2.7 Polystyrene Wallpaper Backings
3.2.8 PVC Skirting.

3.2.1 Flexible PVC Coverings

A good example of a flexible surfacing material is provided by the "Corlon" of Armstrong Cork Co. Ltd.

Four designs are available—Supreme, Granette, Starglow and Tesserette, in 0·045 in. overall thickness. All these designs are in pastel pale colours ideally suited to blend with any decorative scheme and both Supreme and Starglow series have metallic particles inlaid in the wearing surface. All designs are available in 27 in., 45 in. and 72 in. rolls, the roll sizes being as follows:—

Width	Max. and min. roll size	Average length per roll	Average area per roll	Approximate gross weight per roll
27 in.	30–65 lin. ft.	59 lin. ft.	132·75 sq. ft.	40 lb.
45 in.	30–65 lin. ft.	59 lin. ft.	221·25 sq. ft.	59 lb.
72 in.	35·1–60 sq. yd. (17–30 lin. yd.)	75 lin. ft.	50 sq. yd. (450 sq. ft.)	127 lb.

Some of the advantages claimed for "Corlon" are that it can readily be turned round sharp corners; is abrasion resistant; is quiet and cushions impact; resists soap and alkalis; is easy to clean and small surface scratches rub out with use; resists stains; resists temperatures up to 230°F. and does not buckle with heat; costly maintenance of painting is avoided; is hygienic and does not hold dirt; is fade resistant and is relatively fire resistant and does not spread flame.

The following is a list of manufacturers of flexible vinyl covering materials:

Armstrong Cork Co. Ltd.,
Storeys of Lancaster ("Stormur"),
I.C.I. Ltd. ("Vymura") (For "Vynalast" see Section 3.1),
British Xylonite Group of Companies ("Velbex"),
Garland Ltd.,
Stanley Smith and Co. Ltd.,
Wallington, Weston and Co. Ltd.,
Arnoplast Ltd.,
Clearex Products Ltd.,
S. C. Erringron (Hanwell) Ltd.,

Paniquil (Sales) Ltd.,   R. A. Goodall and Co. Ltd.,
Spicers Ltd.,   Pytram Ltd.,
Armoride (Sales) Ltd.,   Thermo Plastics Ltd.,
Commercial Plastics (Sales), Ltd.,   Vacform Plastics Ltd.,
Fablon Ltd.,   Willmotts Ltd.
Greenwich Plastics Ltd.,

An interesting type of special vinyl sheeting is sold by Paniquil (Sales) Ltd. There are, in fact, two sheets: one transparent, one laminated to a bottom vinyl coating which is coloured. Between the two films are locked natural objects such as fibres and foliage which look extremely realistic as they are covered with a film which is almost imperceptible. The name "Royaltex" is given to this type of film.

3.2.2 PVC-coated Fabrics

Fabric-backed pvc is stronger than unsupported sheet and thus may be more suitable in situations where damage is likely to occur. A typical example is "Mural Florestin" made by Armoride Ltd.

Paniquil ceiling modules. Introduced at the 1961 Building Exhibition were the first modules in Paniquil padded and quilted plastics panelling. They incorporate high thermal and sound insulation and are available in a wide range of colours and in designs of 6-and 8-inch squares. (*Paniquil Ltd.*)

The material consists of a specially woven fabric base, to which a coating of tough pvc has been applied mechanically to a controlled thickness. The coating is cured under high temperatures to ensure that the colours will not fade or wash out. The fabric back is mould proof. "Mural Florestin" has excellent durability, particularly in respect of resistance to abrasion. The surface will not scuff, flake or chip, and thus the product, correctly applied, has an extremely long service life during which its appearance does not deteriorate.

It is impervious to dirt, and is thoroughly hygienic and easy to maintain—it can normally be cleaned by a wipe down with a damp cloth, using warm water and soap where grease is present. Strong detergents, polishes and cleaners should not be used. Because of its durability and easy-clean properties, "Mural Florestin" is recommended as highly suitable for situations where wear and tear is heavy, such as corridors, outside lift entrances, and in hotel and catering establishments, hospitals, schools, shops and similar locations.

The material is available in a wide range of plain colours and patterns, all with various surface embossings which provide interesting textured effects and contribute towards its luxurious appearance. Application of "Mural Florestin" is simple. A mould-proof adhesive recommended by the manufacturers is applied to the wall, and not to the back of the material, which is handled dry. The material is supplied in rolls 50 in. wide and 50 yards long.

"Stormur", manufactured by Storeys of Lancaster, also a fabric-backed vinyl, is available in 130 patterns and colourways, illustrating the choice open to designers.

"Plastylon-Mur" is made by Bulgomme and consists of $85 \cdot 6\%$ pure pvc and $14 \cdot 4\%$ cotton support. It is available in 55-in. widths and rolls of 27 yards. It can be shaped to fit corners and round surfaces and is available in a number of patterns including wood grain patterns.

Manufacturers of vinyl backed with fabric are as follows:

Armoride Ltd.,
Storeys of Lancaster,
I.C.I. Ltd. ("Vynide"),
Arlington Plastics Development
    Ltd.,
Bulgomme-Silence Flooring,

Mellowhide Products Ltd.,
Renmore Ltd.,
Bernard Wardle (Everflex) Ltd.,
Robert Pickles Ltd.,
Brifex Ltd.

3.2.3 Quilted PVC and Artificial Stone Wall Facings

The quilted finish of "Paniquil" was described in Section 3.2.1. Another example is "Quilton" supplied by Dalmas, Ltd.

"Quilton" is obtainable in 10 colours—painted lady (red), lilac, spanish gold, verdet (green), cavendish blue, steel grey, summer sky, ice pink, black and white—in two patterns, diamond or button and in alternative finishes of "satin" and "calf". The material is supplied in sealed widths 36 in. wide and can be cut by scissors to any desired shape. The cut edges can be sealed for decorative purposes by a variety of available wood, plastic, or other metal beadings, furnishing braids, self-adhesive tapes, etc., or can be effectively used for display purposes. The standard diamond and button patterns have an $\frac{1}{8}$ in. foam padding.

Manufacturers of these materials are: Dalmas Ltd.; Paniquil (Sales) Ltd.; and Airscrew-Weyroc Ltd. ("Luxweld").

There is an interesting type of decorative finish which gives the impression of a real wall. The pvc is moulded (three dimensionally) to the pattern of a stone wall and can be painted to give any stone finish. The pvc can be stuck to almost any surface. The material is made by Cascelloid Ltd. The sheets are 51⅜ in. × 21⅜ in. and corner pieces are also available. Osma Plastics Ltd. are making a similar product but using glass-reinforced polyester.

3.2.4   Rigid PVC Sheets

A brief description of rigid pvc has already been given in Section 1.3.1. One of the big advantages of the material is its excellent resistance to water and chemicals.

One example of its application is to be found at Smithfield Market, where the market stall partitions have been faced with "Darvic" pvc sheet which provide not only a lasting and hygienic surface but improve the finish of the existing walls. A trial period showed that despite constant battering with heavy frozen carcasses, the plastic proved its value. Approximately 75,000 sq. ft. of "Darvic" was used in the installation.

An even more impressive use was in the Generating Hall of the Kariba Dam. The problem was to meet the conditions imposed by water having a strong alkaline content, which dripped through the roof of the building. The roof was therefore lined with 1,250 sheets of "Darvic" each 41 in. × 66 in. in size, which led the water away, affording complete protection and also making an attractive ceiling as well. This use also illustrates another property of rigid pvc. By a simple vacuum forming process, any shape can be moulded into the surface. In the case of the Kariba Dam, the moulding was carried out by Rediweld Ltd. of Crawley, Sussex. They gave the sheets V-corrugations and some lateral stiffened pieces were cemented to the back of each sheet. The edges of the sheets can also be "welded" together (see Section 5.3.8.) to give a continuous sheet. Such techniques as these suggest a great variety of uses under the most diverse conditions.

Manufacturers

Manufacturers of the material include:—I.C.I. Ltd.; British Xylonite Group of Companies; Glass Fibre Developments Ltd. and Storeys of Lancaster.

3.2.5   Application of Plastic Coats

The spraying of pvc on to ceilings is described in Section 3.1.3. A similar treatment may be given to walls.

Polyester resins, with or without glass-fibre reinforcement, and other plastics, may also be sprayed or painted on walls. A wide range of colours is available.

Various plastics for application to walls are made by:

Plastics and Resins Ltd.   Liquid Metal Applicators Ltd.
  ("Lifetime").

"Lifetime" is a semi-liquid compound in one part, which can be applied by either amateurs or professionals by brush or spray-gun. It cures in about 6-8 hours at an average temperature of 50°F. and when cured is extremely elastic, stretching with thermal movements of the substrata. The latter can be almost anything, and the compound is not affected by application to a damp wall, being water-based (which also means that brushes, etc. can be cleaned in water and no solvents are needed provided the material has not cured).

"Lifetime" will insulate, if applied thickly enough, against noise, cold, heat and electricity, as well as being a completely effective damp-proofer. It can also be used internally and can be decorated over. An excellent use is as an adhesive beneath quarry tiles, since it tends to deaden slightly the noise, will damp-proof the floor, and is an extremely powerful adhesive.

"Lifetime" comes in several attractive colours, and is available in five, one or half-gallon cans.

3.2.6 PVC-coated Wallpaper

I.C.I. Ltd. have introduced "Vymura", a paper-backed vinyl. The material is supplied in ready trimmed film-wrapped rolls in standard wallpaper sizes and can be hung in the usual way. There are 49 designs and in tests the paper has withstood scrubbing twice a week for 12 months without any damage.

Fablon Ltd. has also produced a paper-back vinyl wall covering under the name Fablon Vinyl Wall Covering. The material is 27 in. wide, has a textured finish and is sold in 20 pastel shades.

J. and H. Bennett (Flooring) Ltd. also sell "Rado-vinyl," a paper-backed wall-covering. It is available in a wide range of colours.

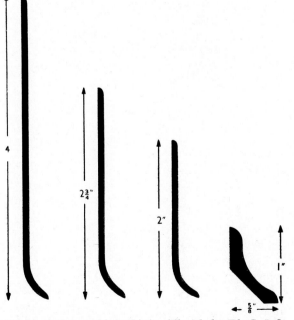

Marley vinyl-covered-base skirting (*The Marley Tile Co Ltd*)

3.2.7 Polystyrene Wallpaper Backings

An interesting development for wall coverings is "New Wall", an expanded polystyrene wallpaper backing made by Newalls Insulation Co. Ltd. It prevents condensation, provides a smooth surface for the wallpaper and is supplied in rolls 30 ft. × 2 ft. × $\frac{1}{16}$ in.

A similar product is "Kotina" made by The Wallpaper Manufacturers Ltd. Supplied in 3 ft. × 4 ft. sheets of either 2 or 5 mm. thickness, it is recommended for application under wallpaper in kitchens, bathrooms or wherever there is trouble with condensation and dampness. In addition to its insulation and acoustic properties, it covers minor cracks and defects in old plaster and provides a perfect decorating surface for wallpaper.

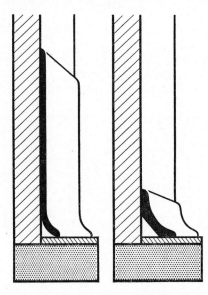

Marley vinyl-covered-base skirting (*The Marley Tile Co Ltd*)

3.2.8 PVC Skirting

The advantages of pvc-base skirtings should be obvious. In general, they provide a smooth, dust-free union between wall and floor and protect the base of the wall from scuff marks. The need for timber skirtings and maintenance is eliminated.

The Marley vinyl-covered-base skirting is extremely flexible before and during fitting and is easily moulded to follow wall contours when required. It is available in six colours, plus black and white, in four sizes (4 in., $2\frac{3}{4}$ in. and 2 in. with a special 1 in. "minicove") and is available in flexible or rigid lengths. It is applied with Marley M21 adhesive. Manufacturers of skirting are:

Marley Tile Co. Ltd.;   Robbin's Linoleum Ltd.

3.3 Wall Tiles
3.3.1 PVC Wall Tiles

By using pvc for wall tiles, much the same advantages are obtained as using the material for floors (Section 2.2). In particular, the tiles will last the life of the building (unlike paper and distemper) and are thus particularly suited to use in large buildings. The colours go right through the tiles; they withstand staining, discoloration, crazing and most common chemicals; they are much less likely to cause condensation on walls than ceramic tiles (for example) and the wide range of colours means that they can be fitted into almost any scheme. PVC wall tiles are made by The Marley Tile Co. Ltd.

"Marleymura" Tiles

The "Marleymura" tiles, being vinyl, are tough, resilient and resistant to hard usage. One of the big advantages is that they are easy to clean and simple washing keeps them bright and new. However, Marley Superwax does give a lustrous sheen. The tiles are available in five pastel tints—green, blue, yellow, grey and pink, as well as black. The size is 12 in. × 6 in. The tiles can easily be cut to other shapes if required.

Marley Vinyl Wall Tiles

The Marley wall tiles are available in nine colours, plain and marbled patterns, including black. The sizes are $4\frac{1}{2}$ in. × $4\frac{1}{2}$ in., 6 in. × 6 in. and 9 in.× 6 in., except for flecked and stippled patterns which are available in one size only—$4\frac{1}{2}$ in. × $4\frac{1}{2}$ in. The thickness is $\frac{1}{16}$ in. The slightly rounded edges of the tiles ensure clearly defined but close butting joints. Capping and feature strip is available in nine colours, $\frac{3}{4}$ in. wide. The tiles can be fixed with a special adhesive to virtually any dry and firm surface.

Specifications for New Works—For Cement Rendering or Plastering (Materials and Finish)

The wall surfaces to receive Marley wall tiling should be rendered in cement and sand, finished with a steel float or finished with hard wall plaster. The surfaces should be thoroughly dry before the tiles are fixed.

Angles

Internal and external 90° angles can be finished with the right-angle strip produced for the purpose or the tiles may be carried to the angle, as may be desired.

Curves and Bullnoses

Curves and bullnoses should not be tiled.

Fixing

Marley wall tile cement as recommended by the manufacturer should be used.

Protection Against Dampness

Marley wall tiles should not be fixed to walls subject to penetration of dampness behind the tiling, as, for example, due to absence of horizontal damp-proof courses, 1th embankments and so on.

Where tiling is brought down to the sides of baths or the back or sides of sinks or lavatory basins or at other points where water may lodge, the tiling should be kept above the edge of the fitting and a fillet of waterproof mastic inserted below the lower edge of the tiling and the edge of the fitting.

Waxing
After fixing, the tiles should be waxed with Marley Superwax and lightly buffed.

Fixing Marley Tiles to Walls

The method recommended by Marley for fixing their tiles to walls is as follows:

"Marleymura" can be applied to any wall that is clean, smooth, firm and dry. Wallpaper, flaking paint, etc., should be removed first.
(1) The starting line should be straight and level near or at the bottom of the wall. Measure the height to be covered, and adjust the starting line so that there is not a row of small cut pieces at the top or bottom.
(2) The recommended tiling procedure is to take a wall area that can be tiled within an hour (approx. 2–4 sq. yd. according to porosity). Apply Marley wall tile cement No. 1 on to this area. With a pointing trowel apply blobs of adhesive to the wall and spread out with horizontal strokes with a "half pitch" trowel (notches $\frac{1}{16}$ in. deep at $\frac{1}{8}$ in. centre cut at 60° to edge). The adhesive will take about half-an-hour to go off on surfaces of normal porosity and the area should be covered within one hour of commencing to fix tiles. When the tile is pressed home, at least 60% of the back of the tile should be covered with adhesive. This should be ascertained by trial, and it is a check on the correct condition of the adhesive.
(3) Commencing at the bottom left-hand corner, place the first tile in position, pressing it home with a clean cloth.
(4) Using the right-angled gauge, fix the next tile: there will be a space between the tiles equal to the thickness of the gauge.
(5) Continue tiling along and upwards until the area is covered. Fill in as necessary with the cut tiles at top and/or bottom.
Note: To cover rounded surfaces, slightly warm the tiles before fixing, but do not bring them into contact with a naked flame.
(6) If adhesive gets on to the face of the tile remove by careful treatment with a knife or fine steel wool.
Next comes the gauge-jointing with "Marleyfilla", a white, cellulose-based filling material.
(1) Wax the tiles with Marley Superwax or similar polish to afford protection during the jointing.
(2) Fill in the joints with Marleyfilla, using a broadknife.
(3) Remove any surplus with a damp sponge.
(4) After the joints have hardened, the wall can be washed, or polished with Marley Superwax.
(5) If there is a lack of absorption in the wall surface so that the adhesive does not stiffen with sufficient rapidity to prevent sliding, the joints should be filled as may be necessary or, at any rate, at the end of each day's work.

Marley wall tile cement No. 1 is recommended for the installation of "Marleymura". One gallon covers approximately 12 sq. yd. of tiling.

The tools required are: a rule, spirit level and plumb line, for marking out starting lines; right-angle gauge; broadknife; sponge; scissors (if much cutting is involved, a tile-cutting machine is recommended); adhesive spreader (the broadknife can be used).

Paniquil (Sales) Ltd. also produce their product in tile form as 2 ft. × 2 ft. squares. It is a decorative soft foam-padded pvc leathercloth bonded by hardboard.

3.3.2 Polystyrene Wall Tiles

One of the big advantages of polystyrene wall tiles is that they reduce condensation to a minimum. They are, therefore, widely used in bathrooms. In this connection, Jablo Plastics Industries Ltd. manufacture an insulation and anti-condensation lining for use behind wallpaper.

Polystyrene wall tiles are usually smaller than vinyl types and look much more like those made of ceramic materials. They are, however, much lighter than either of these, are rigid, relatively unbreakable and can be readily sawn by unskilled labour where this is necessary to fill awkward corners and strips. The plastic is highly water resistant (one of the best materials for this), is available in a wide range of delicate colours and gives a pleasing appearance.

Manufacturers

Manufacturers of these products are: James Halstead Ltd.; Plysu Sales Ltd. and Evered and Co. Ltd. Plysu Sales Ltd. make an interesting product consisting of preformed sheets 12 in. × 12 in., comprising 256 miniature polystyrene tiles on a flexible fabric backing. They are available in a variety of attractive colour effects.

Robinson Bros. Cork Growers Ltd. manufacture expanded polystyrene wall tiles. Warmafoam Ltd. also manufacture this product.

3.4 Plastic Laminates and Boards

A laminate is by definition a combination of any two or more materials. A brief account of the subject has already been given in Section 3.1.

By far the most common type of laminate is the decorative variety which is based on melamine-formaldehyde resins. Other types, however, include phenolic which are dark in colour and more often used for cladding, and polyester-glass (or polyester-paper) both of which are acquiring increasing importance. Also included in this section are the plastic-surfaced hardboards which are, strictly, laminates since they are combinations of two materials.

Another form of laminate which may be mentioned at this stage is the "sandwich"-type laminate. Here, two surfaces (frequently a melamine laminate) enclose a core, usually a cellular material. Such sandwich products make excellent structural materials for partitioning and details are given in Section 3.5.1.

All of the laminates have certain properties in common: they resist commonly used household materials such as ink, water, spirits, greases and detergents, and temperatures of up to 300°F. or more. Many of them are resistant to cigarette burns. The attractive appearance is combined with cleanliness as well as great toughness and durability. The colours and appear-

7

ance are permanent and are not affected by damp. The surfaces do not support mildews or fungoid growths and are therefore valuable materials to use under most conditions.

3.4.1 Decorative Laminates

Decorative laminates are available from the following concerns:

Harrison and Sons, Ltd.
Fablon Ltd. (*Fablonite*).
North British Plastics Ltd. (*Planex*).
The Phoenix Timber Co. Ltd.
  (*Coronet*).
Getalit Ltd. (*Getalit*).
The Arborite Co. (U.K.) Ltd.
  (*Arborite*).
A. S. Lester Ltd. (*Decopon*).

Wallington Weston and Co. Ltd.
  (*Marlica*).
Formica Ltd. (*Formica*).
Bakelite Ltd. (*Warerite*).
Perstorp Products (G.B.) Ltd.
  (*Perstorp*).
Holoplast Ltd. (*Decorplast*).
Commercial Plastics (Sales), Ltd.

Here are some details of various products available.

Bakelite Ltd.

Warerite is available in $\frac{1}{16}$-in. veneers, satin being the usual finish although a glossy finish is made to order. The standard sizes are 10 ft. × 4 ft. and 9 ft. × 4 ft. There are 30 designs, 5 marbles, 10 plain colours and 9 woodprints, most in a variety of colours. There is also *Wonderboard*, a structural board faced with *Warerite*.

Apart from the normal types of *Warerite* decorative panels, a new type of fire-retardant decorative plastics laminate, which meets the requirements of Class I BS. 476 in respect of flame-spread properties, has been developed by Bakelite Ltd. and is now being added to the *Warerite* range. The new material, designated DU/78/FR, is particularly suitable for use in railway carriages, as well as on ships, aircraft, and other transport. It is of special interest to designers, architects and specifying authorities in the building field for use in lifts, escalators, stairways, corridors and similar locations in public buildings and places of entertainment.

Warerite Fire-Retardant Veneer DU/78/FR, which can be made in any of the wide range of *Warerite* colours or patterns, is usually used as a surfacing veneer on various types of core material and improves the fire-resisting properties of a structure. It can also be employed to up-grade the flame-spread properties of combustible components such as wood, particle board, hardboard and insulation board. Alternatively, it can be used to decorate non-combustible components such as asbestos and plasterboard without down-grading their BS. 476 classification.

Decorative laminates usually comply with the requirements of Class 2 BS. 476 in respect of flame-spread properties. The new laminate, in addition to meeting the requirement of Class 1 BS. 476, has also been proved by the Swedish Box Test and is certified as Class "F" by Det Norske Veritas. With this qualification the material is acceptable for installation in passenger vessels and similar craft.

Getalit Ltd.

Getalit is available from stockists in four standard sheet sizes $116\frac{1}{3}$ in. × 51 in., $98\frac{3}{8}$ in. × $33\frac{3}{4}$ in., $98\frac{3}{8}$ in. × 48 in. and $84\frac{1}{4}$ in. × 40 in. The standard thickness is $\frac{1}{20}$ in. but other thicknesses can be supplied to order. The range includes a large selection of plain colours and these, together with a number of realistic marble effects, have proved popular with architects and designers throughout many countries. In recent years a considerable demand has grown for wood-grain effects and the manufacturer's close association with timber for over 30 years has resulted in representations of a high standard.

The Arborite Co. (U.K.) Ltd.

Arborite panel sizes are 48 in. × 96 in. and 48 in. × 120 in. Other panel sizes, including 60 in. × 144 in., are available on request. It is available in either a high-gloss finish or a matt finish and is $\frac{1}{16}$ in. thick. A range of 80 colours and patterns is available.

Arborite Edge Trim is available in strips $1\frac{5}{8}$ in. wide by 10 ft. long. It is $0 \cdot 030$ in. thick and will take a 3 in. outside radius. Edge trim, which can be cut with scissors, eliminates the use of metal mouldings on counter and table edges and has all the qualities of *Arborite*. It is ideal for self-edging coffee tables, all types of furniture pieces and bar tops, etc.

A new development, solid grade *Arborite*, which can be made in various thicknesses from $\frac{1}{8}$ in. to $1\frac{1}{2}$ in., is an homogeneous laminated plastic with exceptionally high impact resistance and durability which can be used for easy-to-maintain partitioning, work tops and furniture. Being immensely strong, solid grade *Arborite* dispenses with the use of corestock material and enables partitioning and built-in fitments to be made without a wooden or metal framework. Both sides of solid grade are decorative.

A. S. Lester Ltd.

Decopon is supplied in two finishes, gloss and satin (eggshell). The whole range consists of nearly 70 patterns and colours, including 21 plain colours. Dimensions are 280 cm. × 125 cm. approximately 9 ft. 3 in. × 4 ft. $1\frac{1}{4}$ in. and the thickness is $1 \cdot 2 – 1 \cdot 3$ mm.

Marley Products

Marleytop Super is a product comprising a chipboard core with a thin high-pressure veneer on the one side and varied balancers on the reverse. This is an improvement on the original *Marleytop* in respect of additional resistance to wear and heat and enables the whole 70 patterns of *Marlica* to be made available for *Marleytop Super* in the standard sizes of 8 ft. × 4 ft. and 6 ft. × 4 ft. and in thicknesses of $\frac{1}{2}$ in., $\frac{5}{8}$ in. and $\frac{3}{4}$ in.

Marleybord Super is a chipboard—hardboard "sandwich". The object of the construction is to give good resistance to bowing and distortion. The decorative surface is a sheet of *Marleybord*, whilst the reverse can be either a second sheet of *Marleybord* or plain hardboard as required by the customer. This material is available in sheets 8 ft. × 4 ft. and 6 ft. × 4 ft. in two overall thicknesses of $\frac{5}{8}$ in. and $\frac{3}{4}$ in. in the new extended *Marleybord* range.

Standard $\frac{1}{20}$ in. *Marlica* is available in a wide range of patterns and matching pvc. The standard sizes are 8 ft. × 4 ft. and 6 ft. × 4 ft., whilst 8 ft. × 3 ft. and 6 ft. × 3 ft. sheets can be supplied by arrangement.

The *Marleybord* range has been expanded from the original 22 patterns to 56. For many of these patterns matching pvc sheeting is available. Standard-size sheets are 8 ft. × 4 ft. and 6 ft. × 4 ft. in $\frac{1}{8}$ in. thickness.

Formica Ltd.

Formica is available in standard sheets 8 ft. × 4 ft. To illustrate the extensive range of products, the following is a description of some *Formica* patterns.

Abstract-impressionist designs included in the architectural range are: "Aeriel" —a modern effect, in two colourways, of intersecting horizontal and vertical lines, giving regular areas of colour and reminiscent of architects' townscapes: "Current" —an intriguing suggestion of flow and movement in low relief black on white: "Screen"—in two colourways and based on a simple arrangement of circles in an abstract pattern: "Strata"—lines of movement against a white background, creating a contour effect when seen from a height: "Grafitto"—an Italianate, sketched effect, bold and graceful: "Tidemark"—a striking pattern of depth and character, which can be used, as may most of these designs, to give either horizontal or vertical emphasis: "Horizons"—similar in effect and versatility, with blue-grey lines converging colour against white: "Reflex Major" and "Reflex Minor"—a rugged, masculine pattern in two scales, which could be used most effectively in a linked interior-exterior scheme: "Mazette"—a linear design in two colourways, giving a fascinating, three-dimensional impression: "Frost"—a crisp effect of frost on glass, in two colourways: "Flint"—a vivid, visual representation of solid, sturdy flint walls, its sombreness relieved by clear white: "Wasdale"—another eminently versatile pattern, in two colourways, with linear movement predominant.

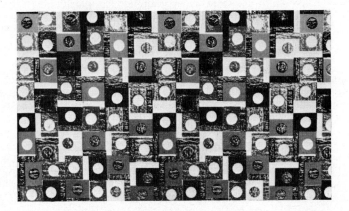

"Morse" from the "Formica Architectural Range" (*Formica Ltd*)

Traditional formalized patterns in the range are: "Tartan"—with its pierced-screen effect: "Morse"—a gay, forceful design of circles on rectangular shapes: "Sance"—a typical renaissance architectural effect, interpreted in modern terms: "Cathedral"—an interesting effect created by the use of English cathedral ground plans—in two colourways: "Traditional"—a pleasingly integrated, if unspectacular, design of grey on grey-white: "Meadow"—a fresh floral and leaf effect of great precision and delicacy: "Tobacco"—a black-on-white leaf pattern: "Blossom"—another attractive leaf and flower pattern in two colourways, both with a crisp, white background: "Fireflower"—a dramatic, full floral effect in warm and vital red: "Sylvan"—a graceful and lovely design showing leaf sprays and blossom in repeat motif, impeccably reproduced on a white background: "Ionic" a finely shaded reproduction of Ionic pillars taken from an Adam engraving: "Foliage"—another leaf pattern in blue-grey on white: and, finally, "Tile"—a traditional tile pattern, showing alternating squares of two different designs in warm gold on black.

There are many more designs than this. The two main products are the $\frac{1}{16}$ in. veneer and *Formica Beauty Board.*

Holoplast Ltd.

Decorplast is available in 75 different standard colours and patterns, including 20 wood grains, these being available in sizes up to 10 ft. × 4 ft. *Chequerplast* is also available with an embossed surface which is used for many industrial applications, including floors.

Perstorp Products (G.B.) Ltd.

Swedish *Perstorp* is manufactured in four different normal qualities:—
(1) *Perstorp Standard*, in 1·5 mm. (0·059 in.) thickness. All-round quality for horizontal as well as vertical surfacing.
(2) *Perstorp Relief*, in 1·5 mm. (0·059 in.) thickness. Same quality as Swedish "Perstorp" Original, but having a relief surface with only slight light reflection. Intended for decorative vertical surfacing.
(3) *Perstorp Minor*, in 1·05 mm. (0·041 in.) thickness. Specially suited for joinery and furniture.
(4) *Perstorp Exterior*, in 1·1 mm. (0·043 in.) thickness. Specially suited to all exterior purposes—such as doors, walls, balconies and outdoor tables—being polyester resin impregnated glass fibre as against phenolic resin paper based.

Perstorp Standard can be manufactured as double-sided, in several different grades, and with special patterns and motifs. It is also available in qualities that satisfy the demands of the Swedish building regulations of 1960 as regards fireproof surface layer Class 1 (quality FP 1) and fire-resistant surface layer Class II (quality FP 11).

The material can be manufactured in any thickness from 1·5 to 20 mm. (0·059 in.–0·787 in.). In most cases the decorative laminates are glued to an underlay material, and experience shows that the *Perstorp* normal qualities are the most suitable from the economical and practical viewpoints. Sometimes, however, it is desirable to use decorative laminates without any underlay, and in such cases it is recommended to use thicker material. In general, thicknesses of up to 5 mm. (0·197 in.) are sufficient in order to obtain satisfactory stability.

A glossy surface often produces irritating light reflections. Therefore, *Perstorp Standard* normally has a surface that can be called satin. It is available in a wide range of colours and designs with glossy finish and with two decorative surfaces. Such sheets for instance, are used for screen walls, and in such cases, thicknesses from 3 to 5 mm. (0·118 in.–0·197 in.) are most frequent.

In the matter of special patterns and motifs there are many possibilities: patterned textiles, wallpaper patterns, sketches, inked-in drawings, crayon drawings and water-colour paintings can be pressed into the panel.

3.4.2 *Technical Properties and Machining*

In order to illustrate the technical properties of all laminates and instructions for machining, those given for Swedish *Perstorp* can be used as an example.

Technical Properties of Swedish Perstorp

Approximate values		Perstorp Standard	Perstorp Minor	Perstorp Exterior
Specific gravity		1·4	1·4	1·4
Weight		0·45 lb./sq. ft.	0·3 lb./sq. ft.	0·37–0·39/sq. ft.
Thickness		1/16 in.	0·0413 in.	0·394–0·433 in.
Flexural strength	along	>14,000 p.s.i.	>14,000 p.s.i.	17,100 p.s.i.
	across	>11,300 p.s.i.	>12,000 p.s.i.	
Impact strength	along	>0·30 ft./lb.	>0·30 ft./lb.	214 p.s.i.
	across	>0·25 ft./lb.	>0·25 ft./lb.	(Dynstat)
Tensile strength	along	>12,800 p.s.i.	>12,800 p.s.i.	7,100 p.s i.
	across	>10,000 p.s.i.	>9,000 p.s.i.	
Abrasion resistance (tested as per NEMA standard LP 2-1.06)	Patterned	As per NEMA Standard Cl. 1	Slightly lower than as per NEMA standard Cl. 1	500 revs.
	Plain-coloured	As per NEMA Standard Cl. 1	As per NEMA standard Cl. 1	
Modulus of elasticity	about	1,400,000 p.s.i.	1,400,000 p.s.i.	—
Thermal conductivity	about	1·1 B.Th.U./ft. h°F.	1·1 B.Th.U./ft. h°F.	1·36 B.Th.U./ft. h°F.
Dimensional change at variations in relative air humidity between 30 and 80%	along	1·5%	1·5%	0·8%
	across	3·0%	3·0%	
Coefficient of heat expansion	along	8×10^{-6} in./in.°F.	8×10^{-6} in./in.°F.	8×10^{-6} in./in.°F.
	across	9×10^{-6} in./in.°F.	9×10^{-6} in./in.°F.	
Heat resistance (short-time exposure)		max. 300°F.	max. 300°F.	max. 300°F.

Light Resistance

The light resistance can be tested according to several different methods. The best one for practical use is DIN 53388, using the sun as light-source. The test implies grading the light-resistance according to well-known norms, from 1 ("very bad") up to 8 ("best possible"). The light resistance of *Perstorp Standard, Relief, Minor* and *Exterior*, corresponds to norm 6, or better.

Heat Resistance

The heat resistance is checked as per the NEMA standard for decorative laminates, LP 2-1·08, which means exposure to a maximum temperature of 360°F. for 20 minutes. This test guarantees that a pot of boiling water can be placed on the material without damaging it. On the other hand, the sheet can be damaged by hot frying-pans and smoothing irons, the temperatures of which are often very high.

Perstorp is not damaged by a burning match, nor normally by a burning cigarette.

The smallest bending radius that can be recommended when gluing on curved surfaces and in cold condition is: *Perstorp Standard* and *Relief* 12 in.; *Minor* and *Exterior* 7⅞ in.

These figures concern bending with the decorative face outwards. When bending with the decorative face inwards, the radii can be about 25% smaller.

Chemical Resistance

Tests of the material were conducted by the Skånska Ättikfabriken AB's Central Laboratories in accordance with internationally recognized NEMA standards for laminated plastics (LP2-1.10, National Electrical Manufacturers Association, U.S.A.).

Test pieces were exposed to chemicals for a 16-hour period at a temperature of 24ºC. To prevent evaporation, each test piece was covered by a sheet of glass. At the conclusion of the test period each piece was washed in water and an alcohol solution. The following figures compare test results of *Perstorp Standard* and *Minor* with the standards prescribed by NEMA.

Rating Scale: 0 = No attack. No changes in colour or in surface structure; 1 = Slight attack, noticeable in reflected light; 2 = Slightly etched; 3 = Severely etched, pattern destroyed.

In the case of the following materials the test results showed that, with the exception of ink and iodine, which had a rating scale of 1, the remainder had a rating scale of 0, thus all of them met the standards prescribed by NEMA. Test time was 16 hours.

Medium	NEMA Standard
Petrol	0
Water	0
Alcohol 96%	0
Amyl acetate	0
Acetone	0
Carbon tetrachloride	0
Insecticide	0
Household soap	0
Fatty alcohol	0
Trisodium phosphate	0
Olive oil	0
Citric acid 10%	0

Medium	NEMA Standard
Coffee	0
Mustard	0
Sodium bisulphite	0
Wax	0
Shoe polish	0
Ink	1
Iodine, 1% in alcohol	1
Ammonia, 10%	0
Urea, 6·6%	0
Phenol 5%	0
Hydrogen peroxide	0

Apart from the obligatory NEMA tests, similar tests were carried out with a further selection of strong chemicals with the following results:

Medium	Time, hr.	Test result
Hydrochloric acid, concentrated	65	2—3
Hydrochloric acid, diluted	65	1—2
Sulphuric acid, concentrated	65	3
Sulphuric acid, 55%	65	1—2
Nitric acid, concentrated	65	3
Hydrofluoric acid, concentrated	65	1—3
Cresylic acid	65	0
Caustic soda lye, 20%	7×24	1
Ammonium sulphide, 10%	75	0
Acetic acid, concentrated	65	0
Acetic acid, 55%	65	0
Sodium chloride, 10%	65	0
Sodium nitrate, 10%	65	0
Sodium sulphate, 10%	65	0
Sodium acetate, 10%	65	0
Sodium sulphide, 10%	65	0
Sodium sulphite, 10%	65	0
Potassium iodide, 10%	65	0
Potassium iodate, 10%	65	0
Potassium ferrocyanide, 10%	65	0

Machining Instructions

Perstorp panels (and similar laminates) can be worked with ordinary hand tools and wood-working machines. Excellent results are obtained with both hand- and machine-working, provided that the correct methods for this type of material are used. It is essential that the tools be sharp.

The panel should be fed rapidly and steadily through the saw, decorative side up, at the rate of about 0·5 metres per sec. (about 90 ft. per min.). Feeding too rapidly or too slowly will cause overheating and premature dulling of the blade.

The blade should normally project about 40 mm. ($1\frac{1}{2}$ in.) above the table. Reducing this height will give a better finish on the cut surface but will also increase the rate of wear on the blade. Conversely, increasing the height of the blade above the table will leave a rougher cut face but will reduce wear on the blade. The sawbench should be firm and steady. The use of spring-loaded rollers to hold the panel against the table is recommended. The operating costs per unit sawed are about the same with carbon steel and carbide blades. The advantage of using carbide is, of course, that fewer blade changes are required, and also that the blade can be used for most types of work.

Circular Saw

Carbon steel blade

Surface speed:	40 to 50 metres per sec. (7,800 to 9,800 ft. per min.)
	(Blade diam. of 300 mm. (12 in.) running at 2,800 r.p.m. is recommended)
Tooth spacing: (fine)	approx. 7 per inch
Blade thickness:	2 to 3 mm. ($\frac{1}{16}$ in. to $\frac{1}{8}$ in.)
Set:	Light
Hook:	Slight forward (5–10°)
Hardness:	approx. 46 Rockwell C.

Blade with carbide-tipped teeth

Surface speed:	approx. 60 metres per sec. (10,800 ft. per min.)
	(Blade diam. of 300 mm. (12 in.) running at 4,000 r.p.m. is recommended)
Tooth spacing:	72 or more on a 300 mm. (12 in.) blade
Tooth thickness:	3·5 to 4·5 mm. ($\frac{9}{64}$ in. to $\frac{11}{64}$ in.)
Set:	None
Hook:	Slight forward (5–10°)
Quality of tungsten-carbide:	Hard grade, suitable for working in hard and chilled cast-iron, light metals of all kinds, glass, porcelain, etc.

Band Saw

Surface speed:	20 to 25 metres per sec. (about 3,600 to 4,500 ft. per min.)
Tooth spacing:	8 to 12 per inch
Width of blade:	Depends on radius of curves to be cut; ordinarily 10 to 14 mm. ($\frac{3}{8}$ in. to $\frac{9}{64}$ in.)
Feed:	Should be considerably slower than with circular saw. Feed panel right-side up.

Beadings are available to cover butt jointing. This is known as panel trim and is made by, among others, I.C.I. Ltd.

3.4.3 Other Laminates and Suppliers

The most important of other types of laminate are the polyester range of the following manufacturers: Wembley Fibreglass and Plastics Ltd.; Indulex Engineering Co. Ltd. ("Indulite"); British Xylonite Group of Companies, (Polyester-faced paper laminate); Glass Fibre Developments, Ltd., (Polyester laminates for curtain walling, balcony panels, fascias); Armabord Ltd.; Allan Blunn Ltd.; Glas-Roc (Camberley) Ltd. (The last-named concern manufactures a glass-fibre imitation Cotswold and Cornish grey/green masonry panel for exterior and interior use. It is extremely realistic and, of course, eliminates decorating costs).

The possibilities with polyester laminates are great. For example, Wembley Fibreglass and Plastics Ltd. is prepared to take any wallpaper or fabric and convert it into a laminate suitable for panelling. The products are light and impervious to moisture; they can be cleaned with a wet cloth; can be used out-of-doors and where there are corrosive fumes; are crystal clear over the design and have all the attributes of polyesters.

3.4.4 Plastic-faced Boards

Some details, together with the names of manufacturers of plastic-faced boards have already been given in Section 3.4.1, and here are some further products in this catagory.

Plastics Fabrication Co. Ltd.

Polypanol-H/F is the registered trade name of a decorative pvc-surfaced hardboard manufactured by Plastics Fabrication Co. Ltd. and marketed by Plastics Marketing Co. Ltd. of Sevenoaks, Kent. It comes in a variety of plain colours, wood-grains and patterns in sizes up to 12 ft. × 4 ft. (Popular size 8 ft. × 4 ft.).

Its characteristics are: Low price for a plastic-faced board; tough hard surface which will not easily scratch or rub off and one which can be easily and repeatedly cleaned with soap and water or a mild detergent without deterioration; attractive colours and surface emboss; colour fastness; realistic wood-grain patterns on standard range; surface highly resistant to most household commodities and liquids; will not spread flame and the flame-resistant F.R. grade has an excellent fire rating for most purposes involving fire-hazard regulations. The light-weight semi-flexible 2 mm. grade is particularly suitable for curved surfaces.

Polypanol-H/F

Grades, Colours, Patterns and Grains

Grades	Sizes	Thickness	Approx. Weight
Standard	8 ft. × 4 ft. (popular) 12 ft. × 4 ft., 10 ft. × 4 ft., 9 ft. × 4 ft., 6 ft. × 4 ft., 5 ft. × 4 ft., 4 ft. × 4 ft.	$\frac{1}{8}$ in.	2,900 sq. ft. per ton.
	8 ft. × 4 ft., 4 ft. × 4 ft.	$\frac{1}{4}$ in.	—
Light-weight Semi-flexible "LW"	10 ft. × 4 ft., 8 ft. × 4 ft. 5 ft. × 4 ft.	2 mm.	4,400 sq. ft. per ton
Flame-resistant "F.R.1" Eternit "D" base	8 ft. × 4 ft.	$\frac{1}{8}$ in.	
Flame-resistant "F.R.2" Flame-proofed Hardboard base	8 ft. × 4 ft.	$\frac{1}{8}$ in.	2,700 sq. ft. per ton.

Polypanol-H/F can be manipulated in a manner very similar to standard good quality hardboard with the usual joinery tools, provided the following precautions are taken:

The surface being decorative, it is inadvisable to nail, screw or pin through the face of the board unless the fixing holes are to be covered with a moulding or by other means. If it should be necessary to break the surface skin it may be touched up with a paint of a similar shade with reasonable results.

It is recommended that the edges of the board be protected from moisture or other damage by covering with a timber, plastic or metal moulding or framing, or by specifying wrapped edges (extra charge) when ordering.

When using synthetic rubber-type adhesives of the contact bonding variety, it is essential that the surplus volatile solvents in the adhesive be allowed to disperse before the two surfaces are brought together, otherwise certain solvents may penetrate the hardboard and affect the pvc surface. It is advisable to check with the supplier on the suitability of any particular adhesive.

Recommended adhesives are:—

For contact bonding site work to a variety of surfaces including timber and plaster—Tretobond 425 or 404; for press work to timber, expanded polystyrene and certain other surfaces—Aerolite 306 "Cascamite One Shot".

There are, of course, many other adhesives which will give satisfactory results but it is recommended that the adhesive manufacturer be consulted before using any particular type.

When it is intended to fix panels of large area firmly in position by means of pins, screws or other means, it is advisable to dampen lightly the back of the boards 72 hours before erection to obtain maximum expansion. This will ensure that the panels will not buckle due to expansion after erection. When dampening the back of the boards, care should be taken not to apply excess water to the edges of the panels as this may cause wrinkling along the edges. A light, even sprinkling or sponging of the back of the board is all that is necessary.

When fixing a number of full-size wall panels side by side, it is recommended that a small gap ($\frac{1}{16}$ in. or in certain cases less, depending on the humidity conditions) be left between panels to allow for any expansion that may take place.

Great care should be taken to see that the synthetic rubber adhesives used are not inadvertently applied to the decorative surface because most of the solvents which are normally used for removing these adhesives will affect the pvc surface to some degree. If it is necessary to remove such an adhesive, the manufacturers recommend carbon tetrachloride.

Laconite Ltd.

Laconite plastic-coated wallboards are manufactured from a quality hardboard faced with a plastic coating which is durable and hygienic and has a high finish. This glossy surface is impervious to dirt and moisture and a wipe with a damp cloth will remove all dirt and grease and restore the original lustre. In spite of its glazed appearance, the surface is warm to touch. The panels are either plain or embossed to impart a tiled effect.

Laconite is used wherever a permanently hygienic and easily cleaned surface is required on walls and ceilings—in kitchens, canteens, toilets, washrooms, bathrooms and shops. It is not suitable for external use, nor is it intended as a working surface, but it can be used with confidence for lining shelves and other horizontal surfaces subject to only light wear. With normal care, its hard durable surface will last a lifetime.

Like all hardboard, *Laconite* should be thoroughly damped some 48 hours before fixing, a pint or so of water at room temperature being worked into the back of each panel, to within 3 in. of the edges, with a sponge, soft broom or hard brush. The panels should then be laid on a floor or other level surface until required. If any panel is not used within three days, it should be re-damped with about half the quantity of water and left for a further 24 hours. *Unless this pre-treatment is carried out, the panels will buckle after fixing.* If considerable cutting and fitting are necessary, it is advisable to leave the pre-treatment until after the panels have been cut to size, ⅛ in. being allowed for every 4 ft. of panel for subsequent expansion.

The material is supplied in standard panels 8 ft. × 4 ft. and 6 ft. × 4 ft. by ⅛ in. thick. The panels are easily cut with ordinary carpenters' tools: for straight cuts a hand saw, or, better, a panel saw, for curved cuts a keyhole, pad or fretsaw. Those with power tools can use a jig-saw fitted with the appropriate blade. The coated side should be uppermost and the panel well supported on each side of the cut. After cutting, the edge should not require more than a light bevelling, on the coated edge, with a smooth file or sandpaper.

Small holes in the panels should be made with a twist drill, medium-sized holes with a centre or auger bit. Large holes can be made with an expansive bit, but this requires practice and the inexperienced may find it easier to drill a small hole and enlarge it with a suitable saw, such as a pad saw, finishing with a half-round file.

Laconite can be bent, without pre-treatment, to any radius down to about 30 in., with the finished surface on either the inside or the outside of the bend. Tighter bends (with radii down to about 15 in.) can be made by working the panel by degrees round a wooden frame, hot water being scrubbed into the reverse side every two or three hours. When the required radius is achieved, the panel should be bound round the frame and left for 48 hours. If the bend is to be unsupported, the radius of the frame should be a few inches smaller than the radius of the finished bend, since the panel will spring back a little when released.

If the surface to be covered consists of rough brickwork or plaster in poor condition, vertical wooden battens some 2 in. wide by ½ in. thick should be secured to it with wall nails, or plugs and screws, at 12 in. or 16 in. centres, with cross battens at similar intervals. Battens should coincide with the positions of all joints and panels should be bonded to the battens.

As an alternative, panels may be pinned or screwed to the battens. Begin at the centre of a panel and work outwards towards the edges. Use only rustproofed pins or chromed screws.

In some cases, it may be preferable to cover the wall with blockboard or chipboard, to which the *Laconite* panels may be bonded.

Airscrew-Weyroc Ltd.

Hardec is a material combining a colourful hard-wearing melamine plastic face and plain plastic backing built on to a core of hardboard. This balanced construction minimizes warping and ensures maximum flatness and rigidity under the most exacting conditions. *Hardec* is made in a range of colours and patterns including linen prints and wood grains. The melamine surface of *Hardec* is tough and hardwearing and the colours extremely fast to sunlight. Fading does not occur in normal domestic or industrial use. The material withstands stains from ink, coffee, tea, alcoholic drink, weak acid and many other chemicals: it is not readily marked by hot plates, teapots, steam or boiling water, and it is largely resistant to cigarette burns. For all practical purposes it is scratch- and chip-proof.

Wherever there is moisture, the edges must be well protected. A bedding mastic should be used in joints before the fillets are put on, and for individual panels an edging should be used with a protective coating in the fixing holes.

A new material known as *Wonderboard* is being made by this company in conjunction with Bakelite Ltd. It is a chipboard with decorative surface veneers.

Manufacturers of plastic-faced boards include: Plastics Marketing Co. Ltd. ("Polypanol—H/F"); Laconite Ltd. ("Laconite"); Airscrew-Weyroc Ltd. ("Hardec"); North British Plastics Ltd.; Masonite Ltd.; Thames Plywood Manufacturers Ltd.; Bryce, White and Co. Ltd.; Celluglos Products Ltd. (pvc bonded to plywood); Tensile Products Ltd. ("Uniplast" plastic-faced panels); Formica Ltd.

3.5 Plastics in Construction

The object of sandwich constructions is to exploit the strength of thin shells so that lightweight structures are possible. There are two covering faces held at a distance from one another by a material of low specific gravity. Such parts can be heavily stressed both in the plane of the sheets and at right angles to them. Longitudinal and transverse forces are entirely absorbed by the faces which are protected from indentation by the support offered over their whole area by the lightweight core.

The supporting cores can consist of honey-comb materials or rigid plastic foams. The former method is described below and the latter product can be achieved by all the usual methods. One of the most interesting of these is to produce a rigid foam *in situ* between the two faces. One such material is *Moltopren*, the components for which (including the special mixing, metering and dispensing equipment) are sold in the U.K. by J. M. Steel and Co. Ltd., who will also provide an interesting booklet on the subject of sandwich constructions by Peter Hoppe.

3.5.1 Sandwich Constructions for Curtain Walling

A well-known example of this is found in *Holoplast*. This panel consists of two flanges and interconnecting webs to provide maximum rigidity and strength. These webs form cavities suitable for thermal or sound insulation fillings. The panels are widely used for interior partitions and as in-filling panels for exterior curtain walls where, filled with a suitable insulation material, they have a "U" value as great as or greater than 11 in.-cavity brick walls yet they are only $1\frac{1}{2}$ in. to 2 in. thick.

Typical examples of the use of this material may be given. Over 75,000 sq. ft. of *Holoplast* curtain walling, worth nearly £300,000, was used in two office blocks erected as part of the Barbican redevelopment scheme in the City of London.

St. Alphage House incorporates infill panels of grey Muroglass and vertically sliding windows. The aluminium sections are anodized and sprayed with butyrate lacquer. A feature of the curtain walling system at St. Alphage House, which is an adaption of the standard *Holoplast* system, is the use of 20-ft.-high, two-storey assemblies of modular width. The interlocking split-mullion design allows each assembly to expand and contract separately, both in the vertical and horizontal direction in such a way that thermal movement does not affect the weatherproof qualities of the curtain walling.

The two-storey-high assemblies for Lee House—which are also of inter-locking split-mullion design—have blue armourclad infill panels with pivoted windows, and the mill-finish aluminium sections are also sprayed with butyrate.

The *Holoplast* system lends itself to speedy erection. The complete curtain wall construction is prefabricated and assembled at the factory of Holoplast Ltd., and delivered to the site in bulk. The curtain walls have the additional advantage that they do not need painting or normal maintenance—any cleaning that may be necessary can be carried out quite simply with soap and water. The hard surface of the infill panels resist smoke and dirt, and the aluminium frames are resistant to corrosion.

Holoplast curtain walling is now available with neoprene glazing and clip-on beads. Neoprene structural gaskets, which have been used for 14 years in the U.S.A. and are now being introduced in Britain, provide a self-sealing and resilient frame for glazing panels and opening lights. The lip of the gasket is pulled forward to allow the glass or panel to be set in place and a neoprene filler strip is then pressed into the slot, forcing the lip tight against the glass or panel. No metal pressure stop is needed and replacement of the glass or panel is easily effected. The gaskets are prefabricated to the required size, corners being moulded and vulcanised to the straight members. Opening lights can be provided within this system.

Venesta Manufacturing Ltd. have developed an interesting new product. This is *Instant Building Board*, made from expanded polystyrene faced both sides with $\frac{1}{8}$ in. hardboard. This new material is rapidly winning acceptance as a time- and labour-saving material for general panelling and partitioning. The expanded polystyrene core gives the board bulk and rigidity, yet adds very little to the weight of the hardboard faces—a full-size board 2 in. thick weighs only 48 lb., easily handled by one man. The core also gives the board exceptional thermal insulation properties: the 1-in. thick board has a thermal conductivity of 0·285 B.Th.U./sq. ft./°F., equivalent to a 11-in. brick wall. Thicknesses available are 1, $1\frac{1}{2}$ and 2 in., with plain hardboard, or with pvc, or stove enamelled finish.

Expanded Polystyrene Composites

Other composites of expanded polystyrene include: for interior use—expanded polystyrene faced with asbestos or plasterboard: for exterior use—expanded polystyrene faced with eternit emaille asbestos.

Manufacturers

Manufacturers of this type of laminate are: Holoplast Ltd.; Jablo Plastics Industries Ltd.; British Xylonite Group of Companies; Tensile Products Ltd.; Robinson Building Techniques Ltd. (expanded polystyrene laminates em-ploying outer panels of hardboard, plywood, decorative laminates, alumin-ium, asbestos and pvc).

3.5.2 Cladding

Cladding with plastic sheets for roofing is described in Section 4.2. Exactly the same applies to vertical wall cladding.

However, *Marleyclad*, a rigid corrugated vinyl cladding for internal and external use is more particularly for vertical applications. The corrugations measure $\frac{5}{8}$ in. peak to peak and are $\frac{3}{16}$ in. deep. There is no limitation on length up to 500 feet.

U.A.M. Plastics Ltd. is manufacturing *Heliotrex* translucent curtain walling panel. It is made of glass-fibre reinforced polyester and has a light transmission of 62% with a "U" value of 0·34.

The panels can be made in any size up to 8 ft. by 4 ft. and consist of two flat sheets of *Unilux* glass-fibre reinforced polyester resin separated by a corrugated sheet of the same material. The finished thickness of the complete panel is about $1\frac{1}{4}$ in., its weight being $1\frac{1}{2}$ lb./sq. ft. Since the fire-retardant grade of *Unilux* is used, the panels are graded Ext. SAA under BS.476. They can be used with any curtain walling system and with conventional bedding materials.

A new type of cladding material is being made by James Booth Aluminium Ltd. of Birmingham. This is vinyl-coated aluminium, grey in colour, of Trough "A" profile and formed from 20 s.w.g. Mangalal N53 aluminium sheet. A recent example of its use is the switch-house superstructure at Ferrybridge "C" coal-fired power station.

Industrial Exchange Co. Ltd. are selling special laminates known as *Indulex* for wall cladding, although they are suitable as structural members for low buildings.

The external face is of glass-reinforced polyester resin, the actual surface being an embossed polyester gel coat. The next layer is asbestos cement followed by a core of foam (polystyrene, pvc, phenolic or glass) followed by another sheet of asbestos cement and last a vapour barrier of aluminium foil in a polyester gel coat. Window and door frames can be incorporated in the panels during manufacture.

Perstorp Exterior is a weatherproof panel of glass-reinforced polyester. It is specially intended for the outside covering of news stands, doors, walls, etc. The material has a matt surface and is available in nine matching colours. Sizes are 2050 × 930 mm. and 780 × 1230 mm.

The expansion and contraction of *Perstorp Exterior* due to temperature variations are so small that they can generally be disregarded. The coefficient of thermal expansion is only about 0·015 mm. per metre and per °C. (0·0035 in. per ft. and per °F.). Dimensional changes may amount to 0·8 mm./m. (0·01 in./ft.) due to variations in the relative humidity of the air between 30% and 80%. As these dimensional changes are comparatively small, no special measures need to be taken for conditioning.

Wembley Fibreglass and Plastics Ltd. will also produce exterior decorative polyester cladding panels to special order from customer's own paper designs.

3.5.3 Doors

Doors are usually made in the form of a sandwich construction with either a laminate surface and/or an expanded plastic core. Manufacturers are as follow: F. Hills and Sons Ltd., (Melamine-faced flush doors); British Werno Ltd., (The "Nieder" sliding door with a hard melamine surface); Peak Displays Ltd., (Sliding doors glazed with "Perspex"); Jablo Plastics Industries Ltd., (Doors with expanded polystyrene core); Osma Plastics Ltd., (Cellular structure for doors and partitions); Duraflex Housecrafts Ltd., (Special door seal from rubber).

Another door based on plastics is the folding door which is vinyl covered. A typical example is *Marleyfold*. These doors operate on the bellows principle. Flexible doors are also made by William Newman & Sons Ltd. and J. Avery & Co. Ltd.

Home Fittings (G.B.) Ltd. make *Modernfold* and *Soundmaster* expanding walls, both sides being covered with *Everflex 131* back-coated vinyl-coated fabrics. Both products conform to BS. 3424 and BS.476, Part 2, 1955 Flammability Test. There is also a cheaper priced *Wall Fold* in 26 colours.

Bolton Gate Co. Ltd. produce their *Wonderfold*, a lightweight folding leathercloth partition in five colours.

3.5.4 Panels

Panels can be made from almost any plastic products. An example of glass-fibre panels may be given from the range of Kelscreen Co. Ltd.

Such panels are translucent and can incorporate many attractive materials such as textured fabrics, modern fibres, metallic sequins, real leaves, grasses and the like. They are extremely serviceable and easily washed with soap and water. They are shatter-proof, scratch resistant and light-fast. These panels (marketed by the U.A.M. Group) can also be made in Vinyl. Another manufacturer is the British Xylonite Group of Companies.

Another important panelling material is profiled *Perspex*. This is made by I.C.I. Ltd. in such standard colours as Opal 040, Opal 068, Yellow 261, Red 461, Green 663 and Blue 762, although other colours can be obtained. The material is profiled in the manner of corrugated sheet but it is available in one size only—70 in. × 42 in. It is tough, completely weather resistant and never requires painting. Door canopies, windbreaks, screens and decorative panels can all be made with this material. Profiled sheet has been particularly used in open-plan houses. Peak Displays Ltd., make sliding doors glazed in *Perspex*.

Metal panelling is now being coated with pvc and polythene as protection from corrosion and to give added colour. Mullions have been coated in the same way.

Manufacturers

Manufacturers are: Ayrshire Metal Products Ltd., (pvc); Plastic Coatings Ltd., (polythene and pvc); British Xylonite Group of Companies, (Mullions coated with pvc).

The latest material of this type is a vinyl sheet/steel laminate which can be employed for exterior cladding, interior panelling, ceilings, ducting, etc. Examples of the product are made by:

John Summers and Sons Ltd.

(*Stelvetite*—in any colour—made in conjunction with BX Plastics Ltd.)

I.C.I. Ltd. (Novar Ltd.)

Dorman Long (Steel) Ltd. are developing plastic-coated steel cladding sheets in a big way. Colours available are black, regency cream, steel grey, silver sage, golden brown, sky grey, terra cotta, manor blue and austin green. One colour on one side and a different one on the other are also available to give different colours inside and outside buildings. All the usual tests for weathering etc. have been carried out and the results are excellent. The sheets can be pressed and formed without affecting adhesion of the pvc to the steel, and although there is no protection at sheared edges, there is no appreciable corrosion creep under the pvc. Various sections are available, including corrugated, trough rib section and broad rib section. Various flashings, sealants and filler pieces are also produced.

Ruberoid Co. Ltd. manufacture a system of lightweight insulated wall cladding. The outer skin is available in plastic-coated galvanised steel or aluminium in a range of colours.

3.5.5   Miscellaneous

An interesting use of plastics, in conjunction with more conventional materials, is provided by H. and R. Johnson Ltd.

This company provides prefabricated tile partitions using ceramic glazed tiles. The surfaces of the panels are separated by accurately gauged plastic spacers specially made to allow the free running of concrete through them.

Pilkington's Tiles Ltd. manufacture a similar product *Ceramiclad*. These are lightweight polyurethane filled panels for curtain walling, cladding, partitions and murals and are faced with glazed ceramic tiles. They are available in sizes up to 8 ft. × 4 ft.

3.6   Plastic Glazing Products

The traditional materials for window frames are still wood and metal. This is in spite of the fact that wood readily warps and steel and other metals, particularly aluminium, corrode, pit and stain. The onset of these defects is delayed by galvanizing or by the application of paints but difficulties often occur sooner or later. In any case, maintenance costs, particularly with tall buildings, are very high. Where galvanized steel and pvc are considered to be technically equal, then the problem of maintenance may well decide the issue.

Architects and builders are well aware of the limitations of wood and metal but until recently there was little they could do about it. What they really required was a completely new material which did not deteriorate or distort, or a covering which was unaffected by weathering. These requirements at one stage seemed formidable and insoluble but they have now been satisfied, at least from the technical point of view, even though the economics are a little troublesome.

As with so many other difficulties, plastics provide the answer to these problems. To be more specific, it is pvc. The material has all the necessary

8

properties and, in addition, can be readily fabricated into a wide variety of shapes and sizes. It can thus be used for any window system and manufacturers are promising a minimum of 15 years' trouble-free service without maintenance. This, it would seem, is a development which the architect must urgently follow and adopt.

3.6.1 Properties of PVC

Both rigid and flexible pvc have excellent weathering resistance. In the cable field for example, the material is used out-of-doors in the hot sun of the Arabian desert. They are also highly water, oxygen and ozone resistant so that they are ideal for window frames. A figure of 15 years life has been quoted—it might well prove to be 50.

The materials have been adopted extensively for their processing properties just as much as for their chemical properties. They can be extruded very easily (when warmed to plastic condition) and produce a wide variety of profiled shapes. Hollow rectangles, for instance, can be slipped over shaped wood.

Rigid pvc is likely to be the most important material for window frames. Dimensionally it is very stable (slide-rules are made from it), it is highly chemical resistant and very stiff. It is likely to be the window frame material of the future.

With this background of information, the present and future use of the material for window frames will be considered.

3.6.2 Reasons for Using PVC

Wood is popular for window frames for a number of reasons. It is cheap, easy to convert by comparatively simple equipment and has good thermal characteristics. However, it has to be protected from weathering, fungoid growth and rotting and attack by boring insects.

Metals, though in some cases more expensive, are also used extensively. Although they are not subject to the same degree of warping as wood, they readily corrode (in the case of steel, hot galvanizing is, of course, an important method of protection). For both metals and wood, therefore, multiple coats of paint are required at comparatively frequent intervals. This can be particularly expensive with tall industrial and commercial buildings and any method of overcoming the problem, even though more expensive initially, must surely make the project cheaper in the end.

It is useful to look at the defects of wood and metal to see how pvc can overcome them. In the case of weathering, many years experience has shown pvc to be an ideal material for out-of-door applications.

The water resistance of pvc can best be illustrated by immersion figures. Those given in the following table were obtained on both flexible and rigid pvc by complete immersion of samples in water at 20°C.

These figures are given only as examples since they can vary considerably with the composition of the compound. As will be seen, rigid pvc is considerably superior to the flexible variety. Sunlight resistance is equally impressive so that little deterioration need be expected. A life of 15–20 years can be anticipated for the flexible material and at least 50 years for the rigid material.

Water Resistance of PVC

Time Immersed	Flexible (% water absorbed)	Rigid (% water absorbed)
24 hours	0·09	0·01
1 week	0·14	0·02
2 weeks	0·19	0·04
3 weeks	0·24	0·06
4 weeks	0·32	0·09
2 months	0·43	0·12
6 months	0·72	0·18
12 months	1·21	0·23

In the case of fungoid and similar growths, pvc is naturally quite resistant. However, if it is to be installed in districts which are particularly prone to supporting fungoid growths, then special ingredients can be added to the pvc to provide added protection.

As far as metal and wood are concerned, they are both protected from the deleterious influences mentioned by covering with pvc. As far as dimensional stability is concerned, this is very good, particularly with the rigid variety. The flexible type might change its shape somewhat over a period of years, but the rigid material is one of the most dimensionally stable materials known. This is illustrated by its use for making precision instruments.

Thus there is no doubt about the value of pvc as a substitute or complementary material for wood and metal. It is now necessary to see how it is used.

3.6.3 PVC as a Complementary Material

The most commonly used protective method at the present time is to cover wood or metal frames with pvc sheaths. This system retains the merits of the conventional materials and confers on them the advantages of pvc. Not least of these is that the pvc is self-coloured and therefore no painting is necessary. PVC can be supplied in a wide variety of attractive colours, including white and cream, so that the architect can indulge in any colour scheme he wishes. Over the years, such frames need not be painted, but merely cleaned at long intervals, which will undoubtedly cut down maintenance costs. However, should any change in colour scheme be desired, the pvc surfaces will take paints quite readily, exactly as with normal constructional materials.

Since pvc is so simple to extrude, a number of most attractive shapes can be produced if required. They permit the provision of a system which allows condensate to be drained off. Double glazing can also be carried out quite readily by the use of special flexible extruded pvc sections. The extrusions are particularly smooth and look clean and hygienic.

3.6.4 All-PVC Windows

However attractive a new material may be, the cost must be taken into account. In the case of pvc-covered window frames, it has been estimated that wood-pvc costs about 2s. 6d. per sq. ft. more than conventional painted wooden frames. On the other hand, wood-pvc is about 2s. cheaper than painted metal frames.

Solid rigid pvc window frames (without wood or metal cores) are more expensive initially than any of the foregoing systems. They have been made and installed, however, by welding solid extrusions at the corners. In spite of the cost they are undoubtedly the best type of window system that can be installed at the present time. They have all the advantages of pvc and are virtually indestructible. In this connection, they are fire resistant and will burn only in a strong flame, extinguishing when the flame is removed.

Although such systems would be expensive at the moment, it may well be possible to bring the price down. Instead of manufacturing the frames by extrusion and hand welding, if the demand became high enough, it would be possible to make them automatically by injection moulding. Whether this development comes is largely up to the architect. Only he can decide on a size that could be standardized and so provide for economical production on a large scale.

The architect must give serious consideration to these matters. The maintenance costs on many tall buildings now being erected will be enormous. They could virtually be eliminated by adopting one or other of the pvc systems. Initially, the cost will be higher and in building estimating there is a natural tendency not to consider these more expensive materials. If any tender, however, states the fact that pvc windows are to be specified at a greater initial cost but the saving will be a matter of thousands of pounds sterling a year, then the architect will be performing a service to himself and his client.

3.6.5 Manufacturers and Their Products

Tensile Products Ltd.; Melwood Thermoplastics Ltd.; Austins of East Ham Ltd.; Leon Ellis Manufacturing Co. Ltd.; Henry Hope and Sons Ltd.; Plasticable Ltd. (glazing sections).

Examples of actual products may be given with reference to those made by Henry Hope and Sons Ltd. and Tensile Products Ltd. The "Ferroplast" windows made by Henry Hope are pvc-covered steel windows and their "Polyclad" system is for holding glass in position without putty or clips, again using pvc for protection.

The following is the specification for Hope's "Ferroplast" windows:

Steel core is hot-dip galvanized after fabrication.

Electrically welded corners of both steel core and pvc cladding make "Ferroplast" windows strong and weathertight.

Multi-colour frames are possible with "Ferroplast" construction. Different colours can be used for the inside and outside of any window; glazing beads are usually white.

Colour range: yellow, red, buff, blue, grey, green, black and white.

Weatherproof glazing is ensured by a combined aluminium and pvc bead, which is removable for glass replacement. Windows are inside glazed.

No painting or other maintenance is needed for "Ferroplast" windows.

Excellent insulation for heat and sound. Completely draughtproof.

Quiet and easy to operate—no slamming.

Fittings: hinges and pivots are bronze, satin chrome finish.

"Cremone" bolts fitted to side hung and vertically pivoted casements have anodised aluminium handles with chromium-plated brass rods.

In the case of Tensile Products Ltd. their "Metleplast" system combines rigid pvc extruded sections with a completely enclosed aluminium core. Both component materials are permanently bonded by the principle of interlocking sections, the aluminium core being reinforced at the corners by a concealed bracket.

The fittings, designed for maintenance-free operation, are made from nylon, giving exceptional strength, freedom from corrosion and high resistance to abrasion. A patent release pin enables the window to be completely reversed for easy cleaning.

The fittings are available in white, black, grey or cream. The pigment is an integral part of the pvc extrusion and requires no maintenance whatsoever. Nylon window catches are available in white, grey and black.

The method of fixing used is extremely simple and adaptable to almost any type of building construction. An aluminium fixing lug is snapped into the window frame by means of an interlocking joint at one end. The other end of the aluminium lug is malleable and can be plugged or built into the brickwork or steel framework. The fixing lug is designed to slide along the outside channel of the window frame and be affixed at the most convenient point. A unique feature is that when a window is fixed all fixing screws are concealed.

3.7 Insulation with Foam

Detailed information on insulation is given in Section 4.4 for roofs. The following additional information is provided concerning walls.

A polyurethane foam may be applied to walls by spraying as has already been described for roofs. The spaces between cavity walls may be filled in the same way if required.

That normally employed for the insulation of walls is polystyrene foam in the form of sheets. These can be applied direct to brick walls with cement mortar and can be finished with mortar or any gypsum-type plaster. The sheets may also be inserted in cavity walls without any difficulty.

It is clear that timber buildings can be readily insulated with polystyrene foam sheets. These sheets may be nailed to timber supports and finished with hardboard or any other material. Buildings can be made in this way with no other type of wall and they can obviously be used for cold storage.

In the case of concrete structures, the polystyrene board can be placed in the shuttering before the concrete is poured. The polystyrene sheets can also be applied to existing structures by the use of suitable adhesives. In an operation such as this, the adhesive should be applied to the backs of the boards. One or two "U" values will be of interest. Taking a 9 in. external wall as a basis, "U" values approximating to the following will be obtained: with 1 in. board $0 \cdot 15$; $1\frac{1}{2}$ in. board $0 \cdot 11$; 2 in. board $0 \cdot 09$.

3.8 Miscellaneous

3.8.1 PVC-covered Wire Fences

If chain-link and similar wire fences are covered with pvc, then considerable protection is afforded and long life will be achieved. Such products are made by: Rylands Brothers Ltd.; A. J. Binns Ltd.; Plastic Coatings Ltd. (this firm will collect many types of metal objects and cover them with pvc, polythene or other plastics); British Ropes Ltd.; Tinsley Wire Industries Ltd.; Barnards Ltd.; Expandite Ltd.

One advantage of plastic protection over galvanizing is the large number of colours which are available.

3.8.2   Venetian Blinds

Light-weight Venetian blinds can be made from a number of plastics. One example with orientated sheet is made by P. I. Christensen and Co. Ltd. Another concern, which uses pvc. is Avery Airflex Ltd. Another with styrene-butadiene in a range of non-fading pastel colours is made by E. Hilburn (Blinds) Ltd.

Part 4

ROOFS AND CEILINGS

CONTENTS

4.1 Introduction

4.2 Plastics for Roof Lights
  4.2.1 "Perspex" for Roof Lights
  4.2.2 Glass-fibre/Polyester Products for Roof Lights
  4.2.3 PVC for Roof Lights

4.3 Laminated Plastics for Roof Cladding

4.4 Foamed Plastics for Insulation
  4.4.1 Foam for Roofs
  4.4.2 "Styrocell" with Sheeted Roofs
  4.4.3 Recommended Specification for Under-sheeted Roofs using Clips
  4.4.4 General Building Techniques
  4.4.5 "Styrocell" with Tiled Roofs
  4.4.6 Recommended Specification for Tiled Roofs Over Rafters
  4.4.7 Recommended Specification for Tiled Roofs Under Rafters
  4.4.8 "Styrocell" in Concrete Roofing
  4.4.9 Foam for Ceilings
  4.4.10 "Styrocell" with Timber Joists
  4.4.11 Recommended Specification Under Timber Joists
  4.4.12 Recommended Specification Over Timber Joists
  4.4.13 Eaves and Ridge Filler Blocks
  4.4.14 Foam "In Situ"
  4.4.15 Type R.329 "Celspray" "Freon"-Blown

4.5 Plastics for Translucent Ceilings
  4.5.1 Supporting Framework
  4.5.2 Panels
  4.5.3 Thermal Insulation

4.6 Ceiling Finishes

4.7 Acoustic Tiles

Part 4

ROOFS AND CEILINGS

4.1 Introduction

Up to the present time, plastics have not made a big impact as material for roofs and ceilings. The conventional timber joists, tiles, bitumen-treated linings, plaster and boards still hold undisputed sway because they are perfectly satisfactory products and are reasonable in cost. Moreover, with exceptions to be mentioned later, plastics are not at their present stage of development meant for such structural purposes.

It is, of course, possible to build satisfactory roofs from laminated plastics and this aspect is considered in Part 9. Usually, such materials are adopted for special reasons and they are relatively expensive.

Plastics do, nevertheless, have a valuable and growing part to play in the construction of roofs and ceilings. The most important of these applications may be summarized as follows:

4.2 "Perspex", polyester and vinyl plastics as roof lights.
4.3 Laminated plastics for roof cladding.
4.4 Foamed plastics for thermal insulation.
4.5 Plastics for translucent ceilings.
4.6 PVC for decorative ceilings.
4.7 Plastics as acoustic tiles.

A new development coming along is to spray a vinyl coating over a roof. This has all the usual properties of pvc and gives a completely waterproof and weatherproof coating. Quite apart from this the colour range possible is extensive. One company concerned with the project is R. A. Brand and Co. Ltd. and further details can be found in Section 3.1.3.

Plastics and Resins Ltd. have produced a semi-liquid compound which can be applied by brush or spray. It can even be applied to damp surfaces and cures in a few hours to a continuous, impervious and immovable plastic skin. It is available in several colours and can be applied to almost any surface.

Tretol Ltd. manufacture *Tretoplast*, a jointless plastic skin for walls and ceilings. It is a pvc-based film, applied as a heavy liquid by spray, which dries to form a rough, flexible and continuous skin to a thickness of approximately 30/1000 of an inch. When applied over a ceiling construction of insulation or plasterboard, this skin is strong enough to permit an appreciable degree of flexing at the joints between the boards. *Tretoplast* "film-forms" readily over cracks or fissures which occur in brickwork and concrete and eliminates completely any focal points for mould growth or collection of dust. The material is waterproof, can be easily cleaned down by hosing or detergent washes and has excellent resistance to steam, acids and alkalis. It provides its own decoration and is available in colours, including white, the colour persisting throughout the thickness of the skin.

4.2 Plastics for Roof Lights

The best known of these are the corrugated "Perspex" sheets for applying to corrugated roofs, but corrugated vinyl sheets are now becoming available. "Perspex" is also made in the form of shaped products for dome lights. Polyester plastics are the strongest of all and may be obtained corrugated or flat. They are not, however, as transparent as "Perspex" (neither is pvc) and give a diffused light only.

4.2.1 "Perspex" for Roof Lights

Some detailed properties of "Perspex", including mechanical and thermal properties' and methods of machining and cementing, are given in Section 5.5.11.

Corrugated "Perspex" is a tough material which has been specially developed for roof lighting. A wide range of profiles is available to match other corrugated roofing sheets and the material is easy to install in exactly the same way as such sheets. The main advantage of "Perspex" sheets is that they can bring lighting to any point of a corrugated roofed building by simply replacing one or more of the existing sheets. Apart from straight corrugated sheets, more profiles are available in the curved form for barrel vault roofs and similar constructions.

The normal "Perspex" is clear but colours can also be supplied. One of these is Opal 030 which is a diffusing material with good light transmission properties.

Double-skin forms of "Perspex" roof lights can be employed to improve thermal insulation of roofs. The sheets should be spaced about $\frac{3}{4}$ in. apart and this halves the rate of heat loss.

An interesting development is the use of "Perspex" sheet for self-venting roof lights. This is possible because if the temperature of the building rises above 150°C., the material will become soft and pliable and be released from its fixings at the top and sides. Thus, it will hang down providing a vent for the discharge of heat and smoke, and the introduction of fire hoses. In some tests carried out, "Perspex sheet" was shown to fall in 10 minutes at 150°C. and in 6 minutes at 175°C.

When installing this type of roof light the bottom edge of the sheet is fixed in the usual way. The top edge, however, is supported, but not fixed along its width, on a $\frac{3}{16}$ in. thick piece of flat "Perspex" which is fixed to the roofing sheet and a supporting purlin by a normal fixing method. The top edge of the corrugated sheet is positioned not less than $\frac{1}{2}$ in. from the edge of the purlin so that at the appropriate temperatures, the ledge of flat "Perspex" will soften and fold downwards, thus allowing the main sheet to do the same.

"Perspex" is also being incorporated into flat roofs in the form of doming lanterns. The transmission of 90% light gives effective lighting below. To fit the "Perspex" lantern lights, the curb, upstands and gables supporting the sheets can be made from concrete, timber, light metal pressings or polyester structures. It is possible to obtain internal clear widths of lanterns from 2 ft. to 8 ft. in 6-in. increments. This is obtained without interruption of light by glazing bars or framing as with normal materials. Another advantage is the saving in weight in that "Perspex" sheet is only 25% of the weight of $\frac{1}{4}$ in. wired glass, not to mention the saving effected by the elimination of glazing bars, etc. In fixing the lanterns to the curbs, simple designs have been formulated employing a "Welvic" washer (produced by I.C.I. Ltd.) and standard nuts and bolts. The use of the pvc washers ensures wider division and allows for thermal expansion.

So far as cost is concerned, "Perspex" compares favourably with other materials. In addition, its high light transmission means that fewer roof lights will be necessary in that, with its use, an area as little as 10% of the total roof area will give adequate internal illumination.

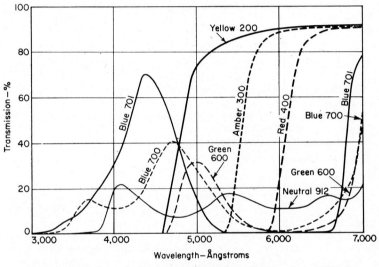

Light transmission of clear coloured "Perspex" sheet $\frac{1}{8}$ inch thick
(*Imperial Chemical Industries Ltd*)

Apart from corrugated lanterns, a number of firms manufacture dome lights. These have the usual advantages—half the weight of cast glass with a light transmission of 92% compared with 80%—and in addition, by using the correct shades (opal), can provide protection from sun glare. The designs which can be used are virtually unlimited since "Perspex" is easy to shape during manufacture. The limit of size is approximately 118 in. × 70 in. Domes made from the material are cheaper than those made from cast glass.

Manufacturers

The following is a list of "Perspex" roofing material manufacturers.

W. J. Cox (Sales) Ltd.; W. Freer Ltd.; Phipps Plastics Products Ltd. (their dome-lights are marketed by Henry Hope and Sons Ltd., Halford Works, Smethwick, Birmingham); Moto Plastics Ltd. (their domelights are marketed by Cordar Ltd.); Orbex Ltd.; T. and W. Ide Ltd. ("Twidex" acrylic domes, and hinged ventilating units in aluminium for these); The Rubberoid Co. Ltd. (also aluminium curbs); Cordar Ltd. (The products of Cordar Ltd. are available in clear or opal "Perspex" and, occasionally, colours. The products can be circular, rect-angular or square in most standard sizes. The company also manufactures single- and double-skin insulated roof lights to give a "U" value of 0·42 For use with "Perspex" roof lights, the company manufactures a 45° splayed polyester glass-fibre curb which can be insulated on site to equal the roof deck. The chief advant-age of the 45° splay is economy. For example, a 3 ft. × 3 ft. nett light dome can accommodate a 4 ft. × 4 ft. roof opening). Newdome Ltd.; E. D. Hinchliffe and Sons Ltd.; Duplus Domes Ltd.; Rolinx Ltd. ("Lumidomes"); Robin Plastics Ltd. (This company has introduced from Belgium the *Lantern-O-Plastic*, a floating skydome made from "Perspex". Condensation is fully drained off to the outside. Double or treble skinned domes can be provided where necessary).

Some examples of the above products, made by W. J. Cox, are given below:

PVC "Coxdomes"

The Mark I is a circular "Coxdome" with clear/diffusing single skin. The diameters range from 24 in. to 72 in. Fittings are also provided.

The Mark III is a rectangular "Coxdome" with clear/diffusing single skin. Sizes range from 24 in. × 24 in. to 118 in. × 70 in.

The Mark IV is a rectangular "Coxdome" with clear/diffusing opal, but with a double skin. Sizes range from 24 in. × 24 in. to 68 in. × 44 in.

A continuous rooflight is also available. The "U" value of a single skin is 1·00 ($\frac{3}{16}$ in thick) and 0·95 ($\frac{1}{4}$ in. thick) and for a double skin 0·42.

W. J. Cox is currently developing an extension of the "Coxdome" range to be formed from wire-reinforced pvc sheeting. They have already produced rooflights to the same pattern as their "Coxdome" Mark III in sizes up to 48 in. × 36 in. and are confident that this same material will be manufactured in both Mark III and Mark IV Double-Dome shapes to sizes up to and including 96 in. × 48 in. This is a new development in the plastics field as this material—"Darvic" pvc sheet reinforced with 34 s.w.g. × $\frac{1}{8}$ in. square wire mesh embedded, has now received from the D.S.I.R. a designation External F.AA. It will be appreciated that this is a major step forward in the manufacture of plastic rooflights.

4.2.2 Glass-fibre/Polyester Products for Roof Lights

A detailed description of glass-reinforced polyester products is given in Section 5.7.

The most common form is a rigid sheet usually corrugated but it can be flat.

Some of the outstanding characteristics of this material from the point of view of roof lighting are:

(1) Non-corrosive under usual atmospheric conditions;
(2) structural material which can have built-in colour;
(3) excellent insulator of electricity;
(4) transparent to radio-frequency waves;
(5) good thermal insulator compared with other structural materials;
(6) good sound and vibration damping effect;
(7) can be made translucent and coloured;
(8) high impact and tensile strengths (tensile strength 20,000 lb. per sq. in.);
(9) resistant to most chemicals;

(10) water absorption—0·5% approx.;

(11) coefficient of linear expansion—12 × 10⁻⁶ per °C.;

(12) thermal conductivity of chopped strand mat laminate—1·6 B.Th.U. in./ft.²h. deg. F.;

(C.F. thermal conductivity of structural steel: 300 B.Th.U. in./ft.²h. deg. F.)

The materials are the strongest plastic types available for roofs.

The following is a list of glass-reinforced polyester roofing product manufacturers:

Allan Blunn Ltd.

Some of the advantages claimed for this company's material, known as "Galt Glass", are light weight, resistance to shattering, the ability to be machined with conventional tools, the avoidance of glare and the ability to give the utmost light transmission. The types available include corrugated roof lights, dome lights and decorative sheet. The corrugated roof lights are available in 44 different profiles to match all standard roof materials in lengths of 3 ft. to 10 ft. in 6 in. increments.

Galt glass fibre reinforced dome lights (*Allan Blunn Ltd*)

Ceiling profiles can be made in longer lengths to special order. The dome lights are supplied to conventional spherical and rectangular patterns in popular sizes and also in the modular barrel type for continuous-run roof lighting. Double-skinned domes for insulation purposes are available in certain sizes. Decorative panels in colour, which avoids painting and maintenance for illuminated ceilings and concealed lighting effects, are available. They are applied in flat sheets with reeded or stippled surfaces and the special Continental corrugated profile.

Wembley Fibreglass and Plastics Ltd.

This company will produce corrugated or other roofing products in any required profile and will match any corrugated sheet sent to it. Products are translucent or opaque, or coloured. Domes etc. will also be made to order.

Universal Laminated Plastics Ltd.

The proprietary name for the material is "Verplex". Grade A is unaffected by temperatures from −40°C. to +120°C. and Grade B by temperatures from −40°C. to +200°C. Either grade can be made non-inflammable for an extra charge.

B.I.P. Reinforced Products Ltd.

This company's product is "Filon". The light transmission is high for this material and is from 83% to 85% in the translucent quality. Any length of sheet can be provided, limited only by transport and handling facilities. Where colours are used, the product is opaque and light transmission varies from 0% to 65% according to colour. Standard colours only in flat sheet 1¼ in. double reed, 4 in. shiplap and 8 in.–3 in. iron profiles are available. A first-class self-extinguishing quality can be supplied if required. "Filon" has the approval of the Ministry of Works, the War Department, the Air Ministry and the L.C.C.

Newalls Insulation Co. Ltd.

"Interclad" is the name of this company's product which is a glass-fibre mat used as insulation. For ease of estimating requirements "Interclad", in various sizes and thicknesses, is packed to give coverage units of 100 sq. ft. as laid.

Description:	Glass-fibres bonded with thermosetting resin into tough, but light and pliable mat, free from shot, rot-proof, odourless and non-hygroscopic.
Nominal Density:	¾ lb./ft.^{3}
Thermal Conductivity:	0·26 B.Th.U. in./ft.^{2} h. deg. F. at normal ambient temperature.
Sizes:	(a) 60 ft. × 21 in. × 1 in. thick—105 sq. ft.
	(b) 75 ft. × 16½ in. × 1 in. thick—103 sq. ft.
	(c) 30 ft. × 3 ft. 4 in. × 1 in. thick—100 sq. ft.
	(d) 34 ft. × 3 ft. × 1 in. thick—102 sq. ft.

The Rubberoid Co. Ltd.

Domelights.

Hartington Conway and Co. Ltd.

"Litaglass".

Fablon Ltd.

"Rilite".

Sommerfields Ltd.

"Corrolite".

Reinforced Plastic Developments

"Contirol" glass-fibre rolls, in range of fast colours.

Cascelloid Ltd.

"Cascalite". A number of different colours and thicknesses of material are available, including 6 oz., 7 oz. and 8 oz. Different profiles are also available to match other materials on the market such as asbestos cement, aluminium and iron.

For normal use, the standard materials are perfectly satisfactory. Where special fire regulations are in force, then special fire-resistant grades can often be provided (to B.S. 476: Part 3: 1958).

U.A.M. Group of Companies

This company manufactures "Unilux" reinforced sheeting in a wide range of colours and profiles, together with dome and barrel lights.

Installation Pointers

(1) The materials can be drilled easily and can be cut with a fine-tooth saw or abrasive wheel, if necessary.
(2) Care should be taken not to distort the sheets by over-tightening fittings.
(3) Use bolts, hook bolts, screws or drive nails with galvanized, bituminous felt or pvc washers.
(4) It is desirable that a weather-seal strip or sealing compound be used between overlaps.
(5) Seam bolts should be employed on overlaps.
(6) The roofs are immune to atmospheric pollution and should therefore require no maintenance. They may be cleaned when required with water and detergent.

4.2.3 PVC for Roof Lights

Rigid pvc is being used on an increasing scale for roof lights. It has excellent chemical, weathering and fire-resistance properties and is available in a variety of colours. The corrugated sheets have all the valuable characteristics associated with pvc.

Some manufacturers of this product are:

BX Plastics Ltd.

This company manufactures corrugated "Cobex". One of the major advantages of this tough, corrosion-resistant rigid vinyl sheet is its non-inflammability. Made in profiles to match asbestos sheeting, translucent coloured "Cobex" excludes glare without restricting the entry of natural light; the new extruded sheet is available in all standard lengths, 20 ft. stock lengths or longer if required. Rigid vinyl is waterproof, will not warp and is light and easy to handle. It is not only very economical but also reduces labour costs because it needs no framing, cementing or flashing.

The Marley Tile Co. Ltd.

This company manufactures an extruded corrugated vinyl sheeting called

"Marleyglaze". Produced in a natural translucence as well as in red, green, yellow and blue, "Marleyglaze" is extremely tough and durable. It is designed for use as a roof sheeting and may also be incorporated in interior design to provide such things as partition walls.

An example of the use of the material was as a permanent awning for crew protection on m.v. Sapele Palm. Thirty panels in natural colour, each 10 ft. × 2 ft. 6 in. with a 3 in. profile were used.

Allied Structural Plastics Ltd.

This company produce "Aspect" translucent pvc sheeting. It is extruded from the rigid pvc compound in profiles to suit asbestos cement sheets, standard 3-in. corrugated, standard six, major six, big six, Canada tiles, Atlas tiles and Trafford tiles. The thickness of the sheet is $\frac{1}{16}$ in. and this results in a natural translucent (82% transmission) sheet which is rigid and tough. It is non-combustible, has a low rate of flame spread, very good resistance to chemical attack and to weather, due to a very low absorption of water. Fixing is straightforward and follows asbestos cement practice. No maintenance is required.

Canopy Design Ltd.

This company produce "Corolux", a corrugated pvc in various profiles and colours. The material is in sheets or cross-corrugated rolls.

Holmsund Ltd.

This company produce rigid pvc sheets in a range of translucent and opaque colours. This is "Carawell" for extensions, lean-to's, etc. PVC roof sheeting may be obtained in corrugated cross-section to match 3-in., standard six, big six, major six, and other commonly used roofing profiles. The 3-in. is usually 30 in. wide and other profiles 43 in. The sheeting is normally used in 3–10 ft. lengths. Longer lengths can be made. The cross-corrugated sheet is either $27\frac{1}{2}$ in. or 48 in. wide. The length of roll is governed by convenience in handling; 30-ft. rolls are common. Formed capping pieces are made from the same material as the pvc roof sheeting.

I.C.I. Ltd.

A relatively new material is a pvc/wire laminate and I.C.I. Ltd. has added clear "Darvic" sheet wire laminate to its development selling range following successful tests on the material at the Fire Research Station. As a result of these tests, carried out on a $\frac{1}{8}$ in. thick single-skin domelight—the laminate was given the highest fire-resistance rating that can be achieved—the External F.AA. rating of BS. 476, Part 3, "External Fire Exposure Roof Test."

It consists of clear pvc sheet with a layer of 8-mesh per in., 34-gauge, galvanized mild steel wire in the centre. The mechanical properties and processing characteristics of the clear material are similar to those of the company's opaque sheet wire laminates, which have been on I.C.I.'s development selling range for some time. It is likely to be used for domelights, rooflights, window louvres, fume cupboards, and special doors and windows.

The laminate is available in 6 ft. × 4 ft. sheets. The clear material is made in thicknesses of 0·080 in. and above, the opaque material in thicknesses of 0·060 in. and above.

Temec Ltd.

This company has a wire-reinforced pvc sheeting in a full range of profiles known as "*S*"-*lon*. The reinforcement consists of 30 s.w.g. $\frac{1}{10}$ in. wire mesh and has received a very high grading as a fire retardant. The company has now also introduced the *Summit* range of corrugated pvc sheeting, either translucent or transparent. Colours are yellow, green, blue and natural and standard widths (2 ft. 2 in. and 3 ft. 7 in.) are available in 6, 8 and 10 ft. lengths.

Pfizer Ltd.

The Chemical Division of this company produce "Vistaglaze", a fully transparent wire-reinforced pvc sheeting. It is available both as flat sheet and corrugated profiles and is inherently non-inflammable and has been awarded the highest grading External S.AA. under BS. 476, Part 3. The colours are glass clear, amber, green and blue. The main use is for roofing and roof lighting.

The pvc/steel laminates mentioned in Section 3.5.4 may also be employed for roof cladding.

William Briggs and Sons Ltd.

This company offers "Bitumetal" roofs in a wide range of coloured decks in either pvc-coated steel or vinyl-coated aluminium.

4.3 Laminated Plastics for Roof Cladding

Instead of transparent or translucent cladding materials, opaque laminated products are also available. These have the advantage over metals of being extremely corrosion resistant and light to handle.

An example is "Corroplast" made by Holoplast Ltd. The material is a laminate of mechanically strong kraft paper impregnated with a special phenol-formaldehyde resin. "Corroplast" is formed into its corrugated shape by high pressure and controlled heat to produce a strong, tough, yet moderately flexible sheet possessing excellent chemical and physical properties and a high strength-weight ratio. With integral colours, the material does not require painting or other maintenance, and can be easily cut or drilled. The resistance to corrosion is in no way affected by this work. It is supplied in sheets 4 ft. wide in lengths of from 4 ft. to 8 ft. 6 in. in increments of 6 in. The standard sheets are available in three colours and the standard size is 8 ft. 6 in. × 4 ft. The inner face can be stove enamelled to improve light reflection. The material has the highest fire resistance rating, External S.AA.

"Corroplast" offers exceptional resistance to corrosive conditions in coastal and industrial areas, and the new finish—a hard, smooth surface made possible by developments in manufacturing techniques—gives greatly improved general performance. The sheet is available in three integral colours—forest green, chestnut red and natural brown.

Ancillaries such as adjustable- and fixed-angle ridges, gable trims and corner pieces, finials and corrugation fillers are available. "Corroplast" is generally fixed with orthodox fittings such as galvanized hooks and drive screws, and a feature is that its resistance to corrosion is in no way affected by cutting or drilling.

9

4.4   Foamed Plastics for Thermal Insulation

The use of plastic foams for the insulation of roofs is an important development since really low "U" values can be achieved. Detailed properties of plastic foams together with suppliers and sizes available are given in Section 1.3.8. Some idea of improvement in thermal properties is given in the following Table for "Flamingo" foam showing the gradual reduction in "U" value with increasing thickness.

Construction	Without insulation	Thickness				
		½ in.	¾ in.	1 in.	1½ in.	2 in.
Concrete 4 in. with asphalt and roofing felt, plastered soffit	0·59	0·24	0·19	0·16	0·12	0·095
Concrete 6 in. with asphalt and roofing felt, plastered soffit	0·52	0·23	0·18	0·15	0·11	0·08
Corrugated asbestos cement sheets	1·40	0·27	0·21	0·16	0·12	0·08
Corrugated iron	1·48	0·28	0·22	0·17	0·12	0·10
Tiled roof on battens, plaster or plasterboard ceiling	0·56	0·24	0·20	0·15	0·11	0·09
Tiled roof on battens, but with roofing felt, plaster or plasterboard ceiling	0·42	0·21	0·17	0·14	0·10	0·08
Timber 1 in. with asphalt or felt. Plaster or plasterboard ceiling.	0·32	0·19	0·16	0·14	0·10	0·08

The B.Th.U. figures quoted are theoretical values, based on laboratory tests under constant conditions. They will remain virtually the same in practice, because of the material's remarkably high water and vapour resistance.

The most important material at the moment is polystyrene foam. This is available in rigid blocks and sheets and is easy to fix, saw, cut and in fact

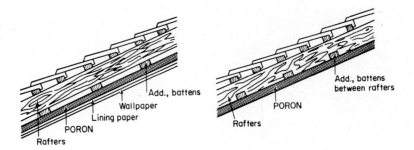

Poron foamed polystyrene roof insulation (*Poron Insulation Ltd*)

fabricate in every way. Thermal conductivity is about 0·23 and density 1·0–2·0 lb. per cu. ft. The material is "closed cell" which means that it is highly water resistant although, in spite of this, waterproofing coatings or membranes are used in association with it.

Apart from the methods of using foams in bulk described below, it is also possible to employ ceiling tiles such as "Marleycel." These are 12 in. square of expanded polystyrene and ½ in. of these is equivalent to 1½ in. of strawboard or 1 in. of vermiculite. They are applied with Marley No. 24 Adhesive.

"Flamingo" expanded polystyrene board used to insulate the factory roof of the King's Langley Engineering Co Ltd. "Flamingo" is made from Montopore expandable polystyrene, manufactured by Monsanto
(*Monsanto Chemicals Ltd*)

4.4.1 Foam for Roofs

Polystyrene foams may be built into roofs in a number of ways. One of the simplest of these is to nail polystyrene boards to the underside of roof rafters using galvanized nails. This will convert a cold and gloomy loft into a bright and usable attic. Where concrete roofs are being built in situ, the polystyrene boards will be placed in the shuttering. Alternatively, they may be laid over the concrete structure and bonded with suitable materials. A sand and cement screed is then poured over the boards although the screeds should have expansion joints cut about every 10 foot square.

Information on the use of foams for roofs is provided by the Shell Chemical Co. Ltd. for their "Styrocell" (the raw material produced by them but converted by various manufacturers.)

4.4.2 "Styrocell" with Sheeted Roofs

The general properties of "Styrocell", particularly its lightness and bondability, make it an ideal insulant for use with lightweight sheet roof construction. In applications of this type, although resistance to the transmission of water and water-vapour is relatively low, some additional safeguards against condensation (e.g. ventilation) must be taken where conditions of high humidity are possible. This can be easily achieved with corrugated sheets, by ensuring that the spaces between the corrugation crests and the "Styrocell" are ventilated at eaves and ridge levels.

4.4.3   Recommended Specification for Under-sheeted Roofs using Clips

Insulation boards of a minimum thickness of $\frac{1}{2}$ in. should be used. The boards should be cut or fitted to run from purlin to purlin. The underside surface of the corrugation valleys should be coated with impact adhesive.

It is also important when fixing "Styrocell" with adhesive, that some form of additional mechanical fixing be provided.

Clips for the appropriate thickness of material should be positioned over the purlins by passing through under the corrugation crests. These should be placed at the board joints so that one clip supports the corners of two adjoining boards. When used with metal purlins, the boards are notched.

Instead of adhesive, light galvanized steel or aluminium "T"-sections can be used in the joints between the boards, and these should rest on the clip.

With corrugated asbestos-cement sheet, the "U" value of the overall construction would be:—$\frac{1}{2}$ in. "Styrocell" $= 0 \cdot 27$; $\frac{3}{4}$ in. $= 0 \cdot 21$; 1 in. $= 0 \cdot 17$.

4.4.4   General Building Techniques

Boards can be applied under and over rafters and timber joists. When applied underneath they should be nailed to the joists through large-diameter washers. This procedure obviates the necessity of relying on an adhesive.

"Styrocell" may also be used in concrete floor and roof constructions. The thickness of concrete laid over the material for flooring should be not less than 1 in. for domestic purposes and over 4 in., probably with reinforcement, for industrial use.

In concrete roof applications, roofing felt is laid immediately over the boards and hot bitumen and chippings may then be laid over the roofing felt.

4.4.5   "Styrocell" with Tiled Roofs

"Styrocell" is eminently suitable for use as insulation to tiled roofs. In applications of this type, although resistance to the transmission of water and water-vapour is relatively high, some additional safeguard against possible water penetration of the tiling, by wind or snow, is recommended. This is particularly desirable where delay is likely to occur between the fixing of the insulation and the subsequent tiling.

4.4.6   Recommended Specification for Tiled Roofs Over Rafters

Insulation boards to be a minimum of $\frac{1}{2}$ in. thick, and laid at right angles to the rafters parallel to the eaves; ensure that the vertical end joints occur over the centre of rafters.

The boards should be secured with $1\frac{1}{2}$ in. galvanized nails at the corners. Counter-battens $1\frac{1}{2}$ in. $\times \frac{3}{4}$ in. to be nailed up the line of the rafters using 3 in.

wire nails. Untearable building paper or felt to be laid over the boards and counter-battens. Normal battening to be carried out with 2 in. wire nails spaced according to the type of tile to be used, and the tiling to be carried out in the normal way.

The overall "U" value for this construction is as follows:—$\frac{1}{2}$ in. "Styrocell" = 0·24; $\frac{3}{4}$ in. = 0·19; 1 in. = 0·16.

4.4.7 Recommended Specification for Tiled Roofs Under Rafters

Insulation boards to be a minimum of $\frac{1}{2}$ in. thick. The boards to be fixed at right angles to the rafters, parallel to the eaves and cut and fitted to ensure that the vertical end joints occur over the centre of rafters. Joints should be staggered in successive rows.

Impact adhesive should be spread liberally on the underside of the rafters. Commencing at the eaves or lowest point, the boards should be pressed securely home against the rafters. They should be additionally supported by means of nailing at the corners. Nails with large pliable washers such as felt or polythene may be used in place of adhesive.

Where the underside surface of the rafters is interrupted by projections, purlins and so on, 1 in. × $\frac{3}{4}$ in. fixing battens should be used so as to support the free edge of the insulation board.

The overall "U" value for this construction is:—$\frac{1}{2}$ in. "Styrocell" = 0·24; $\frac{3}{4}$ in. = 0·19; 1 in. = 0·16.

4.4.8 "Styrocell" in Concrete Roofing

The material, because of its lightness and resistance to rot, is most suitable for use as insulation for concrete roofs with an asphalt or bituminous-felt finish.

In applications of this type it is important that the "Styrocell" be protected from the high temperatures of hot bitumen used for bonding or forming the roof finish. The maximum safe temperature for polystyrene is 160°F. Protection can be provided by a cement and sand binding and a protective layer of roofing felt, laid loose, upon which the roofing finish is then formed. Whilst this treatment can be perfectly satisfactory, care should be exercised in the foot traffic involved in the laying operation. Thus it is preferred that a proper screed be used, particularly since it is usually required for forming roof falls. The recommended method of using a cement screed is as follows.

Insulation boards should be laid over the concrete structure and may be stuck down with dabs of adhesive if desired. A 3:1 sand-cement screed should then be laid over the foam of a thickness of not less than $\frac{3}{4}$ in. A hair felt is then laid and the roofing finish completed in the normal way. Care should be exercised that the temperature of the asphalt does not exceed 420°F.

The overall "U" value for this construction, assuming a 6 in. concrete structure, would be:—$\frac{3}{4}$ in "Styrocell" = 0·19; 1 in. = 0·15; 2 in. = 0·12.

4.4.9 Foam for Ceilings

Where ceilings are finished with the usual plaster board, additional insulation can easily be given. For example, the plaster board and foam board can be fixed to a joist in one operation. Another method is to fix the boards direct to the joists and finish with a skin coat of plaster.

An important use of polystyrene boards with concrete ceilings is to avoid condensation. The polystyrene boards are laid at the bottom of the shuttering with the concrete on top. When the shuttering is removed, plaster may be applied in the usual way. Similarly, polystyrene boards or tiles may be fixed to existing ceilings with adhesives.

The Shell Chemical Co. Ltd., provide the following information in respect of the use of foams for ceilings.

4.4.10   "Styrocell" with Timber Joists

"Styrocell", because of its lightness and rigidity, is eminently suitable for use as a ceiling board. The surface of the boards may either be left undecorated, or painted with plastic emulsion or water-based paints. It can also be plastered.

It is important when fixing the boards with the recommended adhesive that some form of additional mechanical fixing should be provided.

4.4.11   Recommended Specification Under Timber Joists

Insulation boards of a minimum thickness of $\frac{3}{4}$ in. should be used. The boards should be fixed at right angles to the span of the joists so that the end joints occur on the centre of a joist in each case, and they should be staggered in successive rows.

When fitting projecting beams, chimney breasts, fanlights, etc., fixing battens should be provided to support the butting edge.

Impact adhesive should be spread liberally on the underside of the joists. The boards should then be positioned and pressed firmly home, and additionally supported by broad-headed galvanized nails along the line of the joints at about 12 in. centres. Care should be taken to ensure that nails are not driven home too hard. Scrim should be applied to all joints when plastering.

Assuming an undercoated ceiling to a pitched roof, the overall "U" value of the construction shown would be:—$\frac{3}{4}$ in. "Styrocell" $= 0 \cdot 192$; 1 in. $=$ $0 \cdot 124$.

4.4.12   Recommended Specification Over Timber Joists

Insulation boards of a minimum thickness of $\frac{1}{2}$ in. should be used. The boards to be laid at right angles across the joist centres so that the joints occur over the centre of a joist in each case. In fitting projections, rafters, chimney breasts, fixing battens should be provided to support the butting edge.

Where the boards are laid on joists which are to receive the floor finish, 2 in. $\times$ 1 in. battens should be temporarily fixed over the line of each joist, and the boarding floor secured to them. The floor surface, together with its supporting battens, should form an independent raft resting upon the supporting boards and joists. It is important that these battens are not permanently fixed through the foam to the joists and that foam should be packed between the end of the rafters and the wall.

Where boards are used over ceiling joists which are not required to take a floor surface, the battens should be permanently nailed so as to mark the position of the joists and allow treading boards to be laid for subsequent maintenance or repair work.

The overall "U" value of this construction, when used as insulation over ceiling joists in a normal tiled roof, would be:—$\frac{1}{2}$ in. "Styrocell" = 0·28; $\frac{3}{4}$ in. = 0·192; 1 in. = 0·124.

4.4.13   Eaves and Ridge Filler Blocks

A problem in buildings with corrugated roofs is to exclude draughts at the eaves and ridge positions. The conventional types of eaves filling are hard materials which may cause breaks in corrugated asbestos roofing sheets when they are bolted down tightly.

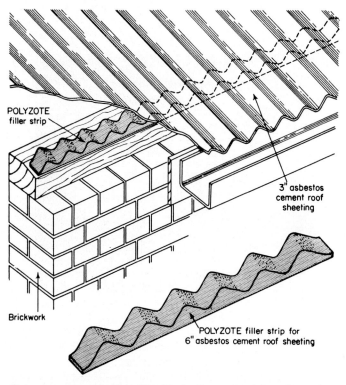

Polyzote eaves and ridge filler blocks for corrugated roof coverings
(*Expanded Rubber Co Ltd*)

"Polyzote," which is an expanded plastic of closed cell construction, has sufficient resilience to allow for pitch variations and thereby eliminates breaking of roofing sheets.

"Polyzote" filler blocks are light, non-porous and rot-proof. They can be supplied in different sections to fit standard asbestos and aluminium corrugated sheets, in lengths of 3 ft. (3 ft. 4 in. for the big six profile only) and in 2 in.

widths. Other widths can be supplied on application from Expanded Plastics Ltd.

4.4.14   Foam "In Situ"

The methods of use of foam so far described involve the fixing of blocks and sheets in position. Another technique of great value is also available and this involves the use of a spray gun and containers to spray polyurethane foams on to any surface.

Foam-in-Place equipment has been developed by The Aerograph-De-Vilbiss Co. Ltd., to apply rigid polyurethane foam by spray, the foam itself being manufactured by The Baxenden Chemical Co. Ltd., especially for this purpose. J. M. Steel and Co. Ltd. also supply the materials and special equipment for foaming on site.

The qualities of foam insulation have long been appreciated in industry, but it is only now, with this revolutionary technique, that the foam can be applied swiftly and without elaborate preparation.

Spraying polyurethane foams (*Aerograph-De Vilbiss Co Ltd*)

The previous alternatives have been: machine mixing, using special and necessarily expensive equipment for the production of foam sheets or blocks, and batch mixing in buckets, using hand or electric stirring.

In either case, it is necessary to use some form of shuttering or battening to retain the foam in position.

In some instances the older methods will remain the most economical method of foam production, but a large number of applications particularly lend themselves to this new simplified spray system.

The foam can be used for the thermo-insulation of roofs, structural steel-work, service pipes, ventilation ducts, and storage tanks; or again, as an anti-drumming agent, for the lining of packing cases as a shock-absorber and water-proofer.

There are other properties too—acoustic, anti-vermin, anti-acid, not to mention the material as a strengthener for panels, etc.

Detailed information on the subject is provided by the Aerograph-DeVilbiss concern in the form of questions and answers.

Q. How is polyurethane foam made?

A. By a chemical reaction between two fluids, called "A" and "B" for practical purposes. Exothermic heat is generated by the reaction which releases "Freon" or equivalent gas. It also polymerizes or cures the mixture, so preventing the escape of the gas and causing the expansion of the material and its conversion into foam.

Q. How does the equipment work?

A. By the use of two pressure feed tanks which feed the two components to the type JGC-505 spray gun which mixes them together in the spray cone.

Q. The foam material as supplied by The Baxenden Chemical Co. Ltd. is termed a "partial pre-polymer"—why?

A. One of the components has already been partially reacted and therefore the final inter-mixing of the two components in the spray cone is only the last stage of the process.

Q. What are the basic chemicals involved?

A. As formulated by Baxenden, component "A" comprises isocyanate, the pre-polymer and "Freon", and "B" polyether resin, "Freon" and the catalyst (in the form of tertiary amines).

Q. How does the type JGC-505 differ from the type JGC-501 and 504 spray guns?

A. The type JGC-505 can handle two viscous fluids. The type JGC-501 and 504 guns can handle only one viscous material and one water-thin additive.

Q. How is the ratio of the two components maintained if no flow meter is used?

A. The ratio is established initially by the physical calibration of the two fluid flows by tank pressures. In the case of the Baxenden material, the ratio is 50:42 by volume for "A" and "B" components respectively. The final result is unaffected by minor fluctuations caused by pressure drops, etc., and no meter is therefore necessary.

Q. How fast can this material be sprayed?

A. About as fast as an operator can handle the gun. Five pints per minute has been found to be a practical rate, although satisfactory tests have been carried out using over double this figure.

Q. What is the viscosity of each component?

A. Ninety-four seconds and 157 seconds Ford Cup No. 4 for components "A" and "B" respectively at a temperature of 68°F.

Q. Why use pressure feed tanks with maximum working pressures of 100 lb. p.s.i. when 30 or 40 lb. would seem to be adequate in practice?

A. Remember that tank pressures are related not only to the flow rate required, but also to viscosity and also by such factors as lengths of fluid hose in use. In many cases, contractors may wish to use far longer fluid lines than the 30 ft.-length with which demonstrations are usually carried out.

Q. *What is the air consumption of the JGC-505 gun?*

A. The type JGC-505 fitted with size 134 air cap consumes approximately 25 to 35 c.f.m. at 75 lb. p.s.i.

Q. *Is any surface preparation required before spraying?*

A. None, beyond the removal of any grease, oil, wax or loose dust.

Q. *Does the foam adhere to metal as well as to other surfaces?*

A. If anything, adhesion is somewhat better when applied to metal than with smooth wood. Any irregularities or contours in the surface naturally assist adhesion.

Q. *Are any precautions necessary to ensure trouble-free operation of the equipment?*

A. It is sometimes an advantage to keep the head of the gun immersed in acetone which prevents build-up of material, or the same purpose can be achieved by fairly frequent applications of acetone to the nozzle by brush.

Q. *How can the equipment be cleaned and how frequently should this be carried out?*

A. By flushing through with acetone. It is unnecessary to clean this equipment more frequently than with conventional materials because of the extended pot life of each component.

Q. *How long does it take for the two components to be converted into foam?*

A. The resin "creams" within seconds of it reaching the surface, rises to its full volume within 30 seconds and becomes hard although friable within 5 minutes. All traces of solvent and isocyanate leave the material within a minute or so of application and the foam cures completely within 24 hours.

Q. *What is the final finished appearance of the foam when cured?*

A. This foam has a puckered appearance although it can be smoothed quite easily with the hand two or three minutes after spraying. In normal circumstances it cures with a fairly hard surface skin.

Q. *What are the properties of this foam?*

A. (a) The foam is completely resistant to water as well as to other fluids.

   (b) polyurethane resin is a chemically inert material and the foam therefore is also resistant to alkalis and acids other than those in their most concentrated form.

   (c) its thermal insulation is of a very high order and is approximately twice as efficient as cork. Thermal insulation efficiency is measured in terms of a "K" factor which in this case is $0 \cdot 11$ to $0 \cdot 14$. The "K" factor of cork is approximately $0 \cdot 24$.

   (d) for general purposes it can be regarded as resistant to weather.

   (e) it withstands heat up to 110°C. (230°F.). There is no known low-temperature limit.

   (f) it has extremely high strength/weight ratio. Even with a density as low as $1 \cdot 1$ to $1 \cdot 5$ lb. per cu. ft. it has a compressive yield strength of 15 lb. p.s.i.

(g) being of "closed" cellular structure, i.e. 80% to 90% of the "Freon" gas-filled cells are independent of one another, polyurethane foam absorbs only a matter of 2% to 3% of water and is therefore extremely buoyant.

(h) its acoustical insulation properties are fair, although h a foam with inter-connecting cells is more efficient. However, because of its surface appearance, this foam would diffuse sound by "random deflection". It also acts as a good anti-drum agent.

(i) its electrical insulation properties are quite good.

(j) it supports combustion, but because of its low density and the lack of solid matter, there is less to burn than with an equivalent volume of material such as wood. In this respect, it is comparable with expanded polystyrene but compares favourably with cork.

(k) when cured, polyurethane is non-poisonous but has no food value and since it prevents the transmission of odours, it can therefore be regarded as pest and vermin proof.

(l) it does not support bacteria life.

(m) although classed as rigid foam, this formulation of foam does absorb shock to a certain extent by distributing it evenly.

(n) the volume of resin needed to make up the foam is very small when compared with dry types of insulants such as cork granules or vermiculite. It is useful to remember that this foam rises to approximately 30 times the volume of the resin when applied under normal conditions.

Q. How toxic are the fumes of the Baxenden material?

A. The fumes should not be inhaled at all if it can be avoided. Inhaling these fumes, even up to five minutes per day, could seriously affect the lungs or throat of the operator in a matter of 2–3 weeks.

Q. What respirator is recommended?

A. We know that the "Plus pressure" respirator manufactured by the R.F.D. Co. Ltd. of Godalming, Surrey, meets with the requirements of the Factory Inspectorate and in the absence of a suitable respirator being offered by ourselves, this type may be recommended.

The specification for the material is as follows:

4.4.15 Type R.329 "Celspray" "Freon"-blown
("Freon" is a Registered Trade Mark of E. I. Dupont de Nemours Co.)

Mixing ratio:	100 parts by weight of Component "A".
	70 parts by weight of Component "B".
Mixing temperature:	60–75°F.
Density:	Minimum 1·1 lb./cu. ft.
	1·4 lb./cu. ft. section cut after spraying.
	1·6 lb./cu. ft. overall average including skin.
K factor:	0·11 to 0·14 B.Th./U./h.sq. ft./°F./in. at 75°F. mean.
Compressive yield strength:	15 lb. per sq. in.

Further information regarding this material may be obtained from The Baxenden Chemical Co. Ltd.

4.5 Plastics for Translucent Ceilings

A growing fashion is the use of luminous ceilings which appear to have uniform brightness. This is achieved by interposing a translucent product between the room and the source of light. The material commonly used for this purpose is a specially formulated pvc.

A typical product is the I.C.I. "Flovic" Foil Translucent White 037 which is a very good diffuser. The material is light in weight and has been designed for heat resistance so that it will not show discoloration, distortion or embrittlement over several years. This achievement, however, has been obtained only at the expense of some flexibility and this must be taken into account in design work. A wide expanse of pvc is not particularly rigid but this can be achieved by the incorporation in the pattern of stiffening ribs, etc.

The operating temperature of the foil should not be greater than 50°C. The material is not easily ignited and in any case is self-extinguishing and is a Class 2 material as defined by B.S.476: Part 1, 1953.

Manufacturers

The following is a list of firms manufacturing this type of installation: Courtney Pope (Electrical) Ltd.; Harris and Sheldon (Display) Ltd.; Ionlite Ltd.; Thorn Electrical Industries Ltd.; Isora Illuminating Ceilings Ltd.; Lumenated Ceilings Ltd. The last-named company manufactures 36-in. square diffusers of tensioned flexible pvc.

A typical practical example of the type of product supplied is provided by the Isora Thermalucent ceilings the claimed features of which are as follows:

(1) A double-layer or "sandwich" panel, giving excellent diffusion but, above all, providing a virtually complete answer to the problem of accumulated dust and dirt becoming visible from below.
(2) The possibility of effecting up to 70% reduction in heat losses.
(3) A new, attractively styled yet extremely strong supporting gridwork.
(4) Translucent panels with all perimeters fully protected against abrasion and accidental damage.

4.5.1 Supporting Framework

This consists of a light but strong 20 s.w.g. galvanized mild-steel grid, normally based on 3 ft. 4 in. centres, which supports the Thermalucent panels. This framework can be painted to any colour specified and is completely demountable, a particular advantage in exhibition and display work or where the ceiling is erected over movable partitions. The bottom flanges of the framing sections, which are V-shaped, present a most attractive appearance as well as ensuring maximum reflection of light.

4.5.2 Panels

Thermalucent panels are extremely light and can be quickly and easily removed from the grid when necessary. Each panel consists of a light, galvanized mild-steel frame over which is stretched and secured two separate membranes, of translucent pvc film (to BSS. 1763/56). A still-air space $1\frac{3}{16}$ in. in depth is thus created, giving excellent thermal insulation and virtually eliminating the problem of dust and dirt on the panels being visible from below.

Isora illuminating PVC ceilings (*Isora Illuminating Ceilings Ltd*)

The Thermalucent system is unique in that a very wide combination of films can be used on the panels. For all practical purposes, the total light transmission of a Thermalucent panel may be obtained by multiplying together the individual light transmission factors of the two films selected.

For example:

upper membrane of Natural pvc = 90% transmission.

lower membrane of Daylight Blue pvc = 78% transmission.

Then total light transmission factor of panel = 90 × 78 = 70% (approximately).

The films are specially-formulated polyvinyl chloride (pvc) 0·006 in. thick, of exceptional strength and toughness. All films conform with BSS. 1763/56 (Type IF sheetings).

They are currently available in the following colours and textures.

	Light transmission factor		Light transmission factor
Natural	90%	Daylight Blue (high diffusion)	54%
Frosted White	88%	Apple Green	53%
Daylight Blue	78%	Rose Pink	51%
Daylight Blue (embossed)	75%	Powder Blue	49%
Golden Yellow	62%	Satin Black	Nil

A wide range of other attractive coloured and patterned films, either translucent or opaque, exists, thus giving infinite scope for unusual or decorated ceilings.

All "Isora" films are classed as "self-extinguishing" and conform with the flammability test described in BSS. 1763/56. "Isora" ceilings have repeatedly received full approval from the London County Council and other Authorities for use in public and other buildings. In addition, the ceiling conforms with the Thermal Insulation (Industrial Buildings) Act 1957, in that it will not enhance the risk of fires breaking out or spreading in the building.

4.5.3   Thermal Insulation

The following data has been provided by the Heating and Ventilating Research Association, Bracknell:

Thermal resistance (R) of Isora Thermalucent ceilings on 3 ft. 4 in. module:

(a) Under open roof (i.e. sheeted or tiled without
             felting or boarding)............   Approx. 1·9

(b) Under sealed roof ....   Approx. 1·4

(Note: the precise value of the thermal resistance will depend on the pitch of the roof: the lower the pitch, the greater the resistance).

Example:

	"U"-Value
Sheeted asbestos roof (no ceiling)	1·40
Above roof with Isora Thermalucent ceiling	0·39

(The ceiling therefore reduces heat loss by 70% under these conditions).

4.5.4   Further Examples

Elco Plastics Ltd. manufacture a number of products in connection with the illumination of ceilings. These briefly are as follows:

"Elcoplas" louvres—A range of polystyrene louvres of $\frac{3}{8}$ in. square to 2 in. square in square and diagonal mesh.

"Specular" louvre—Specially designed louvres giving complete glare control. Polystyrene metalized gold or silver with a polished or matt finish.

"Plasmatic"—A ribbed polystyrene sheet designed specially to meet the need for overall enclosed luminous ceilings.

"Elcoplan"—The latest addition to the Elco range, a new luminous ceiling based on 24 in. modular panels of $\frac{3}{8}$ in. egg crate with no visible means of support.

"Cliplouvres"—Opal polystyrene clip-on type diffusers with either closed or open sides.

A new type of luminous ceiling, not based on pvc, called "Infiniflex" has now been produced by Isora. The appearance of the "Infiniflex" ceiling is remarkable in that an 8-in. module is employed, the small luminous sections being gracefully contoured to avoid an "over-square" appearance. The effect of this size is to make quite small rooms look spacious. A wide range of luminous panels exists, some flat, some vacuum-formed into differing shapes, and some laminated with designs representing spring, summer, autumn and winter. In addition, there are eight types of coloured "Plexiglas" panels which can be used to create focal points of interest and colour in the ceiling. All panels can be fitted with dust-covers, which eliminate the unsightly appearance of dirt, etc., collecting on the luminous ceiling. An unusual and attractive feature is that these dust-covers can also be obtained in colours, thus providing almost unlimited design scope.

A group of nine 8-in. sections forms a 2-ft. square panel frame and this is suspended from the ceiling by a unique method. Each "Infiniflex" panel incorporates a patented swing-hinge device which permits the whole unit to swing down instantly for relamping or cleaning. It is claimed that this technique reduces maintenance costs by as much as 50%.

4.6 Ceiling Finishes

A number of decorative finishes may be achieved on ceilings by employing plastics in various ways. Not only are the finishes attractive but they may be kept fresh by merely washing with water. They also resist corrosive atmospheres. A simple method is to use plastic-surfaced fibre or hardboards or laminates. Plastic-surfaced boards may be obtained from the following companies:

Tentest and Co. Ltd.	Bakelite Ltd.;
(Melamine surface);	A. S. Lester Ltd.;
F. Hills and Sons Ltd.	Airscrew-Weyroc Ltd.
(Melamine);	(Luxboard).

Further companies supplying plastic-surfaced hardboard are given in Section 3.4.9, together with full technical details.

Rather more attractive designs are possible, as illustrated by the products of Paniquil (Sales) Ltd.

This company manufactures two interesting products known as "Paniquil" 43 and "Paniquil" 21. The former is a hardboard to which is bonded a foamed plastic surfaced with pvc. The pvc surface has been moulded to give a quilted appearance. "Paniquil" 21 is a development of this with insulation on both sides of the hardboard. The one side is the same as "Paniquil" 43 but the other has a foamed polystyrene insulation protected by a coating of pvc. The thermal conductivities of the 43 and 21 materials respectively are 0·43 and 0·21.

The products are soft to the touch and are completely washable. The surface design on the pvc can be grained or have a special brushed silk effect. There are six designs and 11 colours.

Foils made of pvc may be used in various ways, as is illustrated by "Vynalast", designed by I.C.I. Ltd. (see Section 3.1). A more simple method of applying pvc is by spraying (see Section 3.1).

4.7 Acoustic Tiles

Decorative effects may be obtained with plastic acoustic tiles which are, of course, intended for sound insulation. They are usually made from pvc or polystyrene.

The properties of polystyrene foam have already been described in some detail. Ceiling tiles from the material (12 in. × 12 in. and 24 in. × 24 in.) are made by:

Jablo Plastics Industries Ltd.;   Nicholls and Clarke Ltd.;
Marley Tile Co. Ltd. ("Celestial"   Robinson Bros. Cork
   tiles, 12 in. × 12 in.);   Growers Ltd.

Decorative acoustic vinyl tiles and pyramids are made by Marley Tile Co. Ltd.

The problems involved may be considered with respect to the Marley products.

Marley acoustic and insulation products—acoustic tiles and pyramid,
Marleycel and Marlith (*The Marley Tile Co Ltd*)

Marley Acoustic Pyramids provide a most convenient and efficient means for the adjustment or correction of acoustic conditions in new buildings, or for correction of conditions in existing buildings, by absorption of noise or the elimination of unwanted reflection. At a frequency of 1,000 cycles per sec., the acoustic absorption reaches the exceptionally high value of 95% and exceeds 60% over the range 125–2,000 cycles per sec. It is considered that noise intensities of 80 decibels or above are in the "dangerous" range. Less robust people may sustain injury through much lower sound intensities.

The Marley pyramid is formed from rigid pvc (in a colour range) perforated and filled with mineral wool. The base of each pyramid is 22 in. square, including a ½ in. flange; the depth is 8½ in. Base covering is 3½ sq. ft. and the surface area of the pyramid is 4 sq. ft.

The acoustic effect of the Marley pyramids depends on a combination of two principles—the use of resonant panels and the absorptive effect of fibrous material.

This combination allows the further following combination of advantages to be secured:

(a) Absence of fibrous dust-catching textures.
(b) Good light reflection.
(c) Easy cleaning.
(d) Facility for decoration by painting—if desired—without loss of acoustic efficiency.
(e) Inability to spread fire. The pyramid consists of rigid pvc resistant to ignition. The absorptive filling is mineral wool. Combustible material is therefore absent from the system.
(f) Rapid fixing involving no disturbance of occupancy.
(g) Minimal damage to structure.
(h) Ready removal and possibility of reinstallation without loss of any value of the pyramids.

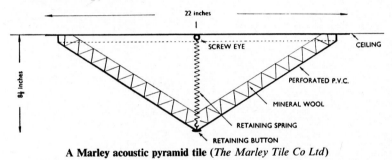

A **Marley acoustic pyramid tile** (*The Marley Tile Co Ltd*)

The Marley "Decortone" vinyl acoustic tiles are formed from pvc into attractive embossed-faced trays with slotted perforation of calculated area, and designed to allow maximum noise absorption throughout the lower middle frequency.

The lightly embossed surface of the perforated vinyl acoustic tile and border tile has an excellent light reflection and produces no glare. A black tissue is placed immediately behind the perforation to enhance their decorative effect and to prevent any tendency of fall-out from the noise-absorbing mineral wool infill. The Marley "Decortone" combines high sound absorbing qualities, together with thermal value of the mineral wool pads in the unit. The tiles are 16 in. × 16 in. and weigh 1 lb. each.

Acoustic tiles may be covered with I.C.I. "Melinex" plastic, the following being suppliers: The Cape Asbestos Co. Ltd. and Wm. Kenyon Ltd.

Tiles covered with pvc are made by J. Avery and Co. (Est. 1834) Ltd.

10

Part 5

PLUMBING

CONTENTS

5.1 Introduction

5.2 Rainwater Goods
  - *5.2.1 Situation Abroad*
  - *5.2.2 Outline of U.K. Developments and Suppliers*
  - *5.2.3 Requirements and Difficulties*
  - *5.2.4 Status and Acceptance*
  - *5.2.5 Advantages of PVC Systems*
  - *5.2.6 The Expansion Problem*
  - *5.2.7 Available Fittings*
  - *5.2.8 Installation and Jointing*

5.3 Pipes
  - *5.3.1 Usage of Plastic Pipes*
  - *5.3.2 Why use Plastics?*
  - *5.3.3 The Plastics Available*
  - *5.3.4 An Installation Comparison*
  - *5.3.5 The Polyolefines*
  - *5.3.6 Rigid PVC and ABS Polymers*
  - *5.3.7 Installation Methods*
  - *5.3.8 Fabrication Methods*
  - *5.3.9 Jointing Methods*
  - *5.3.10 Expansion Joints*
  - *5.3.11 Tapping of Plastic Mains*
  - *5.3.12 Fittings*
  - *5.3.13 Coating of Metal Pipes with Plastics*
  - *5.3.14 Epoxy Resin Pipes*
  - *5.3.15 Polythene Pipes (Detailed Information)*
  - *5.3.16 PVC Pipes (Detailed Information)*

5.4 Accessories and Fittings
  - *5.4.1 Cisterns*

5.5 "Perspex" for Sanitary Ware
  - *5.5.1 Introduction*
  - *5.5.2 General Properties*
  - *5.5.3 Mechanical Properties*
  - *5.5.4 Thermal Properties*
  - *5.5.5 Chemical Properties*
  - *5.5.6 Commercial Products*
  - *5.5.7 Care of "Perspex" Articles*
  - *5.5.8 Sinks and Drainers*
  - *5.5.9 Baths and Wash-basins*
  - *5.5.10 Urinals and Lavatory Basins*

　　　　　5.5.11 *Processing*
　　　　　5.5.12 *Machining*
　　　　　5.5.13 *Connecting*
　　　　　5.5.14 *Shaping*
　5.6　**Plastic Foams for Lagging and Filtration**
　　　　　5.6.1　*Filtration*
　　　　　5.6.2　*Odour Exclusion*
　　　　　5.6.3　*Tank Lagging*
　　　　　5.6.4　*Pipe Lagging*
　5.7　**Polyester Plastics for Plumbing**
　　　　　5.7.1　*Introduction*
　　　　　5.7.2　*General Principles*
　　　　　5.7.3　*Suppliers*
　　　　　5.7.4　*The Materials*
　　　　　5.7.5　*Outline of the Process*
　　　　　5.7.6　*Physical Properties*
　　　　　5.7.7　*The Moulds*
　　　　　5.7.8　*Gel Coat*
　　　　　5.7.9　*The Moulding Proper*
　　　　　5.7.10 *Equipment and Suppliers*
　　　　　5.7.11 *Machining*
　　　　　5.7.12 *Chemical Properties*
　　　　　5.7.13 *Conclusions*
　5.8　**Miscellaneous**
　　　　　5.8.1　*Protecting Tanks*
　　　　　5.8.2　*PTFE for Jointing*

Part 5

PLUMBING

5.1 Introduction

Next to flooring, the best known application of plastics is perhaps for rainwater goods and pipes. These uses, however, are only two aspects of plastics in plumbing of which there are quite a number. Part 5 is therefore divided into the following sections:—

5.2 Rainwater Goods
5.3 Pipes (for cold water plumbing, drainage, mains, etc.)
5.4 Accessories and Fittings (cisterns, floats, etc.)
5.5 "Perspex" for Sanitary Ware (sinks, baths, etc.)
5.6 Plastic Foams for Lagging (pipes, tanks, etc.)
5.7 Polyester Plastics for Plumbing
5.8 Miscellaneous (PTFE tapes and tank linings)

In the case of rainwater goods, the use of pvc for guttering is an obvious application but a comparatively recent development. It is perhaps the most obvious place where plastics will really be useful to the plumbing trade and may well oust conventional materials.

Although the pvc rainwater system looks very much like the conventional type, it is natural to ask why a change should be made. Probably the most important reason is that the system is entirely corrosion resistant and will last indefinitely. It is self-coloured and therefore needs no painting, although it will take paints if it is wished to change colour schemes. Bores are much smoother than cast iron—an obvious advantage. The pvc is also much lighter than metal.

The fittings provided are comprehensive and suitable for all purposes. Apart from guttering and downpipes, there are gutter angles, gutter outlets, fascia brackets, downpipe branches, downpipe shoes, gutter stop ends and so on. There is everything, in fact, which is available for cast-iron systems.

The fixing is simple and easy, the gutter merely snapping into position under the lugs of the fittings and fascia brackets. Pipes can easily be cut to length on site with a hacksaw and assembled quickly with standard fittings. Any surplus pipe cut off can readily be used in another part of the system so that there is no waste. No cementing, drilling, or bolting is required.

As far as plastic pipes are concerned, the general situation is that polythene is used fairly extensively in the U.K. for underground cold-water services. The use of pvc pipe has not been so popular as polythene, although the position is reversed on the Continent, and pvc is now beginning to catch up. It has been estimated that only 15 miles of pvc pipe had been installed up to 1958 in the U.K., but in Holland the figure was 2,300 miles and much higher quantities in both Italy and Japan.

There are several reasons for the difference between the usage of pvc and polythene. The latter particularly shows to advantage in long runs and comparatively small diameters (say below 2 in.) since it can be laid by moleplough in up to 500 ft. lengths. However, its flexibility defeats it at larger diameters and the rigid, strong pvc is better. In any case, thinner walls than with polythene can be used and the pvc has lower gas permeability, an important factor when in the vicinity of gas pipes. Thus pvc is gradually gaining ground and will be extensively used in the future.

Plastic pipes are now relatively common for cold-water systems only. As far as polythene and rigid pvc are concerned, the reason for this is quite simple since both are unsuitable for hot-water systems. This fact has so far probably limited the use of plastic pipes in building because if the hot-water and cold-water systems are combined, then obviously conventional materials will be used. It is only when the systems are separate that plastics come into their own. So far, none of the new plastics has been proved satisfactory for use with hot water.

Pipes are supplied in sizes ranging from about $\frac{3}{8}$ in. to 6 in. nominal bore. Both pvc and polythene are made in normal and heavy gauge material and the pvc also in a light gauge for drainage purposes. Although a wide range of fittings is available for these pipes, they may be handled in many ways as are metal pipes. For example, they can be threaded in the usual way. Bending is quite simple and the heavy gauge is best used for the purpose, a minimum bending radius of five diameters being recommended. However, before bending, the pipe must be softened gradually over its whole length, the heat being allowed to work its way slowly through the wall. After bending the pipe must be allowed to cool until it is rigid again.

Jointing is easily carried out with these pipes. A gas welding torch and stick may be used but the simplest way, from the plumber's point of view, is to use the solvent weld method.

The fittings are even more impressive than the pipes themselves. The "Durapipe" range includes about 450 fittings claimed to be the most comprehensive in Europe. In addition, the moulded 6 in. fittings are claimed to be the largest available and so the plumber has all he needs at his disposal.

Rapid strides are being made in the adoption of plastics for plumbing accessories and fittings. Perhaps the first application in this direction was the plastic toilet seat. In the early days, these were often moulded from a brittle and not particularly attractive phenolic moulding powder. Breakages were common and the reputation of such seats was not very high.

Such troubles are largely a thing of the past. Ekco Plastics Ltd. are producing a range of coloured seats and covers, some examples of the Ekco "Belvedere" being signal red, pastel green, turquoise, peach, and white. These rigid and hard plastics are virtually unbreakable, are hygienic and wiped clean with a damp cloth, can easily be blended with other colour schemes, and are smooth and generally very pleasing. The company also makes a "warm-to-the-touch" polythene which cannot be broken by impact and is particularly clean. It is cheap and available in nine colours.

The use of plastics for other fittings is due to certain inherent properties of the materials. They have an excellent strength to weight ratio, low moisture resistance and excellent corrosion resistance, have a smooth and attractive surface and can be made into a variety of complex shapes. For these reasons, floats and siphons are being made in polythene on an increasing scale. The

"Polyfloat" and "Kingfisher" siphons, made by Shires and Co. (London) Ltd. are typical examples. Polythene sink traps are also examples of the replacement of metals with plastics.

Although lavatory pans have not yet been made in plastics, they undoubtedly will be and the likely material is polypropylene. However, cisterns have been made in white or coloured "Propathene" recently by Cisterns Ltd. of Ilkley. The first injection moulded "Propathene" cistern was introduced to the Australian market some time ago and this "Carona" cistern operates with a finger-tip touchplate and has a self-cleaning action. At each operation it is entirely emptied of water so that no impurities can accumulate in the bottom to cause wear on the outlet valve seat. In addition, the "Propathene" helps to make it silent in use. Because there are no joins in the design it cannot develop a leak.

"Perspex", in its variety of pastel colours is undoubtedly well known to the trade. It is used extensively for bathroom fittings, particularly hand basins and baths. In the latter connection the difference in weight between "Perspex" and cast iron is most obvious. A typical "Perspex" bath weighs only 36 lb. compared with 336 lb. for the equivalent in cast iron.

In the kitchen, sinks, drainers and double drainers are also well known. A more important use is a multi-wash-basin unit. The wash basins are made as a complete unit, with no hidden corners or cracks which at once makes the assembly hygienic and easy to clean.

It is well known that cold-water storage tanks in the roof are liable to corrosion. The trouble is that once a rust spot has started it is likely to be an eventual source of weakness. For existing installations it is possible to buy a prefabricated pvc liner which is, of course, waterproof and corrosion resistant. One firm which makes them is Plastic Liners Ltd. who provide them for tanks of 40, 50, 60, 70, 80 and 100 gallons capacity. The liners have been tested and passed by The British Waterworks Association.

Other products likely to be of considerable interest to the trade are the various foamed products. These are available in either rigid or flexible forms and can be used as acoustic or thermal insulation. Roofs are treated and cavity walls filled with them and they can be used extensively for pipe and tank lagging.

Polyester plastics are used in various plumbing applications. Since they can be used for pipes, cisterns, tanks and rainwater goods because of their strength and lightness, a special section is devoted to them.

5.2 Rainwater Goods

The plastics industry feels that there has been considerable consumer resistance to the adoption of plastic rainwater goods. There is clearly some truth in this, particularly so in the early days, when the prices of guttering, fittings, etc. were higher than the equivalent in cast iron or asbestos-cement.

However, this was not the complete story and manufacturers claim that in spite of this initial higher cost, the installation costs were lower because of the simplified installation techniques. This claim was undoubtedly true, but consumers who had been using cast iron so successfully were rightly hard to convince. Fortunately, the manufacturers of the plastic materials persisted in their efforts, with the result that the use of plastic rainwater goods has greatly expanded. Today, the business is flourishing and there is every indication that the growth will become even more rapid.

Quite apart from any technical considerations, the question of design is an important one. So far, manufacturers have more or less imitated in plastics the products made from conventional materials. There is no reason, however, once the plastics are universally accepted, why new designs should not be adopted. There is considerable scope here for the architect since really complex designs can be produced by the injection moulding process. No doubt, in due course, there will be a revolution in rainwater goods which may considerably alter the outside appearance of houses, offices and factories.

5.2.1   Situation Abroad

The trend on the Continent is always a good indication of what we may be doing in the United Kingdom. This is not necessarily because they have more advanced ideas than we have, but because of relative differences in the price of raw materials. Whatever the reason, far more plastic rainwater goods are at present being used on the Continent than in this country.

Neither Japan nor Italy have any worthwhile iron deposits of their own which has perhaps contributed towards the ready acceptance of plastic rainwater goods. Japan alone is supposed to be using about 40,000 tons of pvc a year for rainwater and soil goods. In Italy the figure is probably about 10,000 tons a year; in Germany 5,000 tons and in Holland 4,000 tons. Exact figures are difficult to determine since the quantities of pvc consumed are often confused with the amount used for pvc pipes.

In Italy, there is no doubt that pvc originally became popular because of the high price of metal. With the drop in price of pvc, however, such rainwater goods were also able to compete with cement-asbestos materials so that they are even replacing these. There is over 11 years' experience of pvc in the country in rainwater installations and more than five years' experience in the use of stack pipes.

To compare the foregoing figures with those for the United Kingdom, in 1952 about 3,000 tons of pvc was used for rainwater goods. It is, of course, not necessarily disadvantageous to have lagged behind in the changeover and, in fact, it is now considered to have been an advantage. The products we are making have a far better finish than the equivalent on the Continent. Quite apart from the rainwater goods themselves, their method of jointing is also inferior to our own because we have been able to design suitable matching parts.

5.2.2   Outline of U.K. Developments and Suppliers

The extent of the early development on the Continent may be gauged from the fact that the Germans were using plastic downpipes in the 1930's. At the same time, zinc-lined wooden troughing for guttering and galvanized goods were employed for other parts of the system. This situation still largely obtains so that the industry may be said to have stood still in this respect.

The extent to which we have lagged behind in this country is indicated by the fact that the Marley Tile Co. Ltd., who undertook much of the pioneer work, marketed their first pvc system as late as 1959. At approximately the same time, Osma Plastics Ltd. introduced a range of gutters and downpipes, although in their case they did not use pvc. They started with glass-reinforced polyester resins although they have now changed to pvc products. Osma also successfully launched their pvc soil, ventilating and wastes goods system in 1963.

Osma Plastics rainwater goods were chosen for this renovated Oast House. Corrosion free, lightweight and easily installed they provide an attractive feature to an unusual dwelling (*Osma Plastics Ltd*)

In the past year or so a number of other companies have also entered the field and it is interesting to make an analogy with Italy. In that country it might have been expected that the manufacturers of cast-iron and cement-asbestos products would have viewed with dismay the onset of plastics which were obviously about to replace their standard lines. They were not dismayed, however, and adopted the commonsense attitude of making plastic rainwater goods themselves.

In this country, in a similar way, Burn Bros., well known in the cast-iron field, are offering rain and soil systems made by their subsidiary, AB Plastics, under the trade name "Terrain". Allied Iron Founders Ltd. also entered the field, manufacturing a soil system under the trade name "Metrex". This system is complementary to their cast-iron range and they are employing metric sizes with the Common Market in view. Yet another firm who manufactures conventional materials is the Universal Asbestos Manufacturing Co. Ltd. This concern has formed a subsidiary, Allied Structural Plastics Ltd., in conjunction with Thermo-Plastics Ltd. The subsidiary of these two companies, one in the conventional rainwater goods field and the other in the plastics field, is manufacturing a plastic rainwater system under the trade name "Aspect".

One of the best known systems of rainwater goods is the "Rymway" range. This system is made by a consortium of three companies—Yorkshire Imperial Plastics Ltd., P. H. Muntz and Barwell Ltd. and The Redland Tile Co. Ltd. Another well-known firm is Alan Barclay (Plastics) Ltd. who manufacture a range of aluminium rainwater systems, and are now licencees and designers of a plastic rainwater system. This includes an integral gutter-fascia section and downpipes. Other companies who manufacture rainwater goods include Chemidus Plastics Ltd., Extrudex Ltd. and the Mentmore Manufacturing Co. Ltd.

5.2.3   Requirements and Difficulties

The requirements of any rainwater system are well established. The first, of course, is that they should have the flow capacity not only to dispose of water in normal times but during freak storms. The materials used should also be capable of withstanding the corrosive action of polluted water which particularly applies to industrial areas. Another critical problem is that of withstanding "frozen up" conditions without breaking. It is sufficient at this stage to state that plastic systems comply with all these requirements.

A problem with plastic waste pipes, which is not encountered with metal or asbestos types, is that of the danger of softening at elevated temperatures. With the advent of washing machines it is possible that quite long periods of flow at temperatures between 190–200°F. will be experienced. Such temperatures might cause permanent damage to rigid pvc. Various solutions to this problem have been considered, including the use of copper inserts in the hope that these will help dissipate heat. The best answer at the present time is to use a steeper angle of fall to give a quick discharge.

One of the comparatively minor problems with pvc systems is that of dimensions. In the early days there was a tendency to reduce the thickness of the rainwater goods below the safe level so as to compete with metal goods. This is a dangerous practice and can result in buckling of installed systems due to expansion. It is now generally agreed that the thickness of all components should be in the order of $0 \cdot 08$ in. to $0 \cdot 10$ in. This thickness is sufficient to ensure rigidity and strength so that builders using them as supports for ladders will not cause damage.

Since metal rainwater goods have been in use for such a long time it is probably not realized to what extent the number of fittings (including different sizes) has grown. It is estimated that there are now some 12,000 of these, which would be a formidable task for the plastics industry to match. This is because expensive moulds are required and the capital outlay would be enormous. Nevertheless, a large number of fittings has been developed as will be indicated. One result of the problem, however, also connected with processing difficulties, is that the upper size limit of pvc gutters at the present time is considered to be about 8 in. The thickness required above this size would make the project uneconomic.

5.2.4 Status and Acceptance

It is fitting to comment on the present status and acceptance of plastic rainwater goods. The plastics industry is obviously optimistic but in view of the "break-through" which has recently occurred, many manufacturers and some authorities believe that all rainwater and soil goods will be made from plastics by about 1975. Obviously, this trend will be speeded up as tests being undertaken by local authorities come to fruition. The L.C.C., for example, are evaluating plastic rainwater goods on a number of sites and if their field trials prove successful, this will no doubt give a lead to the remainder of the country.

Since the distribution of rainwater goods is largely in the hands of builders' merchants, they will obviously influence the acceptance of these materials. Naturally, in this connection, they have not been anxious to increase their capital by the introduction of an alternative system. Most of them now, however, have accepted the situation and are stocking at least the products of one manufacturer. Many of them also feel that metal goods are on the way out and will be replaced by those made of pvc.

The other difficulty associated with acceptance of the new materials is the plumbing trade itself. New techniques are clearly required and obviously there is little experience in the industry. To overcome this, the plastics industry is proposing to undertake various educational schemes to help train plumbers, particularly in the techniques of jointing. Allied Iron Founders Ltd. have organized courses for plumbers in the installation of pvc pipes. Osma Plastics Ltd. are also undertaking a number of lecture tours to explain the system to architects, local government officials and the like.

It will be obvious, therefore, that there is much activity going on on both sides of the industry. Producers and consumers alike are now beginning to appreciate the advantages of plastic rainwater systems and now that this situation has developed there is no doubt that there will be a rapid swing to the new materials.

5.2.5 Advantages of PVC Systems

It is advantageous to begin a review of the practical aspects of pvc rainwater systems by considering their advantages. Some of these are quite practical in their nature, and affect installation techniques.

(1) From the installation point of view one of the most obvious advantages is lightness. It has been effectively demonstrated that one man can easily carry 120 ft. of guttering, which corresponds to the weight of 24 ft. of the same fittings in cast iron.

(2) One of the present defects with the ends of metal fittings is matching-up spigots and sockets. With most pvc rainwater systems the need for this is eliminated. The pipe or guttering is simply cut to size by the use of a hacksaw. The various lengths and fittings can then be joined by various techniques which present no site difficulties.

A development of this advantage is that there is no wastage since the offcuts can be used for short lengths.

(3) In many cases, manufacturers provide that there should be no

preparation of ends on site. Ends are, therefore, held prepared or suitable fittings are provided.

(4) Another practical advantage is that no jointing compounds or special tools are required. Most of the installation, in fact, can be achieved by the use of a hacksaw, drills and screwdriver.

(5) Some of the lengths available are longer than the equivalent metal parts which means fewer joints and a substantial reduction in labour costs on installation.

(6) Other advantages are concerned with operational characteristics. In the first instance the plastic pipes have a smoother bore than the equivalent metal products which gives improved flow.

(7) The pvc systems are corrosion resistant for any conditions likely to be encountered even in the most polluted atmosphere of industrial areas.

(8) The rainwater goods are self-coloured which means that no painting is required. Since the materials are also highly weather resistant, there is no deterioration with time and the colour is not lost, therefore no painting is required for maintenance purposes. However, if the limited colour range available is not satisfactory to the architect, there is no difficulty in painting with conventional paints. No undercoat is required, the only stipulation being that the surface should be clean before the paint is applied.

5.2.6   The Expansion Problem

Although metals expand, the movement is relatively small and little allowance need be made for it. However, in the case of pvc, this has a larger expansion rate which varies with the composition of the material but it is at least 5–10 times as much as that of cast iron. It is, therefore, essential in all pvc installations to make provision for this expansion. It may be noted that although this provision is not so important with cast iron, the fact that no allowance is made often gives rise to leakages at joints due to slight but frequent movements of the system.

The degree of expansion can only be given in general terms but the material supplied by one well-known manufacturer expands approximately $\frac{1}{32}$ in. per 10 ft. length per 10°F. change of temperature. Taking a temperature of 32°F. in the winter and 92°F. or even more in the summer, then this gives an expansion of $6 \times \frac{1}{32}$ in. between the two extremes. The extremes may often be greater than those quoted and it is estimated that a movement of $\frac{1}{4}$ in. is quite likely to be experienced. For this reason it is obvious that suitable joints must be devised to allow for the movement.

Two other points concerned with the thermal characteristics of the material should be mentioned. The most important is connected with handling in cold weather. All pvc compounds become increasingly brittle with a drop in temperature; from about 40°F. downwards the materials become very sensitive and even a moderate blow could cause complete shattering. It is, therefore, necessary to exercise considerable care during installation under such conditions.

This problem brings up the question of storage. Clearly, in cold weather, the guttering should not be stored outside if this can be avoided but should be

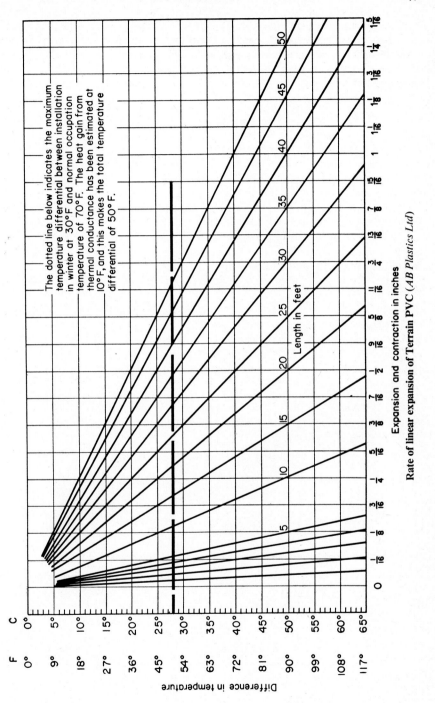

The dotted line below indicates the maximum temperature differential between installation in winter at 30°F and normal occupation temperature of 70°F. The heat gain from thermal conductance has been estimated at 10°F, and this makes the total temperature differential of 50°F.

Length in feet

Expansion and contraction in inches

Rate of linear expansion of Terrain PVC (*AB Plastics Ltd*)

Difference in temperature

kept in some warm room or at least protected from the direct effects of frost. And they must not be kept near hot surfaces otherwise they will be badly damaged. The normal recommendation is fully supported horizontal stacking of gutters and downpipes. Stacking by leaning the ends against a wall is not recommended.

5.2.7 Available Fittings

The manufacturers who are mentioned later should be consulted for full details of their fittings. However, it is possible to give some general guidance concerning those which are available.

The pipes can be obtained in various sizes of which $2\frac{1}{2}$ in. is perhaps the most common. Downpipes of 3 in. diameter are also available and there may be some variations between these by various companies. The pipes are made in various lengths, usually ranging from 6 ft. to 12 ft., although one company offers a length of up to 18 ft. for downpipes.

In the case of guttering, the standard sizes are 4 in., $4\frac{1}{2}$ in. and 5 in. bore. Some companies provide all of these and others only one of them. The lengths normally range from 6 ft. up to 12 ft.

Apart from pipes and guttering, there are many fittings of which the following is a selection:

Single pipe branches ($92\frac{1}{2}°$, $112\frac{1}{2}°$ and 135°); flat pipe heads; shoes; bends with sockets; hose-pipe sockets; inspection pipes; gutter stop ends (internal and external); gutter straps; swannecks (3 in. up to 24 in. projection); gutter angles (90°, 120° and 135°); two-socket gutter outlets; gutter outlets with gutter and stop ends; fascia brackets; gutter running outlet.

Component parts of rainwater goods (*Burn Bros (London) Ltd*)

Most of the fittings are in pvc but a number, particularly brackets and clips, are made from other materials. Fascia brackets, for example, are often die cast from iron aluminium alloys. Gutter brackets are often of hot-dipped galvanized steel or possibly plastic coated. Pipe clips will also usually be made from galvanized steel and screws will be made to match. It will thus be clear that the rainwater goods manufacturers supply a complete range of equipment for the installation of complete systems. Even where the plastics manufacturers do not recommend plastic fittings, they provide the alternative so that a complete range can be obtained from one supplier.

At the present time the colours available are restricted, mainly because of the problem of economics involved with making the same fittings in a wide range of colours. The most common colour is light grey but some companies also make black and cream.

The following are some specific examples of products from various companies:

Osma Plastics Ltd.

The gutters are 3 in., $4\frac{1}{2}$ in. and 6 in. H.R. section; 6 ft. and 12 ft. in length; colours are light grey, black and off-white.

Osma Gutters and Fittings

3 in.	$4\frac{1}{2}$ in.	6 in.	
T.301	T.41		Beaded H.R. gutter 6 ft.
	T.1	T.86	
	T.2	T.87	H.R. Gutter 6 ft.
			12 ft.
T.303	T.3	T.88	90° angle
	T.4		135° angle
T.305	T.5	T.90	Fascia bracket and union clip
T.306	T.6	T.91	Running outlet
T.307	T.7	T.92	Stopend outlet and union clip
T.311	T.11	T.94	Stopend (outside)
	T.12		R.W. head (small)
	T.13		R.W. head (medium)
		T.97	R.W. head (large)

Osma Pipes and Fittings

2 in.	$2\frac{1}{2}$ in.	4 in.	
2/T.6		4/T.6	6 ft.
2/T.8		4/T.8	R.W. pipe 8 ft.
2/T.10		4/T.10	12 ft.
	T.20		R.W. pipe 6 ft.
	T.21		9 ft.
	T.22		R.W. pipe 12 ft.
2/T.26		4/T.24	
		4/T.26	Double socket pipe
	T.23		Pipe connector
		4/T.107	Drain Connector and "O" ring
		4/T.109	Cast iron drain connector and "O" ring
2/T.161		4/T.161	Bend $92\frac{1}{2}$° angle
2/T.162	T.25	4/T.162	Bend $112\frac{1}{2}$° angle
2/T.163		4/T.163	Bend 135° angle
	T.30		Offset—$4\frac{1}{2}$ in. projection
	T.29	4/T.173	„ 6 in. „

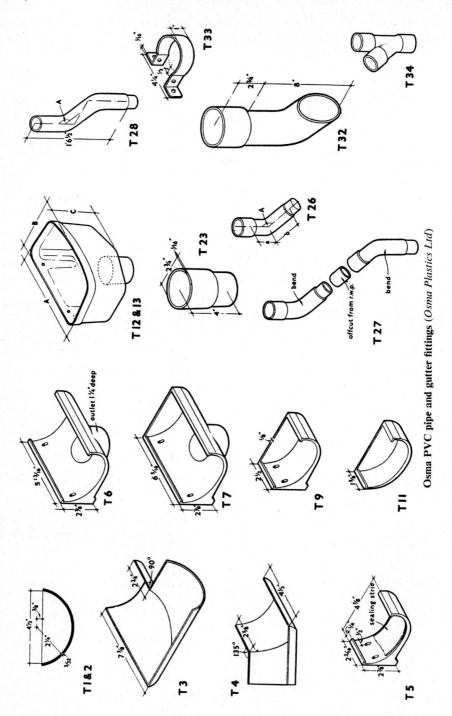

Osma PVC pipe and gutter fittings (*Osma Plastics Ltd*)

Osma Pipes and Fittings (continued)

2 in.	2½ in.	4 in.	
	T.28	4/T.174	Offset—9 in. projection
	T.27	4/T.175	„ 12 in. „
	T.26B		„ 15 in. „
	T.26A		„ 18 in. „
	T.32	4/T.288	Shoe and fixing bracket
2/T.82	T.33	4/T.82	Pipe fixing bracket
2/T.198		4/T.198	Single branch 92½° angle
2/T.208	T.35	4/T.208	„ „ 112½° angle
2/T.218		4/T.218	„ „ 135° angle

PVC pipework 1¼, 1½, 3, 5 and 6 in. is also available in this range, from the comprehensive soil system.

Larger diameter pipework in 7, 8, 9, 12 and 15 in. is also available.

Marley Tile Co. Ltd.

The colours are grey, black and cream and when ordering the prefixes G, B and W respectively should be used.

All rainwater goods, including gutters, downpipes and fittings, to be Marley Vinyl. Gutter brackets to be Marley hot-dipped galvanized-steel (fascia or rafter type) or plastic-coated brackets. Pipe clips to be Marley hot-dipped galvanized-steel base with rigid vinyl strap and 1½ in. No. 12 chrome-, zinc- or cadmium-plated mushroom-head bolt and nut for fixing. Gutter brackets fixing screw to be 1 in. No. 8 cadmium- or zinc-plated. Marley Joint Sealing Compound for gutter joints to be 2½ in. × ⅛ in. The full width of the ribbon of sealing compound is applied to the socket end of the gutter.

Goods	Ref. No.	
	2½ in.	3 in.
R. W. Pipe 6 ft. lengths	P25/6	P30/6
R. W. Pipe 8 ft. lengths	P25/8	P30/8
R. W. Pipe 10 ft. lengths	P25/10	P30/10
R. W. Pipe with 4 in. socket		
(for connecting to 6 ft. lengths		LP30/6
cast-iron 8 ft. lengths		LP30/8
fittings) 10 ft. lengths		LP30/10
Shoes	S25	S30
Bends with sockets 92½°	B251	B301
Bends with sockets 112½°	B252	B302
Bends with sockets 135°	B253	B303
Pipe sockets loose	L25	L30
Inspection pipe	F25	F30
Pipe fittings:		
Branches—single 92½°	Y251	Y301
Branches—single 112½°	Y252	Y302
Branches—single 135°	Y253	Y303
Heads—flat	H253	H303
Clips—socket fixing	C251	C301
Clips—barrel fixing	C252	C302

11

Goods	Ref. No.		
	4 in.	4½ in.	5 in.
Gutter fittings:			
Stopend internal	E401	E451	E501
Stopend external	E402	E452	E502
Brackets—fascia	K401	K451	K501
Brackets—rafter	K402	K452	K502
Brackets—top rafter fixing	K403	K453	K503
Straps	D40	D45	D50

	2½ in.	3 in.
Swannecks projection:		
3 in.	N251	N301
4½ in.	N252	N302
6 in.	N253	N303
9 in.	N254	N304
12 in.	N255	N305
15 in.	N256	N306
18 in.	N257	N307
21 in.	N258	N308
24 in.	N259	N309

	4 in.	4½ in.	5 in.
Clips, angles, etc.:			
Half-round gutter 6 ft. lengths	G40	G45	G50
Union clips	U40	U45	U50
Gutter angles 90°	A404	A454	A504
Gutter angles 120°	A405	A455	A505
Gutter angles 135°	A406	A456	A506
Gutter outlets 2 sockets	O401	O451	O501
Gutter outlets	O402	O452	O502
with socket and stopend			
Gutter outlets	—	O453	O503
with 2 Sockets, 3 in. drop			
Gutter outlets	—	O454	O504
with socket and stopend,			
3 in. drop			

Marley has now produced a 4-in. vinyl soil pipe specially for the British building industry. The pipes and fittings conform with the B.S. Code of Practice 304.

P. H. Muntz and Barwell Ltd.

The rainwater goods made by this company are sold under the trade name "Rymway".

Part Specification
Tensile strength of PVC
    Approximately 7,000 lb. per sq. in. of cross-sectional area.

Coefficient of linear expansion
    Approximately $\frac{1}{16}$ in. per 12 ft. length per 18°F. change of temperature.

Dimensions
    Gutter (half-round, plain ended)—4 in. nom. bore × 0·100 in. wall—in 12 ft. lengths.

Downpipe (plain ended)—2½ in. nom. bore × 0·080 in. wall—in 6 ft., 12 ft. and 18 ft. lengths.

Capacity
Gutter—Cross-sectional area approx. 6 sq. in.
Downpipe—Cross-sectional area approx. 4¼ sq. in.

Weights
Gutter—Approx. 6·6 oz. per foot (5 lb. per 12 ft.).
Downpipe—6 oz. per foot (4½ lb. per 12 ft.).

Gutter and Downpipe Fittings (Injection moulded)
All gutter fittings supplied with factory-fixed all-weather jointing strips.

"Rymway" downpipe connector (*Yorkshire Imperial Plastics Ltd*)

Fascia Brackets
Die-cast, high-grade aluminium alloy, supplied with factory fixed cushioning pad. Brackets supplied complete with 1 in. × No. 10 round-head aluminium-alloy wood screws—rust free and avoiding galvanic action (Note: the cushion must be removed before using with a Gutter Union (R. 11) which has a special close-fitting grove to take the bracket).

Downpipe Clips
PVC with cadmium-plated mild-steel assembly screw and nut and fixing screws, and pvc distance piece. Clip holds downpipe away from wall and allows movement to take up thermal expansion.

Colours
Light grey and black.

An interesting development by Marley is small vinyl gutters and downpipes for garages, sheds, greenhouses, etc. The new system has a 3-in. gutter and a 2-in. pipe.

5.2.8 Installation and Jointing

In jointing and installation the aim of manufacturers has been to make the system as foolproof as possible. It is, therefore, not considered advisable or necessary to use jointing compounds or solvent cementing.

The downpipes are the simplest part of the system to install since the provision of watertight joints is not as important as on guttering. Pipe clips should be fixed at about 6 ft. intervals but as in all installations of plastic rainwater systems, they should not grip the pipe too firmly. The principle is similar to that used in installing plastic pipes so that expansion can occur. The method of connecting two running lengths is to have a downpipe connector. The upper part of the pipe, as a spigot, is fixed into the socket of the connector and the lower part of the pipe, as a socket, receives the lower part of the connector as a spigot. This is a perfectly satisfactory method of jointing provided, of course, that the free end of the pipe is with the flow of water. Some companies will provide prepared ends which allow a simple push fit and, again, this is perfectly satisfactory provided the free end of the pipe is in the direction of flow.

The downpipes are usually fitted to walls by means of metal or plastic fixing clips bolted directly to the wall. Clearly, these bolts have to be fixed into mortar so that some allowance must be made on the pipe for latitude in fixing the clips. The Barclay and "Aspect" systems allow for this by employing a sliding dovetail joint between the downpipe and wall fitting.

Expansion is usually allowed for at the top end of each length of downpipe. A gap of $\frac{1}{4}$ in. should be allowed between the top end of the downpipe and the downpipe connector which is hidden by the band of a pipe clip.

The jointing of guttering presents a greater problem since a watertight joint, which can move, is required. The standard method now adopted is to use a synthetic-rubber sponge on the inside of each end of the gutter union, stopend or angle by the use of various clips and lips on these units, when the guttering snaps into position forming a watertight bond with the unit with the rubber between. This also allows for horizontal movement under expansion. The joint assembly is fixed to the fascia board by bolts. Usually there is a synthetic-rubber sponge on the fascia board to allow for expansion.

A rather more difficult problem is that of jointing with soil and waste systems. In particular, an airtight joint must be achieved between W.C. pedestals and the soil-pipe systems. The most common method at present used is similar to that described for pipe jointing. A spigot and socket joint is used with a synthetic rubber "O" ring between the two when, after assembly, the socket is shrunk over the ring. The Allied Iron Founders system uses this type of joint but the Burn Bros. system has a special expansion coupling. For other jointing in soil systems, both the companies mentioned use solvent cementing with an expansion coupling. (Details of solvent cementing are given in Section 5.3.8).

Suppliers of pvc rainwater aud soil goods are as follows:

P. H. Muntz and Barwell Ltd. ("Rymway");
Osma Plastics Ltd. ("Osma");
Marley Tile Co. Ltd. ("Marley Vinyl");
Yorkshire Imperial Plastics Ltd. ("Rymway");
Redland Tiles Ltd. ("Rymway");
A. B. Plastics Ltd. ("Terrain");
Allied Iron Founders Ltd. ("Metrex");

Allied Structural Plastics Ltd. ("Aspect");
Alan Barclay (Plastics) Ltd.;
Chemidus Plastics Ltd.;
Extrudex Ltd.;
Mentmore Manufacturing Co. Ltd.;
La Brecque Engineering Co. Ltd.;
National Plastics Ltd.;
Federated Foundries Ltd.;
Jury Holloware Ltd.;
Aeroplastics Ltd. (Fittings only).

5.3 Pipes

This section divides broadly into two main parts. The first deals mainly (but not exclusively) with general aspects of pipes and coated pipes, but also includes detailed descriptions of installation methods and jointing techniques. The last part deals with detailed information on polythene and pvc pipes including sizes of products made by a few manufacturers taken at random from the list of suppliers to give some indication of the range available.

5.3.1 Usage of Plastic Pipes

The types of plastic employed for pipes have only been used on a large scale since the war. Their serious use for pipes of all kinds is barely 12 years old and their adoption by the general plumber is comparatively small.

If the practice on the Continent is anything to judge by, then this situation will see considerable change over the next few years. Why then has Britain lagged behind? We have all the materials, the extruded pipes and the fittings that everyone else has, we even export fittings to the Continent. It is obvious, therefore, that the British plumbing trade must look at this situation seriously and decide to do something about it. The hot gas welding torch for plastics must become as common as the blow lamp.

There are now a number of different materials used for pipes such as rigid pvc, polythene, H.D. polythene and ABS copolymers. Each one of these must be used under the conditions best suited to its properties. Again, the range of pipes and fittings must be known about and suppliers listed. The properties of such pipes at various temperatures and pressures and after long period of use must be understood.

Apart from such relatively theoretical considerations the average plumber will want to know the practical details. How may pipes be bent and joined and what equipment is required to do it?

General Aspects

Before looking at the situation which obtains today with regard to the use of pipes in the U.K. and the rest of the world, a brief reference to plastic pipes in general would be useful. There are several materials employed and their uses may be divided into several groups.

The principal materials are polythene, high-density (H.D.) polythene, polypropylene, rigid pvc and ABS polymers. Their properties and applications have been dealt with to some extent, and more details are given elsewhere, but the products may be broadly considered at this stage. The first three are known generically as polyolefines and are used for relatively low-pressure systems. The other two are quite unrelated chemically and may be used generally for relatively high-pressure systems.

Several methods of approach to their use may be made. The most important which should be considered is in cold and hot-water systems. Polythene and pvc must not be used with hot water, but there is a possibility that ABS may be. There is no doubt that its properties are such that it will successfully allow the material to be used at the temperature of hot water, but the long-term ageing and flow properties are factors which are not quite so well known. In the case of polypropylene, I.C.I. Ltd., who are one of the important manufacturers of the material, think it a little premature to consider adopting the plastic on a widespread basis. However, polypropylene and ABS polymers are the most promising materials so far for cold- and hot-water plumbing.

Another division which may be made in considering plastic pipes is above ground and below ground use. Which material is used for each application depends on the pipe diameter and the fluid to be carried. Generally, however, any material may be used. Another division is between domestic and industrial (including local utility companies) applications. This is often a matter of pipe size and the divisions will be considered in due course.

World-wide Use of Plastic Pipes

It should be appreciated that statistics are dangerous things and accurate information is not available and in any case it is changing all the time. It is possible, however, to give an overall picture of the situation in the world today.

Probably the biggest user of plastic pipes is Japan with an annual consumption of 60,000 tons of rigid pvc. This is a large figure (remembering the S.G. of pvc is only about 1·4) and one reason for it is the relatively high price of metals in Japan. Most of the pipes are used for carrying potable water, but some are used for sewage and gas mains. It is clear that it will not be long before all pipes used in buildings for low-temperature work will be made of pvc.

Italy, France, Germany and Holland are big users of rigid pvc, although not on the same scale as Japan. The position in Italy, is perhaps, a good indication of the trend since by now pvc pipes and fittings are regarded as just another group of builders' materials. Originally the use of pvc became popular because of the relatively high price of metals, but with a reduction in raw material costs, pvc has more than held its own due to improvements in processing techniques.

An estimated figure for Italy for 1960 gives 12,000 tons of pvc, about half of which was used for conveying drinking water. This adoption of plastics might be thought to give the metal pipe manufacturers serious cause for concern. Such has not been the case because the biggest producers of pvc pipes are either the metal pipe manufacturers or their subsidiaries. This, of course, is how it should be and no manufacturer of metal goods should regard plastics as a competitor. Typical examples include Dalmine, a large manufacturer of steel tubes; del Gres, who were once earthenware pipe manufacturers, as were Ceramica Pozzi, and Sacelit who manufacture mainly asbestos-cement products.

One reason for the more enthusiastic adoption of plastic pipes in Italy is the fact that they are normally incorporated inside the walls. This overcomes weathering problems, but is not necessarily desirable when it comes to repairs.

The position in France and Holland is much the same. In France, pvc is certainly replacing lead in pipe fittings for cisterns. In Holland a consumption of 4,000 to 5,000 tons for water pipes has been estimated.

There is thus no doubt that Continental Europe is enthusiastically adopting plastic pipes, particularly pvc. The position in the English-speaking world is, however, rather different.

U.K. and U.S.A.

In terms of pvc pipes the position in Britain is far from satisfactory. Up to the end of 1958 only about 15 miles of pipes had been installed, although the position is now changing. At about the same time, the figure for Holland was about 2,300 miles and it was greater than this in both Italy and Japan.

This is, however, not the complete picture, since for reasons to be discussed later, polythene has been much more popular than pvc in the U.K. Again, in 1958 the estimated figure for polythene was 30,000 miles, a substantial figure, but one which is misleading. The great majority of the pipe was used for agricultural purposes, most of it underground. The difference between the use of polythene and pvc is reflected in the British Standards. Those for polythene (BS.1972 and 1973) appeared as long ago as 1953 whereas those for pvc pipes have only recently been issued.

The position with regard to pvc in the U.S.A. is even worse than in the U.K. One reason for this has been the relatively high price of pvc polymers in that country. This has had a snowball effect. It means that American manufacturers have not obtained the experience they should have, so they are much behind Western Europe in respect of both fittings and pipes.

5.3.2 Why Use Plastics?

The obvious question to be asked by any plumber is why should he change from materials which have been used for centuries and which, in general, have been perfectly satisfactory? This is a perfectly reasonable attitude and must be closely considered. In so many cases, of course, the plumber is in the hands of the architect and it is the design end of the building industry which must also be considered.

From the point of view of the man who has to handle pipes, the weight is clearly of great importance. Looked at from the point of view of S.G., that of rigid pvc is less than one-sixth that of steel. In terms of pipe weights a 20 ft.

length of 4 in. rigid pvc pipe (Polyorc "B") suitable for a working head of 175 lb. has a weight of only 26 lb. An equivalent pipe of Class B spun iron piping weighs 260 lb. The difference in the problem of handling needs no stressing.

Cost is a feature which needs close examination. If a comparison is made between pvc and spun iron, the advantage is in favour of pvc. This may seem surprising in view of the relatively high raw material price of the pvc. The difference is in the much cheaper production costs of pvc pipes. Polythene pipes (definitely polypropylene is at the moment) may well prove to be more expensive. If a comparison is made with asbestos-cement, before installation, then the latter is cheaper on an approximate scale of 100 for pvc, 75 for asbestos-cement and 110 for iron.

This is not the complete picture, however. The plastic pipes are much easier to install, and mole ploughing can be used. For example, with long lengths of polythene tubing an overall saving of about 40% has been claimed on installation costs. One reason for this is the great ease of jointing, by a solvent or cementing technique (but not for polythene), by hot welding or a form of compression fitting employing a rubber compression ring. Some of these joints can be made in a few minutes, thus cutting costs tremendously. After installation, relative costs are 100 for pvc, 120 for asbestos-cement and 135 for iron. It will be seen that pvc is definitely the cheapest.

There are quite a number of other reasons for fitting plastic pipes. They are corrosion resistant and after years in use can be cut without difficulty and re-sealed—no more badly rusted pipes. Corrosion resistance also means no painting. Again, the bore of the pipe is quite smooth, allowing swept junctions and greater pipe carrying capacity. The pipes are good heat insulators, resist chemicals and have relative flexibility.

5.3.3   The Plastics Available

The principal plastics now available on a commercial scale in the form of pipes are low-density (L.D.) polythene; high-density (H.D.) polythene; polypropylene; rigid pvc; and ABS types. These are the chemical names. Unfortunately, there are also trade names which sometimes make identification difficult and examples will be given.

A choice between the different plastics will have to be made on a number of counts. The most obvious is probably to use the material which has the best properties for a given job. This is not always easy since the properties of the different materials are sometimes quite similar. Next there is the ease of installation, which affects cost, and will often influence the choice. Finally, there is the question of direct cost. It is impossible to be specific about this since it is not only a question of the difference in price between raw materials, but the manufacturer's efficiency of extrusion, the wall thickness (and tolerances) used and the type of fittings. Only general indications can be given, therefore, and prices from individual manufacturers must be obtained.

A brief study of each of the plastics will indicate their general characteristics and help to show how each one differs from the other.

(a) L.D. Polythene (see also Section 1.3.3)

This is the most common material used for pipes at the present time.

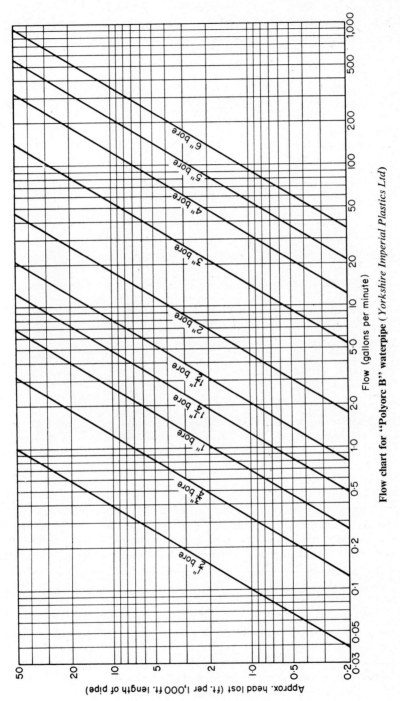

Flow chart for "Polyorc B" waterpipe (*Yorkshire Imperial Plastics Ltd*)

It is fairly resistant to chemicals, non-toxic and non-contaminating, light, resists freezing and is a good electrical insulator.

(b) H.D. Polythene

This material is made by a low-pressure process (the name Ziegler for this process will often be heard) and the term high density is only relative, since the L.D. and H.D. densities (really S.G.'s) are 0·92 and 0·94. Its advantage lies in that it is rather tougher and has a higher softening point than L.D. polythene. It will, therefore, be used where these properties are of importance.

Polythene tube waste and warning pipes (*Maesteg U.D.C. and Imperial Chemical Industries Ltd*)

(c) Polypropylene

This material is comparatively new and consequently has not yet become well established. It feels very much like the two polythenes and has many similar characteristics. However, its softening point is considerably higher and it may, one day, when various difficulties have been overcome, be the plastic which will be used for hot-water plumbing.

(d) Rigid PVC

This is quite a different material to the polyolefines. In particular, it is quite stiff and it burns only when in a flame and is self-extinguishing when the flame is removed. The polyolefines burn quite readily. It has roughly the same temperature characteristics as polythene, but is much stronger. In this connection, it can be improved by compounding to produce the so-called "high impact types" which are much more "pick" resistant. The chemical resistance of the material is good and unlike polythene, it is impermeable to gases and when carrying potable water can be installed near to gas mains.

(e) *ABS Polymers*

In many ways these materials are similar to pvc, although they are quite a different chemical family. They are, for example, stiff and have good chemical resistance. A well-known trade name for the materials is "Cyclolac". One advantage over pvc is a somewhat higher temperature resistance, although it is not as flame resistant.

All of the foregoing materials are thermoplastics. This means that they have an upper temperature limitation, details of which are given later. Pipes made of thermosetting plastics are available and they could be used for hot-water systems. They are made of "epoxy" and "polyester" resins but unfortunately are much more expensive, are available in comparatively short lengths and are used only for specialized purposes. (Polyester types are mentioned in Section 5.7.13 and epoxy types below).

5.3.4   An Installation Comparison

There is not so much clash between the materials mentioned as might appear at first sight. In practice, the two most important, polythene and rigid pvc, have entered two fairly well-defined different fields, the reasons for which are of interest.

Polythene was the first material to be used for pipes in the U.K. mainly for economic reasons. The two specifications, B.S.1972 and 1973, were issued in 1953 but the pvc specifications have only been issued in the last year or two. This emphasizes the historic preference for polythene.

Now it has become fairly well established that polythene is used for pipes with bores of up to 2 in. in long runs, and pvc for bore sizes above this or for short runs of any size. The reasons for these differences are clear. Polythene is flexible which means that it can be coiled or wound on to drums. The standard length supplied is usually 500 ft. which facilitates laying. Mole ploughing can be readily employed, avoiding expensive trench digging and refilling.

Above 2 in. bore, the polythene is too flexible to support the weight of earth above it, at least in walls of reasonable thickness. Rigid pvc, however, is three times as rigid as polythene and can easily support this weight. It is also much stronger and will withstand much higher pressures for a given wall thickness. The larger diameter pvc is installed in relatively short lengths and, another big advantage, joints may be made by solvent welding which cannot be done with polythene.

What has been said in connection with polythene and pvc more or less applies to the two main groups. These are the polyolefines on the one hand and rigid pvc with the ABS copolymers on the other. The polypropylene, however, is quite stiff and in this respect falls between the two groups.

5.3.5 The Polyolefines

It is convenient to consider these materials as one group and details of their properties are as follow:

	L.D. Polythene	H.D. Polythene	Polypro- pylene
Tensile strength, lb. per sq. in. (average)	1,600	3,200	5,000
Specific gravity	0·92	0·94	0·90
Softening point, °C.	91	120–128	150
Power factor (10° cps)	0·00011	0·0005	0·0009 (at 10^5)

The improved properties in passing from L.D. polythene to polypropylene may be easily observed. It would be advantageous to use polypropylene in preference to the other polyolefines, wherever possible, but unfortunately expense and other technical considerations will often preclude this, at the moment at least.

It might seem preferable to use the H.D. polythene instead of the L.D. polythene but this is not always so. There is a phenomenon called environmental stress cracking which means that if polythene is stressed at normal temperatures and comes into contact with certain materials then it will crack and eventually fail. The materials include detergents, organic acids, esters, aldehydes, ketones, amides, nitro compounds and alcohols (but not beer). The H.D. polythene is worse than L.D. polythene but polypropylene does not suffer at all. If a bend is made at elevated temperatures, the problem does not arise.

The polyolefines can be used with water and most chemicals, except nitric acid and very strong acids, fats and oils and certain solvents, particularly chlorinated ones. At 20°C., however, hardly any ill effects result from even these, but deterioration increases with increasing temperature. Small quantities of contaminates in drainage pipes will not cause trouble.

The polyolefines should not normally be used for conveying gases or be installed near gas pipes when carrying potable water. L.D. polythene should not be used under pressure above 30°C. and not above 60°C. for anything. The H.D. polythene and polypropylene may be used at higher temperatures and pressures but details should be obtained from individual manufacturers.

Regarding installation, the following points should be noted. Expansion is greater than with metals and a temperature rise of 100°F. will give about 7% increase in length. Bending must be carried out at elevated temperatures and details will be given later. The materials may be cut or sawn with normal equipment and ends trimmed with an ordinary knife. Jointing is by all the usual methods except solvent welding.

Some applications include domestic and industrial cold-water services; water supplies and irrigation in agricultural work; for conveying beer, fruit juices, milk, etc.; for laboratory work, for ventilation and general chemical engineering.

5.3.6   Rigid PVC and ABS Polymers

Both of these materials are rigid and supplied in relatively short lengths of about 20 ft. to 25 ft. Some properties are:

	Rigid PVC	ABS Polymers
Tensile strength, p.s.i.	6,000	4,500
Specific gravity	1·3–1·4	1·07–1·09
Softening point, °C.	60–65	80–85

It should be stressed that these properties can be varied considerably by compounding. In general, however, the increased strength, as compared with the polyolefines, can be seen and although the S.G.'s are higher, they are still fairly low compared with metals. The softening properties of rigid pvc are about the same as polythene, but ABS has a little higher temperature resistance which is a good reason for using it.

As far as chemicals are concerned, pvc is particularly resistant. The material is satisfactory for oils, fats and most inorganic salts, dilute-to-medium acids, aliphatic hydrocarbons, methyl and ethyl alcohols. Materials to avoid, include ketones, butyl and higher alcohols, esters, aromatic and chlorinated hydrocarbons, oxidizing acids and halogens.

One advantage of pvc pipes over polythene is that there is no danger of contamination through gas permeation through the walls. A disadvantage, however, is that if water freezes in the pipes they may burst. They must, therefore, be buried below the frost line. The comments made on the relationship of temperature to properties for polythene and expansion also apply with pvc. Jointing can be carried out above ground and therefore only a minimum width of trench is required: solvent welding may be employed. A big advantage of pvc is that it does not support combustion.

ABS polymers, like rigid pvc, may be used in the most corrosive soils. The materials have about the same chemical resistance as pvc, and may be used in similar circumstances and at slightly higher temperatures. The materials, however, do support combustion.

Large quantities of ABS and pvc pipes are used for carrying chemicals, soaps and detergents, soft drinks, oils and fats, natural gas and the like. The pvc, in particular, is used extensively in drainage systems, although large-diameter polythene pipes (up to 36 in.) lining concrete are employed. The pvc is also used by some authorities for coal gas, but if the gas is known to have an aromatic hydrocarbon content, then softening of the pvc is to be expected.

Durapipe and Fittings Ltd. manufacture pipes in this interesting material.

5.3.7   Installation Methods

Similar techniques employed for copper and lead components have been or are being developed for plastics, and although some of the methods and fittings are much the same, others are quite new. A thorough grounding in the various methods must, therefore, be acquired since, although the average plumber might well install plastic pipes with existing or makeshift equipment, he might well cause considerable damage. This might be all the more dangerous since it is quite likely to be invisible.

It is not uncommon practice, for instance, to mark pipes with scribers and knives, but this is not recommended with ordinary rigid pvc or, more particularly, with other plastics. They all tend to have poor notch resistance which means that once the surface has been penetrated, the incision forms a potential source of breakage. Again, the cutting of screw threads in thin-gauge material is not allowed and is even best avoided on heavy-gauge material. It is permissible to cement a plastic sleeve over the end of the pipe and cut threads into that, which is one indication of the different procedure to be adopted between metals and plastics.

Quite apart from the obvious problem during installation of the support for the pipes, there are a number of fundamental plumbing practices which need to be considered. The most important, of course, is jointing and a number of different methods are available. Also to be considered are means of bending, welding, flange making, tapping, mains and service ends connections, expansion joints and the like. All of these features are dealt with on the following pages.

Some Examples of Installations

Before going into details of installation practice it will be of interest to consider a few installations to see the sort of procedure which can be adopted because of the use of plastic pipes. One of the best techniques, even with relatively rigid mains pipes, is to lay the 15–25 ft. pipe lengths (whichever the supplier can provide) alongside the trench, or even some distance from it, and join them into one continuous length. The completed pipe is flexible enough to be laid in the trench quite quickly and will accommodate gentle undulations in the soil.

An example of the use of this principle, which will no doubt become commonplace, was given by the Mid- and South-East Cheshire Water Board. They laid a water main at Northwich, and in order to avoid the disruption of traffic they adopted two ideas. The first of these was to join the short lengths of rigid "Corvic" pvc pipe into a continuous length in a side street. The second was to dig the trench overnight, the pipe being afterwards laid expeditiously.

A rather unusual example is provided by the Newquay and District Water Co., who discovered a fault in a 5 in. cement water main running under the Gannel Estuary. This difficult problem was solved cheaply and quickly by assembling and joining a few hundred feet of $3\frac{1}{2}$ in. rigid pvc "Polyorc B" pipe on the bank and then feeding it through the existing mains. Flanged end connections were then made.

Another advantage of pvc pipes is their light weight and ease of handling over difficult terrain. The Ross and Cromarty County Council had to lay $3\frac{1}{2}$ miles of 6 in. water main over a peat bog on the Isle of Lewis. Normal transport would have been impossible so the pipe was taken from the nearest access point to the points of assembly by helicopter. The 60 yards of pipe weighed only 4 cwt. It may be noted that many pipe manufacturing companies will deliver the pipes in convenient lots if requested to do so.

These are only a few examples of the ways in which plastic pipes can help with installation problems. In this connection the thin plastic wall, giving a small o.d. for a given i.d. is important as is the small increase in o.d. at the joints.

One of the more outstanding reasons for using rigid pvc is "chemical resistance" although the latter expression can cover a multitude of chemicals and conditions. A typical example is a zinc plating bath where the chemicals involved are a severe combination of cyanide, hydrochloric acid, caustic alkalis and chlorine. Metals would not be very satisfactory in such an environment and rigid pvc is a very valuable alternative choice.

A particular example where such an installation was made was at the works of Delaney Galley Ltd. The company are well-known as manufacturers of car heaters and they commissioned a new effluent disposal system for their zinc plating plant at Barking.

An installation of Durapipe "V" PVC pipes and fittings at the Barking factory of Delaney Galley Ltd (*Durapipe and Fittings Ltd*)

For ease of handling and to avoid wastage of space in the effluent plant pumping station, an intricate system was evolved to fit the requisite pipeline within the minimum of space. The major part of this installation was fitted against a wall some 15 ft. long by $5\frac{1}{2}$ ft. high, and to keep the system within these dimensions some 100 pipe fittings were employed. The company responsible for the design and supply of the effluent treatment scheme, Wallace and Tiernan Ltd., decided that pipe and fittings in rigid pvc would be ideal here because of their combination of light weight, ease of installation and specific corrosion resistance. Moreover, the hundreds of different pipe fittings available in rigid pvc enabled this compact system to be devised. There is no reason why the principle should not be extended much further.

The rigid pvc pipe extruded by Durapipe and Fittings Ltd. was chosen. The actual material used by them was "Breon", manufactured by British Geon Ltd., a member of the Distillers Plastics Group. The material is exceptionally light, easy to handle and does not require highly skilled labour for its installation. Injection moulded fittings in "Breon" rigid pvc were also provided by the Durapipe Company—who supply this type of fitting as part of their specialist service to plastic pipe contractors. The method of joining the pipes and fittings was the solvent welding process. This is simple and can be carried out by unskilled labour. At the same time, completely tight joints are achieved so that the technique results in much saving in installation costs. This, incidentally, is a reason for using pvc rather than polythene pipes because the latter cannot be solvent welded.

Three-inch pipelines were mainly used in the installation together with a lesser quantity of 1½ in. pipe. The effluent system has now been in use for over two years and successfully handles some 10,000 g.p.h. This is undoubtedly a striking illustration of the excellence of rigid pvc piping systems used under the most severe conditions.

Mole Ploughing

This particular method of laying pipes can only be used to advantage if reasonable lengths of pipe are to be laid. The minimum length is about 100 feet but preferably more. Only polythene pipes can be laid by the method since they are available in lengths up to 500 feet. This, in fact, is the maximum length which should be laid as above it, ground friction becomes too great and the pipes can be seriously stretched.

Pipes laid by mole ploughing are particularly useful for rural and farm water supplies as well as irrigation and drainage. If fertilizers are added to the water there will be no danger of stoppages because the smooth bore will not trap particles.

Apart from the use of the plough itself, a few comments may be given on the method of handling the polythene pipes. The tubes should be uncoiled or made into a wide circle and laid on the ground in the direction of pulling with the ends sealed to prevent filling with soil. It is preferable not to uncoil during the actual operation as this may cause twisting and possible damage. Joints or fittings should not be pulled in.

Finally, an allowance should be made for thermal contraction, particularly since some stretching may well have occurred. Trouble can be avoided by not having a taut pipe after making the connections.

The use of polythene pipes in rural areas is quite common. Individual feeds to cow byres is a typical example. Irrigation is common and may easily be achieved in the following way. At the intervals where the sprays are required, insert a tee piece sealed by a blank nut. The latter is then pierced with the required number of holes.

Simple Fabrication Techniques

Comparatively simple fabrication techniques such as cutting, sawing and drilling may be readily carried out with plastic pipes. Polythene can be cut quite readily with a sharp knife and shaped in the same manner. The cutting of rigid pvc, however, is much more difficult and it is normally advisable to use a saw.

Polythene may be readily sawn with virtually any saw although one with fine teeth is preferable. Rigid pvc is best cut with a metal saw, rotary if required. The only stipulation is that the saw should be kept as sharp as possible. If any difficulty is experienced, slight warming of the tube will assist.

As far as drilling is concerned, it is quite possible that the normal hand- or power-operated metal-working twist drills will be satisfactory. The main point to observe, particularly with pvc, is that overheating should be avoided otherwise the pvc will be damaged. The feed should be by hand so that the material can be withdrawn if there is any sign of overheating, which is readily detected by an acrid smell. Quite high speeds are permissible, for example 700–1,000 r.p.m. with a feed of 6 in. per min. and a $\frac{1}{2}$ in. drill, and 3,000–3,500 r.p.m. with a feed of 2–3 ft. per min. and a $\frac{1}{8}$ in.-diameter drill.

Normal Installation

Wherever possible plastic pipes should be continuously supported. This applies to both polythene and pvc pipes. Since continuous support is often not possible, however, the techniques here described should be used.

A general point of importance for all plastic pipes is that they should not be positioned near to hot surfaces. In particular, they should be kept away from hot-water pipes, at least by a few inches. Any contact will almost certainly cause failure.

In fixing polythene, the normal metal clips may be employed but the spacing must be closer. This is because the pipes need more support since they are not so rigid, particularly when warm. In addition, they expand and contract so much more than metal, that if not supported at sufficiently close intervals, they will bend and give a most unsightly appearance on walls.

In the case of horizontal runs the spacing should be about 12 times the o.d. of the tube, but this can be increased to 24 × o.d. for vertical runs. In the case of horizontal runs only, any pipes with a bore greater than 1 in. should be supported at 8 × o.d. intervals. The clips should not be so tightened that they cannot accommodate expansion and contraction. If the pipe is laid on a floor, fewer clips will then be necessary.

For the clips to allow sufficient movement they should be the next size up compared with the equivalent for copper pipes. Although not essential, a thin piece of foam rubber between the metal clip and the pipe will avoid any possibility of damage. An alternative which is being adopted on an increasing scale is to use a specially designed plastic clip or grip (Yorkshire Imperial Plastics Ltd.). Some made of polypropylene are on the market for pipe sizes with nominal bores from $\frac{3}{8}$ in. up to 2 in. These clips are screwed to the wall and the pipes snap into them, thus increasing the speed of installation and servicing. The pipes can be easily removed from such a grip and after repair snapped back into place.

Any taps or stopcocks, etc. should be fitted and supported quite independently of the pipework. In no circumstances must plastic pipes support metal fittings.

In the case of rigid pvc pipes the distance between clips can usually be greater than with polythene, as the material is self-supporting. Some examples of distances include: 2 ft. 6 in. for $\frac{1}{2}$ in. bore; 3 ft. 6 in. for 1 in. bore; 4 ft.

12

6 in. for 1½ in. bore; 5 ft. 0 in. for 2 in. and 2½ in. bore and 6 ft. for 3 in. to 6 in. bore. Naturally, some variation around these general dimensions is permissible.

These dimensions will have to be increased if the pipes are to operate at elevated temperatures. Up to 40°C. the spacings need only be reduced, but at temperatures above 50°C., continuous support is necessary. In this connection, thermoplastics are subject to both cold and hot flow. That is to say, that if placed under any pressure at all, gradual flow will occur and possibly damage will result. Consequently, clips should have a reasonably wide bearing surface.

One final point need be mentioned at this stage. The expansion of pvc and polythene is several times greater than that of metal and due allowance must be made for this during installation. With moderate runs it is possible to make this allowance by a suitable disposition of the clips, the best way being to allow a large bend on a wall so that, with loose clips, the polythene can expand into it and contract out of the bend. Another method for really long runs is to have an expansion loop and this is very effective. In some cases, however, this is not suitable or desirable and other techniques will then need to be adopted. Sleeve joints (telescopic) and bellows or diaphragms are obvious methods and are considered later under jointing.

The golden rules to remember in installing plastic pipes are:

(a) The materials are thermoplastic and must not be in contact with hot surfaces.
(b) They must be supported at regular intervals.
(c) Allowance must be made for expansion, particularly by using loose clips.

5.3.8   Fabrication Methods

The three basic techniques with plastic pipe work are bending, welding and solvent cementing. Any one of these operations is likely to be carried out during the simplest installation (with the possible exception of welding) so that plumbers must be skilled in these techniques.

Apart from the three basic manipulative methods, there are also a number of other techniques which are used. A large number of plastic fittings are available which match similar fittings in conventional materials. Jointing also forms a very important part of plumbing with plastic pipes and several methods are employed.

All the methods mentioned which are necessary to make complete plastic pipe installations are now considered.

Bending

Polythene pipes may be bent cold if the inside radius of the bend is not less than 12 times the outside diameter of the pipe. If the clips holding the pipe are removed then the pipe will tend to return to its original shape. It is much more satisfactory to make bends by heat treatment and, with rigid pvc, this is essential.

The bending technique is similar with all materials with the exception that different temperatures are required. With polythene the material will have to be heated to about 100–110°C., and with rigid pvc it will have to be heated to about 130°C.–140°C. A typical method of procedure is to plug one end of the tube and to hold it upright. Cold sand is next poured in to just below the point where the bend is expected to start. Hot sand at the temperature mentioned is next poured in to the end of the bend when the tube is then filled up with cold sand. The tube is plugged, and when it has warmed up is bent in the desired manner using a suitable jig and held in position until cool. Cold water may be poured on to accelerate cooling.

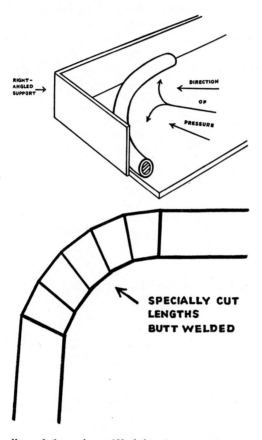

Bending polythene pipes—(*Yorkshire Imperial Plastics Ltd*)

Alternative methods exist. The tube can be filled with cold sand and then placed in an oven or dipped in hot oil or glycerine. The use of a blow lamp blowing gently on the outside of the pipe is not recommended. This is because the material has poor thermal conductivity and there is considerable danger of overheating and thus degrading the material. Instead of sand inside the tube, it is possible to inflate a suitable hose.

Welding

The simplest method of welding two pipes together is to cut the two ends square and place the surfaces in contact with a hot plate for a short time. The two ends are then pushed together and held under pressure for a minute or two until the weld has cooled. A very strong butt joint can be obtained in this way. Times and temperatures must be found by experience but are likely to be about 110°C. and 150°C. for polythene and pvc respectively, with times of under one minute. The foregoing technique can be applied only in certain cases and certainly not when the pipe has already been placed in position. In this case, a more normal type of welding is undertaken which in principle is similar to metal welding. Welding rods of $\frac{1}{8}$ in. or $\frac{1}{16}$ in. diameter can be obtained. The only equipment required is a special welding torch heated by gas or electricity. In effect, the plastic is melted by a stream of hot nitrogen.

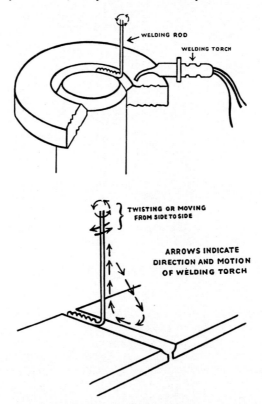

Welding plastics (*Yorkshire Imperial Plastics Ltd*)

To make a weld, the edges of the material are externally chamfered to an angle of 45° to 60°. The edges are held together, the welding rod is held between the thumb and forefinger and heat is applied simultaneously to the rod and edges. Obviously, the rod is placed down in the gap at the point

furthest away from the operator and welding carried out towards the operator. Although some practice is required with this technique, if the surfaces
involved are clean, then no difficulty should be experienced.

The use of this welding technique allows pipes to be joined together, and
flanges or T-junctions to be made. The method is widely used for joining
lengths of large pipes on site.

Cementing

One of the commonest and simplest methods of making a joint is to
cement two pipes together. No specialized equipment is required although
suitable cements will have to be purchased.

Spigot and socket joint (*Stewarts and Lloyds Ltd*)

In effect, a spigot and socket joint is manufactured. The outside of the
spigot and the inside of the socket must be cleaned of grease and dust. A coat
of cement is then applied to each surface and allowed to dry. A second coat is
then applied advantageously, using a brush in both cases. The pipes are joined
immediately (i.e. without waiting for solvents to evaporate) and the joints are
then left undisturbed for as long as possible. A minimum of six hours is
recommended but 24 hours would be better.

Apart from joining two pipes together, the solvent technique can be used
for attaching the various fittings. The method must only be used for fittings
with plain surfaces, however.

It should be stressed that the solvent method can be employed only with
rigid pvc and ABS pipes. None of the polyolefine family can be solvent
welded.

5.3.9   Jointing Methods

The simplest jointing method is the spigot and socket joint employing a cement. In some cases the joint can be made with only solvent, such as methyl ethyl ketone.

Pipes can be obtained from suppliers already manufactured with prepared ends for this type of joint but by taking any pipe, heating the end and enlarging the bore with a suitable size pipe, a socket can be made.

Another effective jointing method is the shrink socket joint. In this, a rubber "O" ring is placed on the plain end of the mating tube which is then slid into a socket. This socket has previously been made by heat treatment and therefore retains residual strains. As soon as heat is applied to it, therefore, by means of a blow lamp, it will be found that it will shrink over the "O" ring and make close contact on either side of the ring. The "O" ring is thus compressed and makes a watertight seal. The method has been extensively used on the Continent for underground services.

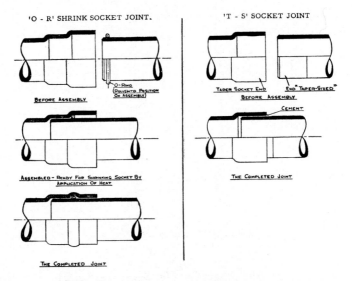

Plastic pipe joints (*Yorkshire Imperial Plastics Ltd*)

It is possible to use compression fittings with plastic pipes just as it is with copper. In fact, the same fittings are employed, modification only being required because of the outside diameter of some of the pipes. It may be necessary to build up the outside diameter of the tube to the equivalent B.S.659 copper tubing size. These fittings do, of course, allow polythene pipes to be connected to cocks and valves, taps and the like, and alloy metal and plastic pipes to be connected even where the outside diameters are different.

In the case of some pvc pipes, the outside diameters conform to those of steel pipes to B.S.1387. In such a case, Viking Johnson couplings may be employed. Similarly, the same company's adaptors may be employed to make connections between plastic pipes and flanged cast-iron pipes. A similar method uses a pvc flange on the pvc pipe and a cast-iron or steel flange on the metal pipe. The pvc flange is solvent cemented to the pvc pipe and the two pipes are joined together by means of a gasket.

5.3.10   Expansion Joints

As previously pointed out, the coefficient of expansion of plastic pipes is relatively high, for which allowances must be made during installation. The use of suitable bends to compensate for the expansion has already been mentioned previously. Other methods exist, however.

One such is to use sleeve joints. These consist of external sleeves with circular joint rings and backing flanges which will accommodate axial expansion. The technique can be used only for gases and liquids which do not give deposits.

Bellows and diaphragms can be employed as in other systems. Although the method is effective, it is not always easy to obtain components with materials which will resist chemicals being transported in the pipes. However, bellows are now being made in neoprene, silicone rubber and "Viton" which can be used at quite widely varying temperatures and with many different chemicals.

Unit expansion bends can be employed. In Germany the Lyre expansion bend has been used extensively but there are limitations to all of these types. For example, the bend must be made in one piece and in the case of pvc, the lengths available are only 16 to 20 ft. This therefore limits the maximum tube diameter to 2 in. or $2\frac{1}{2}$ in. due to the limitation on bending radii.

Screw-type high density polythene pipe fittings (*Shell Chemical Co Ltd and Yorkshire Imperial Plastics Ltd*)

5.3.11   Tapping of Plastic Mains

It is possible to tap plastic water mains for service connections, under pressure if required. It is necessary, however, to reinforce with suitable metal tapping saddles into which the ferrules should be screwed. They should not be screwed directly into mains.

Suitable saddles are available and can be provided in both gunmetal and malleable iron, but a check should be made that the saddles are suitable for the plastic pipes. When ordering, they should be specified to suit the outside diameters of plastic pipes.

5.3.12   Fittings

The widest variety of fittings is now available for plastic pipe work. These are obtainable in ABS, pvc and some of the polyolefine materials.

Selection of thermoplastic fittings (*Durapipe and Fittings Ltd*)

The types of fittings to be expected are T-pieces, 90° elbows, 45° elbows, 90° short bends, end plugs, reducing sockets, socket unions, flanges, saddles, bottle traps and the like. Many of these are available with both plain surfaces for solvent welding and threaded ends.

Many of the pipe manufacturers produce a wide range of fittings. Some of them are standard types but others have specialized designs. For example, there is an all-plastic fitting which can be used for jointing, preserving full bore, and requiring no heat or jointing compounds. In this connection, it may be noted that jointing compounds should not be used as they may cause difficulties, and wrenches should be employed with the greatest caution as damage can easily result. Many plastic fittings can easily be tightened up by hand. A tool is sold by one company for forming a bulge at the end of a tube in the cold. This then acts as a seal and for retaining the plastic fitting on the tube. (Tools from Yorkshire Imperial Plastics Ltd., and Wednesbury Tube Co. Ltd.)

Some examples of fittings obtainable from various companies are as follow:

BTR Industries Ltd. (PVC Fittings)
(Note: measurements are in inches)

45° Elbow $\frac{1}{2}$–6 nominal pipe size with o.d.'s of $1\frac{3}{8}$–$7\frac{23}{32}$. Both threaded and socket types, this applying to all fittings where appropriate.

90° Elbow	Sizes as 45° elbow.
Tee	Sizes as 45° elbow
Caps	$\frac{1}{2}$–4 and o.d.'s $1\frac{3}{8}$–$5\frac{7}{16}$.
Couplings	$\frac{1}{2}$–6 and o.d.'s $1\frac{3}{8}$–$7\frac{5}{8}$.
Reducing coupling	$\frac{3}{4} \times \frac{1}{2}$ to $2 \times 1\frac{1}{2}$ and o.d.'s $1\frac{9}{16}$–3 (large end) to $1\frac{3}{8}$–$2\frac{1}{2}$ (small end).
Reduced bushing	$\frac{3}{4} \times \frac{1}{2}$ to 6×4.
Socket flange	$\frac{1}{2}$–8.
Blind flange	$\frac{1}{2}$–8.
Union	$\frac{1}{2}$–3 with o.d.'s $2\frac{3}{8}$–$5\frac{5}{8}$.
Plugs	$\frac{1}{2}$–4.
Plug valve	$\frac{1}{2}$–2.

Aero Plastics Ltd. (*PVC Fittings*)

4 × 135° bend.
4 × 92$\frac{1}{2}$° bend.
4 × 104° bend.
4 × 112$\frac{1}{2}$° bend.
4 × 4 × 135° junction.
4 × 92$\frac{1}{2}$° junction.
4 × 104° junction.
4 straight coupling.
4 plug.
4 cap.

All these fittings are for use with 4 in. nominal pipe and have sockets designed for gap-filling solvent cement jointing. The bends and branches, with the exception of the two 135° fittings, are all fully swept.

Polypropylene Fittings

These fittings are designed specially for use with pitch-fibre pipe. They are all-socket type, the sockets having a 4° inclusive taper. The joints are made by driving the pitch-fibre pipe, which has a spigot with a 4° inclusive taper, into the socket of the fitting. The joint is permanent and tight under all conditions of use. The range of fittings include:

4 in.	90° Short-radius bend
	45° Short-radius bend
	4 × 90° Junction
	4 × 135° Junction
	Adaptor

6 in.   90° Short-radius bend
                            45° Short-radius bend
                            6 × 135° Junction
                            Adaptor
                            End female cap

4 in. or 6 in.   135° Junction

Durapipe and Fittings Ltd. (*Pipe in ABS and High Impact PVC. Fittings in ABS and unplasticised PVC*)

(Note: measurements are in inches)

90° Elbow (Female) Nominal Bore $\frac{3}{8}$, $\frac{1}{2}$, $\frac{3}{4}$, 1, 1$\frac{1}{4}$, 1$\frac{1}{2}$, 2, 3, 4.
45° Elbow. Nominal Bore $\frac{1}{2}$, $\frac{3}{4}$, 1, 1$\frac{1}{4}$, 1$\frac{1}{2}$, 2, 3.
90° Short Bend (Male). Nominal Bore 6.
End Plug. Nominal Bore $\frac{3}{8}$, $\frac{1}{2}$, $\frac{3}{4}$ and 1.
Tee (Female). Nominal Bore $\frac{3}{8}$, $\frac{1}{2}$, $\frac{3}{4}$, 1, 1$\frac{1}{4}$, 1$\frac{1}{2}$, 2, 3, 4.
Tee 6 in. (Male). Nominal Bore 6.
"Y" Piece. Nominal Bore 1$\frac{1}{4}$, 1$\frac{1}{2}$, 2.
Threaded Bush. Nominal Bore $\frac{1}{2}$-$\frac{3}{8}$, $\frac{3}{4}$-$\frac{1}{2}$, 1-$\frac{3}{4}$.
Reducing Bush. Nominal Bore $\frac{1}{2}$-$\frac{3}{8}$, $\frac{3}{4}$-$\frac{1}{2}$, 1-$\frac{3}{4}$, 1$\frac{1}{4}$-1, 1$\frac{1}{2}$-1$\frac{1}{4}$, 2-1$\frac{1}{2}$, 3-2, 4-3, 1-$\frac{1}{2}$, 1$\frac{1}{2}$-1.
Reducing Socket. Nominal Bore 1$\frac{1}{4}$—1, 1$\frac{1}{2}$—1$\frac{1}{4}$, 2—1$\frac{1}{2}$, 3—2, 6—4.
Socket. Nominal Bore $\frac{3}{8}$, $\frac{1}{2}$, $\frac{3}{4}$, 1, 1$\frac{1}{4}$, 1$\frac{1}{2}$, 2, 3, 4, 6.
End Cap. Nominal Bore $\frac{3}{8}$, $\frac{1}{2}$, $\frac{3}{4}$, 1, 1$\frac{1}{4}$, 1$\frac{1}{2}$, 2, 3, 4.
Socket Union. (Flat Seat) (A neoprene washer is included). Nominal Bore $\frac{3}{8}$, $\frac{1}{2}$, $\frac{3}{4}$, 1, 1$\frac{1}{4}$, 1$\frac{1}{2}$, 2.
A sleeve can be supplied in brass for coupling to metal fittings.
Flanges. "Durapipe" Standard $\frac{1}{2}$, $\frac{3}{4}$, 1, 1$\frac{1}{4}$, 1$\frac{1}{2}$, 2, 3, 4, 6.
British Standard Table "E" $\frac{1}{2}$, $\frac{3}{4}$, 1, 1$\frac{1}{4}$, 1$\frac{1}{2}$, 2, 3, 4, 6.
Saddle. Nominal Bore 3, 4, 6.
   Off takes 1, 1$\frac{1}{4}$, 1$\frac{1}{2}$, 2.
Insert Adaptor. Nominal Bore $\frac{1}{2}$, $\frac{3}{4}$, 1.
Valves and Strainers.

Yorkshire Imperial Plastics Ltd. (PVC)

Straight Coupling; 90° Elbow; Equal Tee (90°); Adaptor Nipple; Barrel Nipple; M.I. Straight Connector; Reducing Bush; Union. Plastic to Plastic; Union Connector. (Cone Joint); End Cap; Cleaning Cap Unit; Bottle Traps.

AB Plastics Ltd. (PVC)

(Note: measurements are in inches)

(*Terrain Soil Fittings*)

Size	Sweep Bend
4 × 4	92$\frac{1}{2}$°
4 × 4	104°
4 × 4	112$\frac{1}{2}$°
4 × 4	135°

Size	Single Sweep Branch
$4 \times 4 \times 4$	$92\frac{1}{2}°$
$4 \times 4 \times 4$	$104°$
$4 \times 4 \times 4$	$135°$

	Double Sweep Branch
$4 \times 4 \times 4 \times 4$	$92\frac{1}{2}°$
$4 \times 4 \times 4 \times 4$	$104°$

4×4	Straight Couplings

	Boss with socket for No. 200 pvc tube
2	PVC tube $87\frac{1}{2}°/92\frac{1}{2}°$
$1\frac{1}{2}$	PVC tube $87\frac{1}{2}°/92\frac{1}{2}°$
$1\frac{1}{4}$	PVC tube $87\frac{1}{2}°/92\frac{1}{2}°$

2, $1\frac{1}{2}$ and $1\frac{1}{4}$	Boss with compression couplings for No. 200 pvc tube $87\frac{1}{2}°/92\frac{1}{2}°$

2, $1\frac{1}{2}$ and $1\frac{1}{4}$	Boss with socket threaded to B.S.P.T. dimensions $87\frac{1}{2}°/92\frac{1}{2}°$

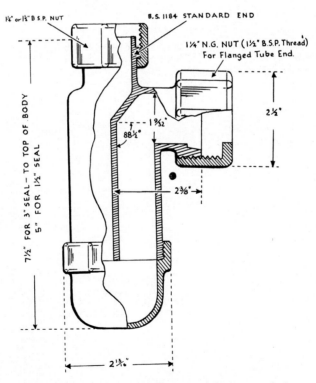

A "Plastronga" (polythene) bottle trap (*Yorkshire Imperial Plastics Ltd*)

Size	
2, 1½ and 1¼	Boss with compression coupling for copper tube to B.S.S. 659 87½°/92½°
4 × 3	Socket reducer
4 × 2	Socket reducer
4 × 1¼	Socket reducer
4 × 6	W.C. connector 6 in.-long O/A (9, 12, 15, 18 and 21 in. long)
4 in. with 2 in. A/S	W.C. connector with anti-siphon connection 9 in.-long O/A and other sizes
4	Cap
4	Plug
4	Caulking bush

I Slide end cap over tube.

2 Place ring in position on ring inserting tool.

3 Push tool into tube and clamp in vice.

4 Turn handle of tool until ring is fully inserted, then screw back approx. ½".

5 Unscrew vice, pull out tool and screw up fitting.

Making a joint with "Wednesbury" plastic tubes and fittings
(*Wednesbury Tube Co Ltd*)

Note: There are many similar products, and similar fittings are available for Terrain waste pipes.

Wednesbury Tube Co. Ltd.

Straight Coupling	PF1
Elbow	PF2
Tee	PF3
MXP Coupling, female	PM3 (Joins metal to plastic)
MXP Coupling, male	PM4
Reducing bushes	PR1
MXP Adaptor, male and female	PM1 and 2

Paragon Plastics Ltd.

This company produces a polypropylene waste system with $1\frac{1}{2}$ in. and 3 in. seal. It is suitable for boiling water.

Other Manufacturers

Other manufacturers of plastic pipe fittings are: P. H. Muntz and Barwell Ltd.; Stewarts and Lloyds Plastics Ltd. Manufacturers of metal compression fittings are: Yorkshire Imperial Plastics Ltd. and Conex-Terna Ltd.

5.3.13   Coating of Metal Pipes with Plastics

If a metal pipe system is in a particularly vulnerable situation and corrosion is excessive, then internal surface protection of some kind is required. Various paints are available for combating such problems and although reasonably effective the coats are at the best quite thin and the slightest scratch may well cause breakdown.

A way of overcoming the problem has now been devised. The pipes, tanks and other metal components can be dipped in various plastic pastes and a coherent, resistant coating produced. The coatings can range in thickness from a few thousandths of an inch to about $\frac{1}{2}$ in. and this can be achieved in one dip.

Although it is possible to purchase suitable materials and dip in one's own shop, it is preferable to use the services of one of a number of companies which provide these facilities. They have stocks of suitable materials, the correct equipment and will generally collect the components to be treated and return them when finished.

Elimination of Metal Flanges

Until fairly recently, the method of coating the insides of pipe work of moderate size was to paint by hand with a natural- or synthetic-rubber solution. Spraying could not be employed because of the confined space. Because of an excessive number of flanges, the results were generally unsatisfactory.

The reason for the flanges arises because of the impossibility of painting along even quite short lengths of pipe. A "Y"-piece with arms about 2 ft. long is a typical example. It is impracticable by painting to coat the full length of the arms and certainly not the junction of the "Y". Consequently, a short "Y"-piece was usually made with arms a few inches long, each of which was provided with a flange. Other lengths of pipe were then joined to this flange.

It is now possible to eliminate these flanges. The entire "Y"-piece is dipped in the bath of pvc paste and is coated internally and externally with a layer of pvc to any thickness the customer cares to specify. The only flanges now, are on the ends of the arms, and since these are coated with a layer of pvc, this can act as a suitable gasket.

PVC-coated pipes (*British Geon Ltd and Plastic Coatings Ltd*)

Some Principles of the Method

Virtually any type of metal can be coated, with the possible exception of certain zinc alloys. Certainly copper, cast iron and steel present no difficulties. The condition of the metal is of no importance, even heavy rust is of no consequence.

The metal will first be shot-blasted to remove rust and grease. A primer is then applied and this gives a first-class bond between the metal and the pvc. However, if no bond is required at any point, the primer can be left off. Where there is no primer the pvc can be stripped without difficulty.

Both small and large objects can be dipped. Small tanks are available for the former and tanks containing large quantities of pvc paste are available for the latter. One company has a tank containing 24 tons of material. The metal object is heated before dipping, as this assists the pick-up of material. After dipping, the covered object is sintered at an elevated temperature for some time which produces a rough resistant coat.

The coatings produced by the foregoing technique have all the characteristic properties of pvc. They are resistant to weathering, chemicals, acids, alkalis and many solvents, although if solvents or strong corrosive chemicals are involved then manufacturers should be consulted for details.

Treatment with Other Materials

A number of other plastics can be coated on to metals in various ways. They include polythene (L.D. and H.D.), PTFE, PTFCE, nylon and Penton. Not all of them are necessarily applied by dipping since spraying, particularly of large objects, is also widely employed.

Polythene is widely known as a resistant coating and can be used for relatively small objects. However, for various reasons, it is not so important as pvc which is by far the most common material employed. HD polythene, due to its greater toughness, is to be preferred of the two types of polythene.

A PTFE-coated hopper chute (*Plastic Coatings Ltd*)

The best resistant material of all is PTFE but unfortunately the spraying technique imparts microporosity which considerably reduces chemical resistance. However, its close relation, PTFCE, is nearly as good chemically, and can be sprayed to give highly resistant coatings. Unfortunately, it is very expensive. Coatings of PTFE are used because of the low coefficient of friction of the material. If there is a problem with ducting carrying solid materials and these have any tendency to stick, then a coating of PTFE will facilitate the flow.

Penton is an alternative chemical-resistant material with a safe working temperature up to 120°C. PTFE is suitable up to 250°C. and PTFCE up to 200°C., but the Penton is cheaper.

Merits of Nylon

Nylon has been reserved for special treatment since, after pvc, it is likely to have the greatest potential for use by the plumbing trade. This is because of the exceptional toughness of the material, apart from its chemical properties.

Nylon is suitable for use up to 120°C. and is quite good from the chemical resistance point of view, except with respect to resistance to mineral acids. Coupled with this, however, is the toughness of the material and coatings up to 0·025 in. thick are perfectly satisfactory. The abrasion resistance is much better than that of stove enamels which nylon is in many cases replacing.

The most interesting development is in the replacement of chromium plating, the best of which often leaves much to be desired. If the nylon is mixed with molybdenum disulphide, this reduces the friction of the material considerably and gives the coating a metallic lustre. Such a material is beginning to be used on valves a great deal, both internally and externally. The possibilities for taps are also being investigated with quite promising results.

Conclusions

The development of dipping and spraying techniques for plastics has opened a new field of protective materials for the plumber. It is not only a new range of materials but an extension of existing processes as products that could not be treated before can now be effectively dealt with.

The dipping of pipes in plastics is undertaken by Plastic Coatings Ltd.

Audco Ltd. (Newport, Shropshire) have introduced a range of taper plug valves which are coated with Penton, a chlorinated polyether. The valves can be used in corrosive conditions where it was previously necessary to specify nickel alloys or stainless steel. The valves are reliable down to −30°C. and up to 90°C. (the latter at 100 p.s.i. operating pressure).

5.3.14   Epoxy Resin Pipes

Epoxy resins are described in detail in Section 2.4. The following is an example of a commercial epoxy resin pipe made by Bristol Aeroplane Plastics Ltd., Filton House, Filton, Bristol.

The "Epoch" pipe system has been developed specifically to meet the demands of industry for large-bore, highly corrosion-resistant pressure piping.

From a specialized start in aeronautical work soon after the war, it has progressed through performance, process and machine development to become an automatically produced precision product ready for service in a wide range of industries including oil, gas, atomic energy, chemical engineering, brewing and shipping undertakings.

The pipe and fittings are virtually unaffected by soils, sea-water, demineralized water and the majority of dilute acids and alkalis, even up to temperatures of 140°C. This corrosion resistance, in addition to reducing and possibly eliminating maintenance or replacement costs in many applications, also results in high operating efficiency. The mirror-smooth bore of the pipe with its freedom from corrosion defects or build-up of deposits, ensures constant carrying capacity with low friction losses and low pumping costs.

As strong as steel, the pipes are approximately 10 times more flexible than the equivalent steel pressure pipes. They are thus ideal for laying over rough or uneven ground or in locations where soil subsidence is liable to occur. The system comprises pipes and fittings of 6 in. to $15\frac{1}{4}$ in. nominal bore, made from thermosetting epoxide resin reinforced with high-strength glass-fibres. The standard 20 ft. pipes can be supplied bonded together to make 40 ft. or 60 ft. lengths if required. Fittings include both the standard "T"-section, with a branch at 90°, and standard bends catering for radii of $22\frac{1}{2}°$, 45°, $67\frac{1}{2}°$ and 90°. Other fittings such as elbows, restrictors, special adaptors and flanges to meet different specifications can be supplied to order. Two types of flanged fittings are available. The standard pressure flange which meets British and American specifications for the petroleum industry and a low-pressure flange specially designed to reduce cost on low-pressure installations. In addition to the flanged joints, a bonded joint has been developed.

The system is divided into two series. Series "A" covers pressure piping systems operating at 100 p.s.i. and upward. Series "B" covers piping systems up to 100 p.s.i. A full range of fittings is available in both the "A" and "B" Series.

5.3.15 Polythene Pipes (Detailed Information)

The low-density type of polythene is covered in BS.1972, the specification for polythene pipes, where it is referred to as Type 425. Some of the factors specified by BS.1972 are the sizes, maximum and minimum tolerances allowed, coil sizes, tests, etc. and of which details are given later. There is also BS.1973 covering many more sizes and wall thicknesses (the polythene is referred to as Grade "A") but it is preferable for the trade as a whole to use the standard sizes of BS.1972 which most producers stock. H.D. polythene is covered by BS.3284:1961 where the material is referred to as Type 710.

Details of sizes and tolerances of the standard tubes are given in the following tables. (Amendment No. 1).

All polythene pipe is normally supplied black. It is well marked on the outside so that there is no doubt about the various requirements. The markings will include the table number; the name of the manufacturer; the B.S.I. Kite Mark (where appropriate); the British Standard Number; the gauge (normal or heavy); the nominal bore and some form of batch (when extruded) identification. Normal-gauge pipes are marked in red and heavy-gauge pipes are marked in blue.

The Table which follows gives the working pressures for the tubes. The working pressure means that pressure which may be continuously applied at temperatures up to 20°C. (68°F.). For higher temperatures the working press-

13

Dimensions of Polythene Pipes to BS.1972

Table 1. *Normal gauge pipe.*

Nominal bore in.	Outside diameter		Wall thickness	
	min. in.	max. in.	min. in.	max. in.
½	0·667	0·682	0·091	0·102
¾	0·982	1·000	0·122	0·137
1	1·230	1·250	0·122	0·137
1¼	1·477	1·500	0·122	0·137
1½	1·725	1·750	0·137	0·154
2	2·363	2·395	0·183	0·205

Table 2. *Heavy gauge pipe.*

Nominal bore in.	Outside diameter		Wall thickness	
	min. in.	max. in.	min. in.	max. in.
¼	0·532	0·545	0·138	0·155
⅜	0·667	0·682	0·147	0·166
½	0·832	0·848	0·169	0·190
¾	1·043	1·061	0·169	0·190
1	1·311	1·332	0·169	0·190
1¼	1·654	1·679	0·198	0·220
1½	1·888	1·915	0·210	0·232

ure must be progressively reduced for which details are given later. The maximum continuous working temperature of polythene pipes is 60°C. (140°F.) which means that the pipes cannot be used for domestic hot-water systems. Polythene does not melt at 60°C. but merely softens and thus its strength is reduced. This means that it can safely be used for waste pipe applications even if the temperature is likely intermittently to exceed 60°C.

Working Pressures for Polythene Pipes

Nominal bore, in.	Normal Gauge		Heavy Gauge	
	Working pressure,		Working pressure,	
	p.s.i.	ft./head	p.s.i.	ft./head
¼	—	—	285	660
⅜	—	—	230	525
½	130	300	210	480
¾	115	265	150	350
1	90	210	120	255
1¼	75	172	115	245
1½	70	160	105	235
2	70	160	—	—

Referring to these figures, the test pressure applied will depend on the maker of the pipes concerned but in any case an adequate margin of safety is allowed. The heavy-gauge pipe may, of course, be used at higher pressures, but the temperature limitations still apply.

Relationship of Working Pressure to Temperature

Temperature, °C. and °F.		% of Working Pressure (see previous figures)	Temperature, °C. and °F.		% of Working Pressure (see previous figures)
20	68	100	50	122	25
30	86	65	—	—	—
40	104	45	—	—	—

One of the big advantages of polythene pipes is their low S. G. and, therefore, weight. This reduces transport costs and facilitates handling. The weight and size will vary slightly from company to company since they are able to vary the sizes within the limits laid down in BS.1972. However, the figures do not necessarily correspond to the figures of B.S.1972 which are:

If the pipe is coiled this shall be done at a temperature less than 30°C. The internal diameter of the coil shall not be less than 24 times the mean outside diameter of the pipe with a minimum of 2 ft.

Nominal Bore, in.	Recommended minimum internal diameter of coil, ft.
$\frac{1}{2}$ and less	$3\frac{1}{2}$
$\frac{3}{4}$	$3\frac{1}{2}$
1	4
$1\frac{1}{4}$	5
$1\frac{1}{2}$	6
2	7

The ends of the pipes shall be plugged or covered.
If, at the request of the consumer and for the purpose of shipment, pipe is coiled to diameters smaller than those recommended, the material should be recoiled to the larger diameters at the point of delivery.

Coil Sizes and Weights of Polythene Tubes (approx.)

Normal Gauge Tube

Length, ft.	$\frac{1}{2}$ in. I.D. Coil, in.	Wt., lb.	$\frac{3}{4}$ in. I.D. Coil, in.	Wt., lb.	1 in. I.D. Coil, in.	Wt., lb.	$1\frac{1}{4}$ in. I.D. Coil, in.	Wt., lb.	$1\frac{1}{2}$ in. I.D. Coil, in.	Wt., lb.	2 in. I.D. Coil, in.	Wt., lb.
50	28	3·4	42	5·8	42	8·6	51	10·5	56	14·1	58	26
100	28	7·0	42	14·0	44	17·7	54	21·7	60	29	60	53
200	30	14·5	42	29	44	36·0	58	44·2	60	39·5	62	108
250	30	18·0	46	35·9	46	45·8	60	56·1	66	75·2	67	138·5
500	32	35·8	46	71·9	47	93·0	60	112·2	66	150·3	72	277·5

Heavy Gauge Tube

	$\frac{1}{4}$ in.		$\frac{1}{2}$ in.		$\frac{3}{4}$ in.		1 in.		$1\frac{1}{4}$ in.	
50	—	3·4	31	6·8	44	9·9	44	12·4	45	19·1
100	28	7·0	31	14·5	44	20·5	46	25·7	59	39·5
200	28	14·5	31	29·6	44	42·0	46	52·4	59	82·1
250	28	17·1	36	36·2	50	74·2	51	66·1	60	110·2
500	34	35·3	36	75·0	50	105·8	51	132·8	62	202·5

Chemical Properties of Polythene Pipes

The chemical properties of polythene pipes are clearly of the greatest importance in deciding under which conditions they may be installed. The chemical resistance will vary with temperature. The materials here listed are quite safe in continuous contact with polythene up to 60°C. (140°F.).

Chemicals safe with Polythene up to 60°C. (140°F.)

Aluminium salts (and alum)
Ammonium salts (and ammonia)
Antimony chloride
Barium salts
Beer and cider
Bismuth carbonate
Borax
Calcium salts
Carbonic acid
Chlorine water (2%)
Chrome alum
Citric and Formic acids
Copper salts
Detergents (less than 1% soln.)
Dextrose and Glucose
Ethylene and propylene glycol
Formalin (formaldehyde)
Fruit pulp
Glycerine
Hydrobromic acid
Hydrochloric acid
Iron salts
Lactic acid

Lead salts
Magnesium salts
Maleic acid
Mercury salts (and mercury)
Milk
Nickel salts
Oxalic acid
Paper mill liquors
Phosphoric acid (50%)
Potassium salts
Salicylic acid
Salt solution (brine)
Silver salts
Sodium salts (but see figures under chemicals unsafe with polythene)
Sulphur dioxide and sulphurous acid
Tanning extracts and Tannic acid
Tartaric acid (10%)
Tin salts (Stannous)
Vinegar

The following materials are safe only up to 20°C. (68°F.).

Chemicals Safe with Polythene up to 20°C. (68°F.)

Acetic acid (below 60%)
Boron trifluoride
Chromic acid (below 80%)
Hydrofluoric acid (60%)
Hydrogen peroxide
Nitric acid (below 25%)

Perchloric acid
Photographic solutions (not for plate etching)
Picric acid (1%)
Sulphuric acid (70%)

The following materials should not be used with polythene.

Chemicals Unsafe with Polythene

Acetaldehyde
Acetic acid (glacial)
Acetone (and other ketones)
Alcohols
Amyl acetate (and other esters)
Animal oils (and vegetable)
Benzene (and compounds)
Bromine

Ethers
Fluorine
Hypochlorous acid
Iodine
Mineral oils
Nitric acid (over 25%)
Petrol
Phosphoric acid (over 50%)

Carbon disulphide
Carbon tetrachloride
Chlorine (100%)
Chlorosulphonic acid
Chloroform
Creosote
Cresylic acid
Dichlorethylene

Silicone fluids
Sodium hypochlorite (over 15%)
Sulphuric acid (over 70%)
Terpenes
Trichlorethylene
Turpentine
White spirit

The foregoing lists are given only as a guide. Polythene may well be resistant to substances not listed but for further details individual manufacturers should be contacted and in any case it is always advisable to do this. Polythene may also be used with some of the chemicals on an intermittent basis, but here again manufacturers should be consulted.

Wider Range of Polythene Pipes

For many purposes polythene pipes in a wider range of bores and thicknesses than is covered in BS.1973 may be required. Generally, properties and conditions are as for BS.1972 with the differences here outlined. The pipes are supplied in light, medium and heavy gauges; some of the smaller bores have been omitted:

Light-Gauge Pipes to BS.1973

Nominal Bore, in.	Nominal O.D., in.	Maximum Working Pressure, p.s.i. at 20°C. (68°F.)	Approximate Weight per 100 ft., lb.
$\frac{1}{4}$	0·375	150	2·50
$\frac{1}{2}$	0·625	75	4·48
$\frac{3}{4}$	0·875	50	6·45
1	1·250	80	17·43
$1\frac{1}{2}$	1·750	65	25·40
$2\frac{1}{4}$	2·500	35	37·00
$2\frac{3}{4}$	3·000	25	44·80
$3\frac{1}{4}$	3·500	25	52·81
$3\frac{3}{4}$	4·000	20	60·80
$4\frac{5}{8}$	5·000	25	113·25
$5\frac{5}{8}$	6·000	20	136·75

Medium-Gauge Pipes to BS.1973

Nominal Bore, in.	Nominal O.D., in.	Maximum Working Pressure, p.s.i. at 20°C. (68°F.)	Approximate Weight per 100 ft., lb.
$\frac{3}{16}$	0·375	300	3·50
$\frac{9}{16}$	0·750	100	7·73
$\frac{13}{16}$	1·000	65	10·45
$1\frac{3}{8}$	1·750	80	36·95
2	2·500	75	70·45
$2\frac{1}{2}$	3·000	60	86·43
3	3·500	50	101·91

Nominal Bore, in.	Nominal O.D., in.	Maximum Working Pressure, p.s.i. at 20°C. (68°F.)	Approximate Weight per 100 ft. lb.
3½	4·000	45	117·90
4	4·500	35	133·40
4½	5·000	35	148·90
5	5·500	30	164·88
5½	6·000	25	180·38
6	6·500	25	195·85

Heavy-Gauge Pipes to BS.1973

Nominal Bore, in.	Nominal O.D., in.	Maximum Working Pressure, p.s.i. at 20°C. (68°F.)	Approximate Weight per 100 ft., lb.
½	0·75	150	9·98
¾	1·00	100	13·47
1	1·50	150	38·93
1½	2·00	100	54·91
2⅜	3·00	75	105·35
2⅞	3·50	65	124·75
3⅜	4·00	50	144·75
4⅜	5·00	40	183·70
5⅜	6·00	35	222·65

The following details of the products of some manufacturers may prove useful.

P. H. Muntz and Barwell Ltd.

Type 425 "Three Crown" polythene pipe to BS.1972/1953; normal gauge (½, ¾, 1, 1¼, 1½ and 2 inches), and heavy gauge (¼, ⅜, ½, ¾ and 1 inches). All sizes supplied in standard coils of 50 ft., 100 ft. and 500 ft.

Stewarts and Lloyds Plastics Ltd.

Type 425 "S and L" polythene pipe to BS.1972/1953; normal gauge (½, ¾, 1, 1¼ and 2 inches), and heavy gauge (¼, ⅜, ½, ¾, 1, 1¼ and 1½ inches). All sizes available in standard coils 50 ft., 100 ft., 200 ft. and 500 ft. Sizes ½, ¾ and 1 inch are also available in longer lengths on drums ranging from 6,000 ft. for the ½ in. normal gauge down to 1,500 ft. for the 1 in. heavy gauge.

The Wednesbury Tube Co. Ltd.

Type 425 "Wednesbury" polythene pipe to BS.1972/1953; normal gauge (½, ¾, 1, 1¼, 1½ and 2 inches), and heavy gauge (½, ¾, 1, 1¼, 1½ and 2 inches—the 2 in. not to BS.1972). The ½, ¾ and 1 in. normal and heavy gauges are available in 50, 100, 200, 250, 500, 750 and 1,000 ft. coils and the 1¼ in. and 1½ in. normal gauge, and 1¼ in. and 1½ in. heavy gauge are available in 50, 100, 200, 250 and 500 ft. coils. Reels of the following lengths are also available:—Normal—½ in. 5,000 ft., ¾ in. 3,000 ft., 1 in. 2,000 ft. Heavy ½ in. 4,000 ft., ¾ in. 2,500 ft. and 1 in. 1,500 ft.

Wellington Tube Works Ltd.

Type 425 "Wellington" polythene pipe to BS.1972/1953; normal gauge (½, ¾, 1, 1¼, and 1½ and 2 in. nominal bores), and heavy gauge (sizes ¼, ⅜, ½, ¾, 1, 1¼ and 1½ in. nominal bores). Standard coils of 50, 100, 200 and 500 ft.; the 2 in. normal gauge and the 1¼ and 1½ in. heavy gauge in standard coils up to 200 ft. only; coils available down to 25 ft.

Yorkshire Imperial Plastics Ltd.

Type 425 "Polyorc-Alkathene" polythene pipe to BS.1972/1953; normal gauge (½, ¾, 1, 1¼, 1½ and 2 in.), and heavy gauge (¼, ⅜, ½, ¾, 1, 1¼ and 1½ in.). Standard coils available 50, 100, 200 and 500 ft. with 2 in. normal gauge, and 1¼ and 1½ in. heavy gauge available in 25-ft. lengths. Sizes ½, ¾ and 1 in. also available in longer lengths, on metal reels, ranging from 4,000 ft. for the ½ in. normal gauge to 1,500 ft. for the 1 in. heavy gauge. Other lengths on special request. This company also manufactures much larger sizes to BS.1973.

Other producers of polythene tube supplying similar products are as follow:

AB Plastics Ltd.,
Allied Iron Founders Ltd.
  (J. S. & F. Folkard Ltd.),
British Xylonite Group,
Conex-Terna Ltd.,
Chemidus Plastics Ltd.,
Evered and Co. Ltd.,
Extrudex Ltd.,
Formica Ltd.,
Foster Bros. (Plastics) Ltd.,
Kay and Co. (Engineers) Ltd.,
Marley Tile Co. Ltd.,
David Mosely and Sons Ltd.,
Osma Plastics Ltd.,
Peglers Ltd.,
Rediweld Ltd.,
Tenaplas Ltd.,
The U.A.M. Group of Companies.

Details of pipes to BS.3284 for H.D. polythene are given in the table below:

H.D. Polythene Pipes to BS.3284
Sizes are in inches

Nominal Size	Outside Diameter Min.	Max.	Class B W.P. 200 ft. head (87 lb./sq. in.) Mean Wall	Bore Size	Class C W.P. 300 ft. head (130 lb./sq. in.) Mean Wall	Bore Size	Class D W.P. 400 ft. head (173 lb./sq. in.) Mean Wall	Bore Size
General Plastics Pipe Series								
⅜	0·667	0·682	—	—	0·064	½	0·078	½
½	0·832	0·848	0·064	11/16	0·075	11/16	0·097	⅝
¾	1·043	1·061	0·074	⅞	0·094	⅞	0·121	13/16
1	1·311	1·332	0·090	1⅛	0·118	1 1/16	0·153	1
1¼	1·654	1·679	0·101	1 7/16	0·148	1⅜	0·191	1¼
1½	1·888	1·915	0·116	1⅝	0·168	1 9/16	0·219	1 7/16
2	2·363	2·395	0·145	2 1/16	0·211	1 15/16	0·273	1 13/16
BS. 1972 Series								
½	0·671	0·686	—	—	0·064	½	0·079	½
¾	0·982	1·000	0·074	13/16	0·088	13/16	0·114	¾
1	1·230	1·250	0·089	1 1/16	0·110	1	0·143	15/16
1¼	1·477	1·500	0·100	1¼	0·132	1 3/16	0·171	1⅛
1½	1·725	1·750	0·115	1½	0·154	1⅜	0·199	1 5/16
2	2·344	2·375	0·143	2 1/16	0·209	1 15/16	0·271	1 13/16

5.3.16   PVC Pipes (Detailed Information)

The British Standard Specification for pvc pipes for cold-water supply is BS.3505:1962, "Unplasticized PVC Pipe (Type 1140) for Cold Water Supply". The material employed in the specification is the normal type (as distinct from medium- or high-impact types). There are four classes of pipe designed for various maximum working pressures at 20°C. as follow:

Class AA   For a 150 ft. head (65 p.s.i.)
Class B   For a 200 ft. head (87 p.s.i.)
Class C   For a 300 ft. head (130 p.s.i.)
Class D   For a 400 ft. head (173 p.s.i.)

Dimensions of Pipes to BS.3505

Nominal Size, in.	Outside Diameter, in.		Wall thickness, in.							
			Class AA		Class B		Class C		Class D	
	Min.	Max.	Min.	Max.	Min.	Max.	Min.	Max.	Min.	Max.
$\frac{3}{8}$	0·667	0·682	—	—	—	—	—	—	0·050	0·061
$\frac{1}{2}$	0·832	0·848	—	—	—	—	—	—	0·060	0·071
$\frac{3}{4}$	1·043	1·061	—	—	—	—	0·060	0·071	0·075	0·087
1	1·311	1·332	—	—	—	—	0·072	0·084	0·094	0·107
$1\frac{1}{4}$	1·654	1·679	—	—	0·070	0·082	0·091	0·104	0·119	0·133
$1\frac{1}{2}$	2·363	2·395	—	—	0·090	0·103	0·129	0·143	0·170	0·187
2	2·363	2·396	—	—	0·090	0·103	0·129	0·143	0·170	0·187
$2\frac{1}{2}$	2·965	3·003	—	—	0·110	0·124	0·162	0·178	0·213	0·234
3	3·485	3·528	0·115	0·129	0·130	0·144	0·191	0·210	0·250	0·275
$3\frac{1}{2}$	3·985	4·033	0·120	0·134	0·148	0·163	0·218	0·240	0·286	0·315
4	4·485	4·538	0·135	0·150	0·167	0·184	0·245	0·270	0·321	0·353
5	5·471	5·534	0·154	0·170	0·203	0·225	0·299	0·329	0·392	0·431
6	6·590	6·664	0·185	0·204	0·245	0·270	0·360	0·396	0·472	0·519

Where it is proposed to order pipe for use with moulded fittings by the solvent welding technique then closer tolerances are required. Those recommended are:

Pipe Dimensions for Moulded Fittings

Nominal Size, in.	Outside Diameter, in.		Nominal Size, in.	Outside Diameter, in.	
	Min.	Max.		Min.	Max.
$\frac{3}{8}$	0·669	0·679	2	2·366	2·380
$\frac{1}{2}$	0·834	0·844	$2\frac{1}{2}$	2·969	2·985
$\frac{3}{4}$	1·045	1·055	3	3·489	3·505
1	1·313	1·323	$3\frac{1}{2}$	3·990	4·006
$1\frac{1}{4}$	1·636	1·670	4	4·490	4·506
$1\frac{1}{2}$	1·891	1·904	5	5·477	5·497
			6	6·610	6·635

All pipes are required to be marked at intervals of not more than 10 ft.

The marking will show manufacturer's identity, class of pipe and size, table number and the B.S. marking. The colour code will be as follows:

Class AA: yellow; Class B: red; Class C: blue; Class D: green.

The normal lengths will be 10 ft. and 20 ft., although other lengths may be supplied by arrangement. Actually, length is limited because of transport difficulties (the pipes cannot be drummed) and in practice about 25 ft. is usually the maximum.

Working Pressure Considerations

Four ratings of working pressure have been given. To calculate the working pressure for individual requirements, however, the following formula may be used:

Working pressure $= 2st/(D-t)$, where $s =$ maximum permissible working stress at 20°C.; $t =$ wall thickness; $D =$ outside diameter of the pipe.

The only figure in this formula which is subject to variation is the maximum permissible working stress. The short-time tensile strength of the material is 6,000–7,000 lb. per sq. in. but this figure cannot be used since it will not accommodate the long-term creep effect caused by the application of pressure over long periods. It is thus necessary to introduce a high safety factor and experience has shown that a figure of 7:1 is satisfactory. Thus "s" will be 800–1,000 depending on the type of material being employed, but for general purposes it is safe to use a figure of 850 lb. per sq. in.

The figures given were based on a working temperature of 20°C. Rigid pvc must not be used under pressure above 60°C. in any circumstances, and even above 40°C. any use under pressure should be in consultation with the manufacturers. The working pressure is reduced at elevated temperatures expressed as a percentage of the working pressure at 20°C. At 30°C. the figure is 80%; at 40°C. the figure is 60% and at 50°C. 25%.

Apart from reducing the working pressure at elevated temperatures, the pressures given at 20°C. are preferably for use below ground. Above ground it may be advisable to reduce pressures by about 25%.

A series of hydraulic tests are included in BS.3505. In the proof test any pipe shall withstand a pressure equal to twice the working pressure for at least one hour at room temperature without signs of leakage or weeping. In the short-term test, the pipe shall withstand a circumferential stress of 5,700 lb. per sq. in. for at least one hour at 20°C. without sign of leakage or weeping. A long-term test is also specified whereby the extrapolated circumferential burst stress after "50 years" shall not be less than 3,000 lb. per sq. in.

PVC Pipes for Screwed Joints

The dimensions of pipes already given are for use where solvent welding, or other methods of jointing, other than screwed joints, are to be employed. For screwed joints, one of two procedures must be adopted. The first method is to solvent-weld a sleeve on the outside of the end of the pipe to take the screw thread. The second method is to purchase pipe specially designed for the purpose, which means a heavier wall gauge. There is no British Standard Specification for this heavier gauge material but various manufacturers sell suitable products. Some typical dimensions are:

PVC Pipes for Screwed Joints

(sizes in inches)

Nominal Bore	130 ft. head		330 ft. head	
	Wall	Bore	Wall	Bore
⅜	0·105	0·46	0·105	0·46
½	0·125	0·58	0·125	0·58
¾	0·100	0·84	0·145	0·75
1	0·130	1·06	0·185	0·95
1¼	0·140	1·37	0·210	1·23
1½	0·150	1·59	0·235	1·42
2	0·175	2·01	0·280	1·80
2½	0·195	2·58	0·330	2·31
3	0·215	3·04	0·370	2·73
3½	0·235	3·49	0·415	3·13
4	0·265	3·94	0·460	3·55
5	0·295	4·86	—	—
6	0·340	5·78	—	—

Chemical Resistance

In general terms rigid pvc is resistant to most inorganic acids, alkalis and salts as well as many organic chemicals. It is quite resistant to most effluents, salt water, plating solutions, corrosive fumes, soils and the like which lead to its application over a wide field. The material is also perfectly safe with potable water, whether hard or soft, and in the former case it tends to retard the formation of scale. Those materials which do attack it include concentrated oxidizing acids, esters, ketones, aromatic and chlorinated hydrocarbons, organo-nitro compounds, organo-amino compounds, lacquer solvents and acetic anhydride.

Chemical Resistance of Rigid PVC Pipes

Chemical	Maximum Concentration	Maximum Temperature, °C.
Ammonium hydroxide	Saturation	35
Amyl alcohol	Any	31
Beer, etc.	Any	32
Butyl alcohol	Any	31
Castor oil	Any	31
Caustic soda	10%	65
Caustic soda	35%	31
Chlorine water	Saturation	31
Chrome plating solution	—	55
Chromic acid	25%	52
Citric acid	Saturation	65
Coconut oil	Any	31
Cotton seed oil	Any	31

Chemical	Maximum Concentration	Maximum Temperature, °C.
Ethyl alcohol	Any	31
Ethylene glycol	Any	31
Ferric chloride	Saturation	65
Fruit juices	Any	32
Glucose	Any	65
Glycerine	Any	31
Hydrogen peroxide	90%	33
Lactic acid	Any	31
Methyl alcohol	Any	31
Mineral oils	—	31
Nitric acid	10%	65
Nitric acid	35%	32
Oleic acid	Any	31
Propyl alcohol	Any	31
Soaps	Any	65
Sulphuric acid	50%	54
Tannic acid	Saturation	31
Tartaric acid	Saturation	31
Triethanolamine	Any	65

Other Features

Other points of interest concerning rigid pvc pipes are:

(1) Pipes are usually supplied in a grey colour, although natural (a translucent straw colour) is often supplied.
It may be possible to supply other colours on request but, in accordance with BS.3505, the pipes shall not transmit more than 0·2% of the visible light falling on them.

(2) The pipes are suitable for the conveyance of gas which should, however, be free of aromatic hydrocarbons which would cause some surface attack. This may not be serious where small amounts are involved but field trials should be carried out so as to leave no doubts.

(3) Pipes carrying potable water can be laid in close proximity to gas pipes.

(4) Filler rods for welding are available.

(5) No guarantee regarding toxicity is given, but the pipes are normally considered suitable for conveying foodstuffs. Suppliers should be consulted for specific recommendations.

(6) They are good insulators and cannot, therefore, be used for earthing.

(7) A wide range of fittings in rigid pvc is available.

(8) Above 40°C. support should be continuous, and below that every 2 ft. 6 in.– 5ft. 0 in. depending on temperature and size of pipe.

British Standards for PVC Pipe

B.S.3506:1962 has been issued for "Unplasticised PVC Pipe for Industrial Uses", and the details are given in the following table.

Other specifications on pvc pipes are in the course of preparation.

Dimensions and Minimum Burst Pressures of Pipes B.S.3506:1962

Nominal Size, in.	Outside Diameter, in.		Class 1 Non-pressure series		Class 2 Min. burst pressure at 20°C. 390 lb/in^2 (27·4 kg/cm^2)		Class 3 Min. burst pressure at 20°C. 520 lb/in^2 (36·6 kg/cm^2)	
	Wall Thicknesses, in.							
	min.	max.	min.	max.	min.	max.	min.	max.
⅛	0·397	0·409	0·040	0·050	—	—	—	—
¼	0·532	0·545	0·040	0·050	—	—	—	—
⅜	0·669	0·679	0·040	0·050	—	—	—	—
½	0·832	0·848	0·045	0·055	—	—	—	—
¾	1·043	1·061	0·050	0·061	—	—	—	—
1	1·311	1·332	0·055	0·066	—	—	—	—
1¼	1·654	1·679	0·060	0·071	—	—	0·070	0·082
1½	1·888	1·915	0·065	0·076	—	—	0·080	0·092
2	2·363	2·395	0·075	0·087	—	—	0·090	0·103
2½	2·965	3·003	0·085	0·097	—	—	0·110	0·124
3	3·485	3·528	0·095	0·108	0·115	0·129	0·130	0·144
3½	3·985	4·033	0·105	0·118	0·120	0·134	0·148	0·163
4	4·485	4·538	0·115	0·129	0·135	0·150	0·167	0·184
5	5·471	5·534	0·125	0·139	0·154	0·170	0·203	0·223
6	6·590	6·664	0·125	0·139	0·185	0·204	0·245	0·270
7	7·584	7·668	0·125	0·139	0·213	0·234	0·281	0·309
8	8·579	8·673	0·125	0·139	0·241	0·265	0·318	0·350
9	9·574	9·678	0·125	0·139	0·269	0·296	0·355	0·391
10	10·690	10·805	0·125	0·139	0·300	0·330	0·397	0·437

Note 1: Classes 6 and 7 have wall thicknesses equivalent to schedule 40 and 80 respectively and provide thick-wall pipes for special purposes.

Note 2: The pressures specified are minimum short-time burst pressures and do not imply rated working pressures. In selecting the class of pipe to be used for a particular application a safety factor on the burst pressure should be applied depending on the nature and temperature of the fluid and type of installation. For example, for water at 20°C. the safety factor should be 8. Expert advice should be sought.

Note 3: Classes A, B, C and D pipes in B.S.3505, "Unplasticized PVC Pipe (Type 1140) for Cold Water Supply" fully satisfy the requirements of Classes 2, 3, 4 and 5 of Grade 1 of this standard.

Suppliers of PVC Pipe

Rigid pvc pipes can be obtained from the following companies.

Yorkshire Imperial Plastics Ltd.,
Durapipe and Fittings Ltd.,
Stewarts and Lloyds Plastics Ltd.,
British Xylonite Group,

A.B. Plastics Ltd.,
Chemidus Plastics Ltd.,
Extrudex Ltd.,
P. H. Muntz and Barwell Ltd.,

Dimensions and Minimum Burst Pressures of Pipes B.S.3506:1962

Class 4 Min. burst pressure at 20°C. 780 lb/cm² (54·8 kg/cm²)		Class 5 Min. burst pressure at 20°C. 1040 lb/in² (73·1 kg/cm²)		Class 6			Class 7		
				Wall Thickness, in.		Min. burst pressure at 20°C.	Wall Thickness, in.		Min. burst pressure at 20°C.
Wall Thicknesses, in.						lb/in² (kg/cm²)			lb/in² (kg/cm²)
min.	max.	min.	max.	min.	max.		min.	max.	
—	—	0·050	0·061	0·068	0·081	2710 (190·5)	0·095	0·108	4110 (289·0)
—	—	0·050	0·061	0·088	0·100	2610 (183·5)	0·119	0·133	3800 (267·2)
—	—	0·050	0·061	0·091	0·104	2090 (146·9)	0·126	0·140	3080 (216·5)
—	—	0·060	0·071	0·109	0·122	2010 (141·3)	0·147	0·162	2850 (280·4)
0·060	0·071	0·075	0·087	0·113	0·127	1620 (113·9)	0·154	0·170	2310 (162·4)
0·072	0·084	0·094	0·107	0·133	0·148	1510 (106·2)	0·179	0·197	2110 (148·3)
0·091	0·104	0·119	0·133	—	—	—	0·191	0·210	1750 (123·0)
0·103	0·116	0·136	0·151	—	—	—	0·200	0·220	1590 (111·8)
0·129	0·143	0·170	0·187	—	—	—	0·218	0·240	1360 (95·6)
0·162	0·178	0·213	0·234	—	—	—	—	—	—
0·191	0·210	0·250	0·275	—	—	—	—	—	—
0·218	0·240	0·286	0·315	—	—	—	—	—	—
0·245	0·270	0·321	0·353	—	—	—	—	—	—
0·299	0·329	0·392	0·431	—	—	—	—	—	—
0·360	0·396	0·472	0·519	—	—	—	—	—	—
—	—	—	—	—	—	—	—	—	—
—	—	—	—	—	—	—	—	—	—
—	—	—	—	—	—	—	—	—	—
—	—	—	—	—	—	—	—	—	—

U.A.M. Group of Companies (Universal Asbestos Manufacturing Co. Ltd. markets products of Allied Structural Plastics Ltd.),

B.T.R. Industries Ltd., Aeroplastics Ltd.

Some details of pvc pipes available are:

Stewarts and Lloyds Plastics Ltd.

Nom. Bore, in.	Outside Diameter, in.	
	min.	max.
$\frac{3}{8}$	0·669	0·679
$\frac{1}{2}$	0·834	0·844
$\frac{3}{4}$	1·045	1·055
1	1·313	1·323
$1\frac{1}{4}$	1·656	1·670
$1\frac{1}{2}$	1·891	1·904

Nom. Bore, in.	Outside Diameter, in. min.	max.
2	2·366	2·380
2½	2·969	2·985
3	3·990	4·006
4	4·490	4·506
5	5·477	5·497
6	6·610	6·635

Durapipe and Fittings Ltd.

This company manufactures a wide range of pipes in rigid pvc and ABS. All the various standards which have been listed are catered for.

AB Plastics Ltd.

Sizes, in inches, are as follows:

Soil pipe 100

Nom. Size	Outside Diameter (Mean)	Wall Thickness (Min.)
4	4·325	0·125
3	3·218	0·090

Waste pipe 200

2	2·198	0·080
1½	1·628	0·075
1¼	1·428	0·070

BTR Industries Ltd.

Grade	Nominal Size (in.)	O.D. (in.)	I.D. (in.)	Minimum Wall Thickness (in.)
Schedule A	½	0·840	0·750	0·045
	¾	1·050	0·940	0·055
	1	1·325	1·205	0·060
	1¼	1·660	1·520	0·070
	1½	1·900	1·740	0·080
	2	2·375	2·175	0·100
	3	3·500	3·220	0·140
	4	4·500	4·110	0·195
Schedule 40	½	0·840	0·622	0·109
	¾	1·050	0·824	0·113
	1	1·325	1·059	0·133
	1¼	1·660	1·380	0·140
	1½	1·900	1·610	0·145
	2	2·375	2·067	0·154
	3	3·500	3·068	0·216
	4	4·500	4·026	0·237

Grade	Nominal Size (in.)	O.D. (in.)	I.D. (in.)	Minimum Wall Thickness (in.)
Schedule 80	½	0·840	0·546	0·147
	¾	1·050	0·742	0·154
	1	1·325	0·967	0·179
	1¼	1·660	1·278	0·191
	1½	1·900	1·500	0·200
	2	2·375	1·939	0·218
	3	3·500	2·900	0·300
	4	4·500	3·826	0·337

5.4 Accessories and Fittings

The parts included under this heading are cisterns, siphons, ball-valves and lavatory seats. Most of these are made in either polythene or polypropylene or both, except the lavatory seats which are made also in thermosetting plastics.

Some of the obvious reasons for using these materials may be quoted:
(a) Excellent strength to weight ratio.
(b) Low moisture absorption and good resistance to chemical attack.
(c) Non-rusting.
(d) Smooth surface and therefore unobstructed water flow.
(e) Good mechanical strength.
(f) Attractive appearance.
(g) Hygienic (especially applicable to lavatory seats).
(h) Permanent colours.

Suppliers of polypropylene plumbing fittings are as follow:

Cisterns Ltd.,   BTR Industries Ltd.,
Paragon Plastics Ltd.,   L. and P. Plastics Ltd.,
Aeroplastics Ltd.,   Shires and Co. (London) Ltd.

Suppliers of polythene plumbing fittings and accessories are:

R and A. G. Crossland Ltd.,   United Ebonite and Lorival Ltd.,
Folkard (Plastics) Ltd.,   Yorkshire Imperial Plastics Ltd.,
Fordham Pressings Ltd.,   Shires and Co. (London) Ltd.
Kantex Ltd.,

As far as lavatory seats are concerned, Ekco Plastics Ltd. supply both polyolefine and thermosetting types in a variety of colours. Polyester cold-water cisterns are supplied by Wembley Fibreglass and Plastics Ltd., and Osma Plastics Ltd., as well as other manufacturers of polyester products.

Some examples of plastic plumbing fittings may be given.

5.4.1 Cisterns

The "Viking" all-plastics cistern by Cisterns Ltd. has the following specification:

Low-level cistern

Viking 2-, 2½- and 3-gal. BS.1125 plastics low-level cistern comprises the cistern shell and cover in Tufolene, C.P. operating lever, overflow with compression ring, "Flowmaster" siphon, "Alkavalve" silent-filling plastics ballvalve, "Alkafloat" concealed wall supports with screws and washers, high-gloss plastics flushbend, external parts matching ware: operating lever also available in matching ware if required.

High-level cistern

Viking BS.1125 2-, 2½- and 3-gal. high-level cistern. Specification as for low level, but less flushpipe and supplied with plastics operating lever and chain and pull, and outlets screwed 1½ in. or 1¼ in. B.S.P.

Colour range

White and a choice of BS. bath colours to match pottery: ivory, primrose, pink, jade green, light green, turquoise, blue—also non BS. colours, red and mauve.

Viking high- and low-level cisterns are also produced in black composition.

Alkathene (polythene) floats and syphons (*Shires & Co (London) Ltd and Imperial Chemical Industries Ltd*)

The "Lynx" cistern by Shires and Co. (London) Ltd. has the following features:

The cistern is made from polypropylene in a 2-gal. size. The coloured "Lynx", pink, primrose, turquoise, green or white, is rust-proof and impervious to corrosion. The beading is in a toning colour and the streamlined contours give a neat appearance with no unhygienic dust-collecting crevices. The high-gloss surface is easily wiped over with a damp cloth and abrasive cleaners are unnecessary. The coloured "Lynx" cistern incorporates all the features of the black model and is quiet in action. It is fitted with the non-corroding Shires polythene "Kingfisher" siphon mechanism, which ensures a positive action flush first time and refills quickly, quietly and unobtrusively.

There is also the "Hippo" high-level well-bottom plastic cistern.

The "Flomaster" siphon by Cisterns Ltd., has the following features. A big advantage of this type of siphon is the rate of flow which eliminates prevalent flushing problems with BS. W.C. pans, and the consequent waste of water. The "Flomaster" low-level siphon flushes even faster than the BS. high-level-cistern rate-of-flow requirement. Silent in action (the plastic bearings are lubricated by water), the "Flomaster" has a light, easy action and is trouble-free, non-corroding and virtually indestructible.

It has the following specification:

$1\frac{3}{4}$ in. "Flomaster" all-plastics siphon C.O. operating lever; Alkavalve silent-filling plastic ballvalve; $4\frac{1}{2}$ in. Alkafloat; $\frac{3}{4}$ in. plastics overflow and compression ring (to suit $\frac{3}{4}$ in. copper BS.759 or $\frac{3}{4}$ in. Tufolene plastics tubing); heavy gauge high-gloss plastics flushbend and supporting brackets; lead stamping plug.

For white cisterns: C.P. operating lever; white overflow, siphon backnut, union nut, ballvalve backnut; brackets and flushpipe. Operating lever and other external parts are available in both white and a choice of BS. bath colours to match pottery: ivory, primrose, pink, jade, green, turquoise, black, blue, red.

For coloured cisterns: Operating lever C.P. or matching ware—other external parts matching ware only.

Fordham Pressings manufacture the "New Eterna" (low level) and the "Fabula" (high level) plastic cisterns.

The "Alkafloat" is extremely light, yet exceptionally tough, and is made entirely from Tufolene. Every "Alkafloat" is watertight pressure tested. It cannot become waterlogged, is flexible, will not chip, crack, corrode or deteriorate in use and has a high-gloss finish. It is as tough in hot as in cold water, and will even withstand boiling water.

Because of its lightness, it provides "extra lift", thereby reducing the possibility of overflowing. The "Alkafloat" costs no more than other types.

The company's "Alkavalve" plastics diaphragm-type ballvalve has the following features. It is trouble-free with nothing to corrode or to become encrusted or jam. It is made from Tufolene, and is almost silent in action because there are few working parts.

Overflowing is virtually eliminated. The powerful, triple-cam shut-off action resists violent changes of pressure. Filling is rapid, being almost entirely at full bore, as the close-off only becomes effective when the cistern is nearly filled to the water line. Adjustment is by finger screw, horizontally,

14

so as to avoid the cistern shell and internal fittings, and vertically to close off at the water line.

The "Alkavalve" is universal with interchangeable seatings H/P, M/P and L/P. Details are:

Water pressure, lb./in.	Head of Water, ft.	Size of Seating, in./dia.	Pressure of Seating
100–200	230–460	$\frac{1}{8}$	High
40–100	92–230	$\frac{3}{16}$	Medium
20–40	46–92	$\frac{1}{4}$	Low

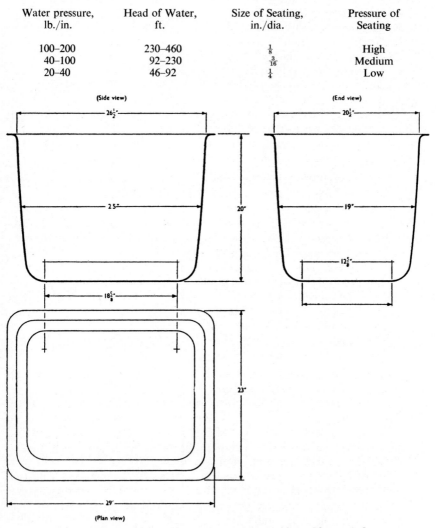

(Side view)

(End view)

(Plan view)

Osma polyester/glass cold water storage cistern (*Osma Plastics Ltd*)

Cisterns Ltd. also manufacture the Viking bath in Tufolene.
Fordham Pressings Ltd. manufacture the well-known "Acquasave".
Wembley Fibreglass and Plastics Ltd. will make cold water tanks to

customer's requirements. Their corrugated types give added rigidity, an important feature not supplied by other manufacturers.

Osma Plastics Ltd., make a water storage cistern and details are given for their 10-gal. and 30–25 gal. sizes.

The 10-gal. cistern is specially designed for use with hot- or cold-water systems. It is particularly suitable as an expansion cistern. The all-glass-fibre product can, in no circumstance, cause or be affected by electrolytic action. Copper and other metallic pipework can be connected with guaranteed freedom from chemical decomposition due to electrolysis.

An overflow of boiling water from the heating system has no adverse effects on the cistern's strength or stability. Hard, soft or high-acid content water cannot affect it. It will not rust or corrode, will not support fungus growth and is even resistant to most chemicals. These features, plus elimination of rust sediment, ensure a permanent, hygienic unit.

The light weight of the cistern—5 lb.—substantially reduces handling and installation costs. Ordinary drilling and cutting tools can be used and there is no difficulty in effecting pipe connections. A wood block should be placed against the inside walls of the cistern to support drilling pressures.

Toughened polystyrene lids are available which provide a perfect dust-proof but not airtight covering. Osmacel lagging sets are also available. These ensure complete thermal insulation against the worst cold conditions, are rot proof, immune from fungus growth or bacteriological attack and cannot deteriorate. Osma cisterns have been specially designed to "nest." This reduces storage space requirements and simplifies transport problems. The following are the sizes available:

10 Gallon Cistern

	Length, in.	Breadth, in.	Depth, in.	Weight (empty)	Capacity, gal. Nominal	Actual
Mean measurements	17¼	12¼	14	5 lb.	10	6⅛
External (including flange)	19½	14½	14			
Base measurement (flat surface)	11 9/16	6 9/16				

Cistern lid 20in. × 15in. with a ½in. flange and nominal radii on corners. Made in high impact polystyrene with raised cruciform for rigidity.

Osmacel lagging sets (for 10 gal. cisterns). Five 1in. thick panels in expanded polystyrene supplied complete with fixing staples and pre-packed. Osmacel B.T.U.'s/in./sq. ft./°F: 0·20–0·25.

30–25 Gallon Cistern

	Length, in.	Breadth, in.	Depth, in.	Weight (empty)
Mean measurements	25	19	20	14½ lb.
External (including flange)	29	23	20	
Base measurement (flat surface)	18¾	12¾		

An interesting new development by Ekco Plastics Ltd. is the "Supersink" made from polypropylene. The material cannot chip or craze and is white right through.

5.5 "Perspex" for Sanitary Ware

5.5.1 Introduction

There are enough "Perspex" baths and sinks in use today to make the material reasonably familiar to the plumbing trade. The use of the material, however, in spite of its many attractive properties, has never become widespread. Since "Perspex" is such an attractive material it is worth considering the subject in some detail to see if its use could not be advantageously extended.

"Perspex" is not the chemical name of the plastic but the trade mark of Imperial Chemical Industries Ltd. The material is also made in the U.S.A. by Rohn and Haas Ltd., and sold as "Oroglas" in the United Kingdom by Charles Lennig and Co. (G.B.) Ltd. "Perspex" having been predominant for so long in the U.K., the material is commonly referred to by this name although both products are referred to generically by the abbreviated chemical name "acrylics".

"Perspex is thermoplastic, which is at once its strength and weakness. Its strength is that it can be softened by heat and therefore shaped. Its weakness, although this is not a very strong one, is that although it is unaffected by warm water, a hot iron would cause considerable damage. The thermal properties will be considered later.

The actual raw materials are manufactured only by I.C.I. Ltd. in the U.K. and Rohm and Haas in the U.S.A. The products are sold in the form of sheets and rods although profiled corrugated shapes are available.

A wide variety of sizes and thicknesses are available. There are many different colours, both transparent and opaque, one standard list having 35 colours. Most sanitary ware manufacturers, however, normally offer only four or five different colours as it would clearly be impossible economically to stock too many.

Machining is quite straightforward and fabricated parts may be joined by cementing. The production of contours, however, needs more special techniques and knowledge which, nevertheless are not beyond the scope of a newcomer to the field. Generally, a fabricator will be employed to make such products and he could also produce articles dictated by the plumber.

At the present time, the plastics industry offers standard ranges of baths, sinks and urinals. Thus the industry itself is trying to lead the field, but there is no reason why the plumbing industry should not assist in this direction or even take over the whole project.

5.5.2 General Properties

"Perspex" in sanitary ware is hardly used out-of-doors. This situation, however, must not preclude the possibility arising in the future since the material has good weathering resistance. Evidence of this is provided by many outdoor signs. The colour change when used outdoors is slight even in tropical climates and this after many years exposure.

The water absorption factor is, of course, important in out-of-door uses. A sample $\frac{1}{4}$ in.-thick stored at 60% R.H. absorbs less than 1·0% water after 270 days exposure. At 100% R.H., the figure is about 2·0%. For direct immersion results are equally impressive. Apart from this, water appears to have no effect on "Perspex", although it may slightly affect its mechanical properties by "plasticization".

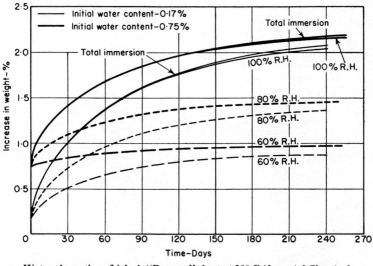

Water absorption of $\frac{1}{4}$-inch "Perspex" sheet at 20° C (*Imperial Chemical Industries Ltd*)

Abrasion resistance is not high but usually satisfactory. It is about as hard as aluminium but, since a depression is made (by an abrasive particle) rather than the material being removed, the surface finish is not affected.

"Perspex" will burn, but only slowly, and is difficult to ignite. There is no after-glow when the flame is removed.

5.5.3   Mechanical Properties
The mechanical properties depend on the temperature and the properties below are considered at room temperature.

Mechanical Properties of "Perspex" at 20°C.

Tensile strength	11,000 lb. per sq. in.
Flexural strength	17,000 lb. per sq. in.
Shear strength	11,000 lb. per sq. in.
Impact strength (Izod)	0·32 ft./lb. per in. of notch
Pyramid hardness (B.S.427)	22
Poisson's ratio	0·35

As will be seen, the tensile properties are good. However, the impact strength is relatively low and must be offset by the thickness chosen and the avoidance of sudden changes in cross section. Laboratory impact tests may be misleading and field trials should be carried out wherever possible.

Another way of determining hardness is to relate it to pencil-scratch hardness between the range 6B to 9H. "Perspex" is one of the hardest of thermoplastics and is scratched by a 9H pencil only.

As with metals, the material is subject to a certain amount of creep under stress. Unlike metals, however, the strain is recoverable at a rate depending on the temperature.

5.5.4   Thermal Properties

In view of its thermoplasticity it is of the utmost importance to consider thermal properties carefully.

Thermal Properties of "Perspex"

Heat distortion temperature	100°C.
1/10 Vicat softening point	110°C.
Demoulding temperature	87°C.
Maximum service temperature	80°C. (Zero stress)
Specific heat	0·35 cal/g.°C.
Coefficient of thermal conductivity (20°C.)	1·3 B.Th.U. in./sq. ft.°F.
Coefficient of thermal expansion (20°C.) (Linear)	$7·2 \times 10^{-5}$ in./in.°C.

One of the most important properties referred to is the demoulding temperature, which will vary by a few degrees either side of 87°C. At this temperature, a shaped object (which has been made by the thermal forming of a sheet) will tend to revert to its original shape, i.e. a sheet. However, any shaped object will operate indefinitely at a temperature as high as 80°C.

Another point is that the coefficient of thermal expansion is about nine times that of metals and allowance must be made for this.

5.5.5   Chemical Properties

As far as the plumbing trade is concerned, the chemical properties may not appear to be of the greatest importance except for resistance to detergents and the like. "Perspex" should be thought of, however, as a material which could be adapted for use as any container-like object since it is so easy to work. Looked at in this way, the chemical properties take on more significance.

In general, the material is chemical resistant. It is resistant to water, alkalis, aqueous inorganic salt solutions and most dilute acids. However, dilute hydrocyanic and hydrofluoric acids and concentrated acids attack the material.

As far as resistance to organic materials is concerned, some do not affect it, others cause swelling, crazing and weakening, and it can be dissolved completely. "Perspex" is not attacked by most foodstuffs which, in turn, are not affected by it. The common chemicals which "craze" it and thus ultimately weaken it mechanically, are here given. (Some of them also eventually dissolve the material).

Chemicals which cause "Perspex" to craze
Alcohol, isopropyl
Amyl acetate (also dissolves)
Carbon tetrachloride (also dissolves)
Chlorine
Cresol (meta) (also dissolves)
Decalin
Petroleum ether (slight only)
Hydrochloric acid (slight only)
Lactic acid (slight only)
Methyl cyclohexanol (rapid action)
Naphtha
n-Octane (slight only)
Olive oil (slight only)
Phosphoric acid
Sulphuric acid
Tritolyl phosphate
White spirit (slight crazing)

The following list shows the effect of other common chemicals and materials on "Perspex".

	20°C.	60°C.	
Acetic acid	U	—	Dissolved
Acetone	U	—	Dissolved
Ethyl alcohol	A	—	Only slight attack
Ammonia (·88)	S	A	
Ammonium chloride	S	—	
Benzene	U	—	Dissolved
Calcium chloride	S	—	
Chromic acid	S	S	Stained
Citric acid	S	S	
Ether	U	—	
Ethylene glycol	S	—	
Formaldehyde	S	—	
Glycerol	S	—	
Nitric acid (10%)	S	—	
Nitric acid (100%)	U	—	
Oil (transformer)	S	—	
(diesel)	S	—	
Potassium permanganate	S	—	Heavy staining
Sodium carbonate	S	—	
Sodium hydroxide	S	—	
Sodium hypochlorite	S	—	
Toluene	U	—	Dissolved

Key: A = Some attack   S = Satisfactory   U = Unsatisfactory.

5.5.6 Commercial Products

It will become clear from an outline of the commercial products available that although much progress has been made, there is still much scope for advancement.

The principal sanitary ware made today is sinks and drainers, wash basins, baths and multi-urinals. Thermo Plastics Ltd. manufacture the last two named and Arrow Plastics Ltd., multi-wash-basin units, but a number of companies manufacture either one or both of the other two and these are:

English Rose Kitchens Ltd.,	Henry Robinson (Fibres) Ltd.,
Graceline Units Ltd.,	V. C. Panels Ltd.,
Harold Moore and Son Ltd.,	W. Freer Ltd.,
Orbex Ltd.,	Arnoplast Ltd.
P. and S. Plastics Ltd.,	Shires and Co. (London) Ltd.,
Shaw Glazed Brick Co. Ltd.,	Wundabath Products Ltd.,
Thermo Plastics Ltd.,	George Howson and Sons Ltd.,
Troman Bros. Ltd.,	Robin Plastics Ltd.,
Wokingham Plastics Ltd.,	W. J. Cox (Sales) Ltd. (Shower
Austin Walters and Son Ltd.,	Enclosures).
Silver Knight Industries Ltd.,	

These companies are manufacturers but there are others who are distributors. There are many of the latter who design their own products but have them made by one or other of the companies mentioned.

It would be wrong to suggest that "Perspex" is extensively used for sanitary ware. At the same time, the material is extremely attractive and this feature will, no doubt, provide an increasingly important sales point. Trials are also proceeding and local authorities in Bristol, Plymouth, Heston, Isleworth and elsewhere have installed substantial quantities of sinks. The trend is therefore growing.

5.5.7 Care of "Perspex" Articles

A number of limitations have been mentioned regarding "Perspex" products. Although these may have sounded formidable, in practice, there is not much likelihood of trouble. Imperial Chemical Industries Ltd., have, however, thought fit to issue the following warnings:

(1) Burning cigarettes must not be stubbed out in or dropped into sinks.

(2) The units are extremely robust and are not affected by boiling water, hot dishes or plates. However, extreme heat is harmful and direct contact with boiling fat, chip pans or casseroles direct from the oven must be avoided.

(3) Scum or grease can be readily removed by soapy water or detergent. Where necessary, mild scouring powders may be used. Metal wool and pads should be avoided.

A notice bearing these warnings is attached to each sink made.

5.5.8 Sinks and Drainers

These units, and the other articles already mentioned, are normally available in a maximum of eight colours. These are primrose, ivory, blue, pink, light green, turquoise, pale pink and dark green.

There are other colours, but most companies restrict their range. Examples include Thermo Plastics, Ltd., (white, ivory, cream and green—special shades on request); P. and S. Plastics Ltd., (cream, pastel green and white); Harold Moore and Son Ltd., (single bowl in primrose, pink, blue, turquoise blue and pastel green), and Troman Bros. Ltd., (white, ivory and sea-green).

All companies naturally make a number of claims for their products and it is useful to summarize these as follows:

The colour is permanent and does not fade or craze; the colour goes right through so that the brilliant polish is always maintained; impervious to water and does not corrode or rust; hot water stays hot longer in the sink; the material is resilient and therefore kinder to dropped crockery; the material will not chip; it is stainproof and thus more hygienic; scratches can easily be removed with modern cleaning powders; the sinks are sound absorbent and therefore there is no metallic "clang"; it is easy to clean; there are no overflow odours; it is resistant to all household cleaners and detergents. It is also resistant to greases and all such household "chemicals".

This is a useful list of claims, but all are justified. Another big advantage is the ability for the entire sink unit (including drainers, soap holders and the like) to be made in one without joints. The hygienic advantage of this is obvious.

Apart from technical properties, the aesthetic qualities hardly need description. Complex curves can be moulded without difficulty, to give most attractive products.

Various standard sizes are available as follows (the figures include drainers):

Sinks (size in inches)	Bowl sizes in inches (left- or right-hand)
42 × 21 — single drainer	19 × 15, 18½ × 14½, 19 × 14½
36 × 18 — single drainer	16 × 13, 15 × 14
63 × 21 — double drainer	20 × 14½, 19 × 14½
54 × 18 — double drainer	—
34 × 14 — single drainer (for caravan or flatlet)	17 × 11½

The units are usually supplied drilled for fitting, as required. Provision for waste and overflow, and chain and plug are regarded as extras.

5.5.9 Baths and Wash-basins

Some of the advantages of "Perspex" baths include light weight, ease of installation and the fact that they are warm to the touch. This is, of course, in addition to the advantages quoted for sinks.

As far as colours are concerned, they will match those of the British Sanitary Pottery Manufacturers' Association. The colours include primrose, pink, blue, green, ivory and white (P. and S. Plastics Ltd.); white, pink, yellow and green (Thermo Plastics Ltd.) and standard pottery colours (Troman Brothers Ltd.).

The baths are normally supplied in cradles, faced if required with shaped "Perspex" panels. Soap holders, shelves and the like can be readily moulded into the baths. Standard taps, handles and so on will also be supplied, including pvc or polythene pipes for the overflow where this has an advantage (see later).

Standard sizes are available ($5\frac{1}{2}$ and 6 ft.) with typical internal dimensions of 66 × $21\frac{1}{2}$ × $15\frac{1}{4}$ in., 66 × 22 × 15 in. and 63 × $22\frac{1}{4}$ × 15 in. Baths are available left hand and right hand. Installation instructions are summarized by P. and S. Plastics Ltd.:—

Use normal sealing compounds between flange of the waste and the bath, with a washer or resilient material. Only moderate pressure should be used to tighten the nut. If a metal pipe and trap are used, they must be accurately aligned so that no sideways or twisting stress is imposed on the bath. Also, since there is inevitably a slight vertical as well as longitudinal movement of the bath in service, it is necessary to ensure that there is sufficient flexibility in the plumbing to allow the trap and waste-pipe fitting to follow these movements, otherwise there is danger of cracking around the waste flange hole in service. If the trap is not bearing against the floor boards or any other structure which would restrict it, and if it is followed by a reasonable length of lead pipe, sufficient flexibility will be obtained, the movement being insufficient to cause any distress to the lead pipe. If a short length of iron piping is used, however, the system will be too rigid. This problem can be overcome by using polythene tube for the waste pipe in conjunction with a metal waste trap.

Wash-basins are also available. That made by Thermo Plastics Ltd. has an overflow which interconnects with the waste. Standard-type wall brackets are suitable for support, though it is recommended that blocks of wood should be mounted in a position to slot firmly into the recesses at the sides of the wash-basin. Waste chain and plug are supplied as extras.

Another product made from "Perspex" is shower trays.

5.5.10   Urinals and Lavatory Basins

Some interesting 3-stall acrylic urinals are made by Thermo Plastics Ltd. The material is impervious to urine and the urinal is easy to clean using normal detergents. Being a one-piece moulding, the absence of joints makes it exceptionally hygienic and problems of seepage are overcome. The urinal has been so designed that with the exception of the inlet pipe and spreaders, all other piping is concealed behind the moulding itself. The plumbing is, therefore, less liable to the type of intentional damage which often occurs when all pipes are exposed. In the event of any piping maintenance being necessary the unit can be removed with minimum disturbance to the surrounding walls or tiles. Since the urinals will nest and the all-up weight is so small, transport, storage and installation are simplified.

The outlets may be left-hand, right-hand, or centre, the standard colour being white. Other colours are available on request. Some dimensions are as follows: Length, 6 ft. $2\frac{1}{2}$ in.; height to top of stall (excluding trough) 3 ft. 9 in.; height overall, 4 ft. $\frac{5}{8}$ in.; depth of trough, $5\frac{1}{4}$ in.; centre-to-centre of stall, 2 in.; projection of side ends, 1 ft. $7\frac{5}{8}$ in. Weight is approximately 70 lb.

Standard fittings (flush pipes, cisterns, etc.) are also sold with the urinal.

Troman Bros. Ltd., manufacture a lavatory basin which has the same advantage as the urinal.

5.5.11 Processing

It may appear to be unnecessary to discuss the processing methods as, in general, the plumber will be dealing with the finished article. Although this is largely true, there are instances where a knowledge of processing techniques is important.

The most practical instance of this is machining. It may well be necessary to drill, tap, saw or otherwise machine "Perspex" during some installation. A second possible application is the addition of parts to existing "Perspex" components. Although this may be achieved by conventional methods (e.g. tapping and screwing) it may also be satisfactorily achieved by cementing. A crack could be repaired in the same way.

Some idea of how a bath, for example, is made could be of value. It will serve to show what limitations there are to the technique so that the fabricator will not be asked to make impossible objects. On the other hand, it will give the plumber ideas as to probable applications for this valuable material.

5.5.12 Machining

"Perspex" is an easy and pleasant material to machine because of its uniform and consistant properties and the complete absence of grain or orientation. In moulded sheet, some slight orientation may occur which may call for special care in some machining operations. These instances, however, are relatively rare. Machining may be done on wood- or metal-working equipment or even with hand tools. The conditions are similar to those required for such metals as brass and aluminium.

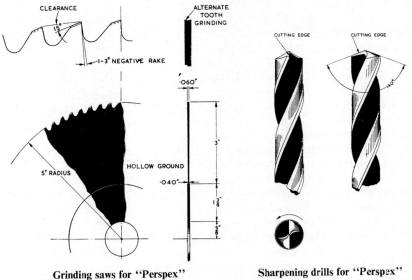

Grinding saws for "Perspex"   Sharpening drills for "Perspex"
(*Imperial Chemical Industries Ltd*)

Good results will be obtained with standard good workshop practice and the following generalizations apply to all types of machining. (Application should be made to I.C.I. Ltd. for full details).

(1) All equipment should be kept in a good, clean condition and adequately guarded to ensure maximum safety for the operatives. Wherever possible, extraction apparatus should be provided to remove swarf and sawdust from the work and its vicinity immediately it is produced.

(2) All tools should be kept well sharpened, paying special attention to the clearance angles and rakes. When grinding tools, holding them in a jig is preferable to judging by eye. In general, all cutting and machining tools should have zero or slightly negative forward rake as this produces a smoother and more uniform surface than do the more conventional types of tools used for light metals. Adequate back clearances are essential.

(3) When machining "Perspex", overheating of the tool should be avoided, to prevent the swarf binding on the tool surfaces. Compressed air blown on the work is a very convenient way of cooling and it also helps to remove swarf.

(4) The "Perspex" should be held firmly in position and solidly supported so as to avoid chattering.

5.5.13 Cementing

The cementing of "Perspex" is a relatively difficult process and the following is only an outline of the subject. Full details may be obtained from I.C.I. Ltd. who issue a detailed brochure on the subject.

There are two types of cement for jointing "Perspex" acrylic materials to themselves. These are: pure solvents (e.g. chloroform, ethylene dichloride, acetic acid) and solutions of methyl methacrylate polymer.

The strength, weathering properties, resistance to the attack of moisture and the ease of preparation of the joints vary with the type of cement used. Joints made with pure solvents are the most easily prepared but give the poorest properties, whereas the cements produce the strongest joints with the best resistance to weathering and moisture, but require more care in preparation.

Most solvents used for jointing acrylic material or preparing acrylic cements may have a toxic effect or may be inflammable. Continuous breathing in of small quantities of the vapour might have a cumulative effect and cause serious illness. Cementing therefore should be carried out in a well-ventilated area in which smoking is prohibited.

An essential feature of the cementing of "Perspex" is that attack by the solvent on the acrylic surface must take place before a satisfactory bond can be obtained. As a result of this attack, the surfaces to be cemented are softened, so that when they are brought together under light pressure they begin to adhere to each other. A curing period is then necessary, during which the solvent in the joint evaporates and disperses within the acrylic material or, with the all-acrylic cements, polymerization takes place. After this curing period, the joint can be handled.

Since solvent attack is an essential feature of the cementing process, it is often necessary to protect the "Perspex" surfaces adjacent to the joint in order to prevent the excess cement flowing over and attacking them.

When making a joint, care must be taken in bringing together the two softened surfaces. This operation should be done gently and without working the two surfaces into one another. Some clamping pressure is necessary to exclude air bubbles, but it should be light and evenly applied.

One of the main difficulties associated with cementing acrylics is to avoid air bubbles within the joint. Careful workmanship, meticulous cleanliness and attention to detail will all help to produce a good joint. One of the important details is to avoid the presence of dissolved air in the cementing medium, which, therefore, should not be shaken immediately before use. Indeed, in many instances, it is desirable to purge the cement of air by evacuation.

5.5.14 Shaping

"Perspex" is a thermoplastic and changes from a rigid to a rubber-like material when heated to high temperatures. In the pliable state it can be shaped by bending or stretching and on cooling will retain that shape to produce a rigid form. The transition from rigidity to rubberiness is not clearly defined but occurs gradually over a wide range of temperatures. The first visible sign is noted at about 85°C. Only at about 120°C., however, does "Perspex" become pliable, but for shaping it is heated to between 150°C. and 170°C.

It is usual to heat the material in an oven, and when it is sufficiently hot, to transfer it to a shaping jig or mould. During the actual shaping operation, the "Perspex" itself is at a uniform temperature in the range 120°C.–150°C.

Shaping may be carried out in a number of ways and it is unnecessary to go into the detail of each. The first essential is obviously a mould but this can be of cheap and simple materials, such as plaster of paris or wood. A female mould is popular but whatever the material, there can be no undercuts which should be kept in mind in designing products.

A heated sheet of "Perspex" is placed over the mould and vacuum is applied to the underside. This pulls the sheet into the shape of the mould. If the mould is of any depth, then the process is "plug assisted", i.e. as the sheet is pulled down a plug (not necessarily to the shape of the object) is pushed in from above.

All methods are similar to the foregoing. A variation is to apply air pressure from above instead of vacuum from below but the result is the same. The methods all require considerable know-how and attention to detail, but the method is basically simple and can produce curved objects without difficulty.

5.6 Plastic Foams for Lagging and Filtration

Some of the detailed properties of plastic foams and suppliers are given in Section 1.3.8 Here it is proposed to provide further information from the point of view mainly of lagging pipes and tanks.

The use of plastic foams for the lagging of pipes and tanks must by now be reasonably familiar to most plumbers. Surprisingly, the method has not been adopted on the scale which one would perhaps have imagined in spite of the convenience of the technique. At this stage of the development of plastic foams, therefore, it is convenient to consider the subject to see what the possibilities really are.

In general, the lagging of pipes is accomplished by wrapping a flexible strip round and round the pipe or fixing shaped lengths to the pipe. In the case of tanks, rigid sheets of polystyrene foam are usually employed and may be strapped or cemented into position.

Another method of application is by spraying. This novel and valuable technique is described in detail in Section 4.4.14.

All types of roofs may be insulated with foamed plastics and specially made sections for eaves are available. Sheets can be used or foam sprayed into place. The sheets may be either nailed on or stuck on with adhesives. (See Section 4.4).

Another minor use of plastic foams in plumbing will already be familiar to plumbers. This is the use of strips of the material to seal the joints between gutters and other parts of rainwater goods. Similar strips may be placed between walls and pedestal basins to avoid any possibility of damage through rocking.

Other uses include filtration and odour exclusion and these will be described.

5.6.1 Filtration

Declon Foam Plastics Ltd. manufacture Scott foams especially for filtration of air or liquids. Polyurethane is the material employed. Such foam filters, apart from their usual properties, have a number of advantages over conventional materials. Virtually no care, for example, is required in handling them and they are much easier to clean than standard products. They may even be washed in water and wrung out.

These foams are made in a number of grades to serve a number of purposes. The porosity ranges from 10 to 80 pores or cells per linear inch. Since most of the filter is air space, it will hold an incredible amount of foreign matter. The effect can be increased by using several layers of material, and thicknesses up to 6 in. (in increments of $\frac{1}{16}$ in.) are available.

It is surprising how many applications there are for foams in filtration. They have already been employed for such purposes as furnaces, swimming pools, air conditioners, industrial panel filters, the precipitation of dusts, the separation of dissimilar liquids and the selective screening of sound waves.

The use of such filters in water circulating systems is an immediate possibility which suggests itself. The corrosion inside pipes used in central heating could easily be prevented from circulating by the use of plastic filters. They would, of course, have to be changed or cleaned periodically but they would nevertheless last a long time. The idea is worth consideration.

5.6.2 Odour Exclusion

No specific examples of odour exclusion can be given but it is known that foamed plastics function very well in this respect. The process is much the same as for dust exclusion and the easiest practical way of using the materials for the purpose is by an adhesive backed strip of the type made by Seal-draught Ltd.

5.6.3 Tank Lagging

Tank-lagging sets are usually sold as five panels comprising two sides, two ends and a lid. Bases are supplied as extras at additional cost. Staples are included and all fitting materials with instructions. The standard material supplied is usually foamed polystyrene 1 in. thick. Details of the standard sizes for metal-type cisterns are given in the following table. Lagging for other size cisterns and cylindrical tanks obviously require other sizes of lagging materials and application should be made to the various suppliers.

Lagging Sets for Standard Cisterns

BS. Size No.	Length, ft.	in.	Width, ft.	in.	Height, ft.	in.
C.1	1	6	1	0	1	0
C.2	2	0	1	0	1	3
C.3	2	0	1	4	1	3
C.4	2	0	1	5	1	5
C.5	2	0	1	6	1	7
C.6	2	3	1	8	1	8
C.7	2	0	2	0	1	7
C.8	2	5	1	10	1	10
C.9	2	6	1	11	2	0
C.10	2	8	2	0	1	11
C.11	3	0	2	0	1	11
C.12	3	0	2	2	2	0
C.13	3	2	2	3	2	3
C.14	4	0	2	0	2	0
C.15	3	2	2	6	2	7
C.16	3	10	2	11	2	11
C.17	5	0	3	0	2	8
C.18	5	0	3	9	3	0
C.19	6	0	4	0	3	4
C.20	6	0	4	0	4	0
C.21	8	0	5	0	4	0

Expanded Rubber and Plastics Ltd. now supply "Polyzote" expanded polystyrene tank-lagging sets to fit the new Osma reinforced plastics water storage cisterns as well as the full range of standard asbestos and galvanized iron tanks.

5.6.4 Pipe Lagging

Both polystyrene and polyurethane foams are employed for lagging pipes. The former, being rigid, is supplied already shaped and has to be strapped to to the pipe in some way. Flexible polyurethane lagging (pre-shaped or in strips) is perhaps more accommodating to awkward bends and corners.

Rigid Types

The types available are best demonstrated with specific examples. "Poron" insulation is supplied in 3 ft. lengths and is for all cold-water pipes and most hot-water systems, although the upper temperature limit is 175°F. The insulation thicknesses supplied as standard are $\frac{1}{2}$, $\frac{3}{4}$, 1, 1$\frac{1}{2}$ and 2 in. The outside diameters of pipes catered for are $\frac{11}{16}$, $\frac{7}{8}$, 1$\frac{1}{16}$, 1$\frac{3}{8}$, 1$\frac{11}{16}$, 1$\frac{7}{8}$, 2$\frac{1}{8}$, 2$\frac{3}{8}$, 2$\frac{5}{8}$ and 3 in. Fixing tape, bands or clips are not included. These products are not usually stuck on by adhesives but by tapes, bands, etc.

Guide to Thickness of Insulation Required

Pipe situation	Cold pipes	Hot pipes
	Minimum thickness, in.	
Unheated or draughty room, passage, corridor or roof space, or space under floor	1	1$\frac{1}{2}$
Normally heated rooms	$\frac{3}{4}$	1
Heated cupboards	$\frac{1}{2}$	$\frac{3}{4}$
Pipes situated outdoors require special attention	1$\frac{1}{2}$	2

"Polyzote" is also available in 3 ft. lengths for the following copper and iron-pipe bore sizes: $\frac{1}{2}$, $\frac{3}{4}$, 1, 1$\frac{1}{4}$, 1$\frac{1}{2}$, 1$\frac{3}{4}$ and 2 in. Other sizes are available to order. Metal fixing bands 8–14 in. long by $\frac{3}{4}$ in. wide can be supplied if required. The lagging is supplied as two shaped halves connected by scrim cloth bonded to the outside as a hinge. Adhesive is not normally used for the main pipe, but it is necessary at bends and for these Bostik 1256 or Tretobond 740 can be used. In the system, bends are lagged by either of two methods, both extremely simple. The "Polyzote" may be cut and mitred to fit the specific requirement; or the bend may be covered using segments of "Polyzote" cut or broken to size, and bound in position with cotton scrim, or with any material to hand.

Flexible Types

"Foamflex" is available in off-white colour in lengths of 9 ft. 9 in. and in sizes to fit pipes of the following nominal bores to comply with BS.1387:1957: $\frac{3}{8}$, $\frac{1}{2}$, $\frac{3}{4}$, 1, 1$\frac{1}{4}$, 1$\frac{1}{2}$, 2, 2$\frac{1}{2}$, 3, 3$\frac{1}{2}$ and 4 in. The depth of cover complies with the requirements of Table 1 of BS.1334:1959.

The material can be fitted both quickly and easily. The sections are supplied slit longitudinally down one side, and are slipped over the pipe.

In order to ensure efficient insulation, it is necessary to seal both the longitudinal and the end joints of "Foamflex". Sealing may be carried out by any one of three methods:—

(1) The use of "Foamflex" adhesive marketed by Semtex, Ltd. Application comprises painting both faces of the joint with the adhesive allowing it to become tacky (approximately 5–10 minutes) and pressing the two surfaces together.

(2) The use of an impact-type adhesive. A wide range of such adhesives is marketed under a variety of trade names.

(3) Self-adhesive pvc tape may be used as a strip sealer over the joints.

The flexibility of "Foamflex" enables it to be carried around slow bends and the material is easily cut to fit bends with sharp internal radii, "T" junctions, etc. No special fittings are necessary. Overpainting is not necessary under conditions of normal hot and cold working, but one coat is sufficient if it is required.

"Raplag" is constructed from foamed polyurethane accurately profiled to ensure a perfect fit when wrapped around the pipe. It is finished with a protective cover of white pvc sheeting (resistant to water, oil and many chemicals) which is provided with a moulded lip along each edge to lock the insulation in place.

The material is suitable for insulating pipes carrying cold and hot water and saturated steam up to 125 p.s.i. (177°C.).

"Raplag" is produced in sizes suitable for $\frac{3}{8}$ in. to 6 in. bore steel pipes (BS.1387:1957) and $\frac{1}{2}$ in. to 2 in. bore copper pipes (BS.659:1955). It is available in two thicknesses—$\frac{3}{4}$ in. and 1 in.—conforming to BS.1334:1959 "Preformed Thermal Insulating Materials for Central Heating and Hot and Cold Water Supply Installations".

In fitting, the exact lengths required can be cut from the standard coil. Slow bends, sockets, unions and other similar fittings can be negotiated in the same manner without cutting or other special preparation. Acute bends, elbows and tee junctions can be covered by simple cutting with a knife or scissors on site. No special tools are required.

Newall's XPS insulation is available for lagging tanks and pipes. Another company producing these products is Warmafoam Ltd.

Other Products

Polyurethane foam backed with adhesive can obviously be of use in a number of places. "Tesamoll" is a self-adhesive plastic foam material, produced in various thicknesses, and in rolls of standard lengths—according to thicknesses. The automatic, continuous methods now employed in the manufacture of the material limit the width of roll in which it can be supplied to $18\frac{1}{2}$ in. The normal range of widths, from $\frac{1}{4}$ in. up to 6 in., is designed to cover most industrial requirements for a continuous strip form with an adhesive backing. The $18\frac{1}{2}$ in. wide material is available to provide sheets of suitable area for stampings and cuttings. "Tesamoll" can be supplied in a range of elementary colours.

A polyvinyl chloride film 0·0015 in.- to 0·0016 in.-thick, with a tensile strength of 22–30 lb./in. of width, is permanently laminated to the foam and forms the carrier for the pressure-sensitive or adhesive mass. The adhesive surface is protected and masked by a grained polyvinylchloride liner, which is also embossed so that it can be easily peeled off as the strip is applied.

Physical Data: Maximum service temperatures (foam) continuous 212°F. dry heat, or 140°F. wet heat. Intermittent, 250°F.;

15

Minimum service temperature (foam)—No reliable information as to limiting factors in lower temperature ranges. Tends to stiffen at 32°F. (freezing) with increasing loss of elasticity roughly proportionate to decrease in temperature. Complete recovery of elasticity on defrosting from 32°F.

The thicknesses of material available include 3 mm., 6 mm. and 9 mm.

5.7 Polyester Plastics for Plumbing
5.7.1 Introduction
The first essential is to define "polyester plastics" and to see why they are, or are likely to be, of value to the plumbing trade. This can only be done by reference to their properties and how they are used (See Section 1.3.7 for brief details).

Basically, a liquid resin is mixed with certain hardeners after which the resin immediately begins to set to a hard infusible product. To give it adequate strength, the resin is reinforced with a glass cloth of some type. The resultant product has excellent chemical resistance and high mechanical strength.

The most important feature is that the process is carried out at room temperature with the simplest of equipment so that with practice, the operation can be carried out in almost any shop with relatively unskilled labour. A wide variety of products can be made by hand, the best known examples being boat hulls and car bodies. As far as plumbing is concerned, water tanks, pipes and rainwater goods have been made in the material. The process is valuable in that a few objects of any desired shape can be made with wooden or plaster moulds. A plumber could, therefore, if he wished, make unusual shapes of cisterns and tanks himself.

There are also many fabricating companies who make up such products and will usually undertake prototype work. The techniques have not yet been adopted extensively by the plumbing trade but they could well be with advantage. The object of the present section is, therefore, to outline the subject so that the full potentialities will be appreciated.

A typical fabricating company is Wembley Fibreglass and Plastics Ltd.

5.7.2 General Principles
Polyester resins are thermosetting with all that this implies. The first interesting feature about the materials is that they are self-coloured. When being made, any colour can be introduced into the mix and it will last the life of the product. Painting is therefore unnecessary.

The second feature is the chemical resistance. This does not only mean that the products can be used with corrosive chemicals but that in the presence of water they do not deteriorate in any way. In addition, they are excellent from the weather resistance point of view even in marine conditions. In this connection they are resistant to attack by sea organisms which accounts for their use as boat hulls. They also resist other growths and can therefore be used in the dampest atmospheres.

Thermal insulation is good which means that to a certain extent, tanks and pipes will be self lagging. Mechanical properties are excellent. This is indicated in comparison with some other structural materials:

Material	Specific Gravity	Tensile Strength, lb. per sq. in.	Comparative Strength on strength/weight basis
Polyester-glass cloth	1·7	51,000	30·0
Steel	7·8	128,000	16·4
Duralumin	2·8	64,000	22·9
Wood (Douglas fir)	0·5	10,000	20·0

The advantages and disadvantages of reinforced polyester plastics may be summarized as follows:

(a) Quite large and complex shapes can be readily and cheaply moulded. The process is slow compared with pressed steel, but the outlay for moulds is negligible by comparison.

(b) There is considerable freedom of design.

(c) The products are resilient and not bent by a blow. However, they are not as rigid as metals and large objects should be reinforced with ribs.

(d) The cost of the raw material is higher than that of steel but this is offset by the cost of moulds and the relatively unskilled labour which can be used.

(e) They have much the best chemical and weathering resistance.

5.7.3 Suppliers

Detailed lists of suppliers of the various ingredients will be given later, but some of the companies in the U.K. manufacturing polyester resins are: Scott Bader and Co. Ltd., British Resin Products Ltd., Beck, Koller and Co. (England) Ltd., and Bakelite, Ltd.

Any of these concerns will supply detailed literature but, in particular, attention may be drawn to two excellent books provided by the manufacturing companies. These are "Cellobond Polyester Resins", supplied by British Resin Products Ltd. and "Polyester Handbook" supplied by Scott Bader and Co. Ltd.

The companies will also sell small quantities of materials for experimental purposes, but Scott Bader also sell an "experimental kit" containing $2\frac{1}{2}$ lb. of resin and appropriate curing ingredients.

5.7.4 The Materials

The principal ingredient is the resin. One important characteristic of this is the viscosity since, if the material is too thick it is difficult to apply to the glass cloth, and if too thin it will run off sloping or vertical surfaces. Medium viscosity resins are best but others can be purchased to give any degree of flow desired. A suitable resin by British Resin Products, Ltd. is Cellobond A2652 and a Scott Bader resin is Crystic 189.

A typical cold-setting formulation is:

	Parts by weight
Resin	100
Catalyst	2–4
Accelerator	1–4

The catalyst hardens up the resin and the accelerator assists with reaction. Catalyst Paste H and Accelerator E are available from Scott Bader and Cellobond Catalyst X7764 and Cellobond Promotor X7761 (the same as the accelerator) from British Resin Products Ltd. The varying proportions of catalyst and accelerator ingredients are given in the formula as an increase in these materials speeds up the setting time.

In making up, the catalyst should be mixed with the resin. After blending, the accelerator may be added but the accelerator and catalyst should never be mixed together first. The mix then rapidly sets, which means that no more than is required for the immediate job should be mixed. It will have a "pot life" of about half-an-hour.

The final principal ingredient is the glass. This can be used as a cloth but it is expensive in this form. The usual material employed is chopped strand mat, a random collection of chopped glass strands bonded together. The strength is not quite as high as with cloth, but is still very good and it is the material used in cars, ships, chemical tanks and the like. Two suppliers are:

> Fibreglass Ltd.
> Fothergill and Harvey Ltd.

Other ingredients are added for various purposes but most of them need be of no concern during early work. The only exception is the colours. To assist dispersion in the resin, these are available in the form of pastes from Scott Bader and Ferro Enamels Ltd.

5.7.5   Outline of the Process

It is proposed to give a more detailed description of the various processes later, but a brief résumé at this point will illustrate the simplicity with which articles can be made.

The most common process is the "wet lay-up" method. A layer of glass mat is laid on the mould (which needs to be treated in various ways) after which it is impregnated with the resin mixture by means of a brush. A further layer of glass is then added, followed by more resin and then more glass until the desired thickness is built up. The action of wetting the glass with the resin makes it take the shape of the mould.

The resultant product is allowed to stand for about an hour during which time it sets quite hard. It may then be removed from the mould and matured by allowing to stand at room temperature for seven days or by heating at 80°C. for three hours.

The process really is as simple as it sounds, although naturally experience is required to get the best results. An existing metal tank may be used as a mould, or a pipe made by wrapping glass round a metal pipe and impregnating with resin.

5.7.6   Physical Properties

The high strength of mouldings made in the way mentioned will illustrate the great potentiality of the materials.

Physical Properties of Reinforced Polyesters

Property	Value
Specific Gravity	1·5–1·6
Compression Strength	18,000–25,000 lb. per sq. in.
Tensile Strength	16,000–25,000 lb. per sq. in.
Impact Strength, Izod. (ft. lb./in. of notch)	10–20
Coefficient of linear expansion	12–15 $\times$ 10^{-6} per °C.
Thermal Conductivity (cal./sec./cm./°C./cm.²)	2–3 $\times$ 10^{-5}

The physical properties given were achieved with chopped glass mat as the reinforcement. The materials are also good electrically with a volume resistivity of 10^{14}—10^{15} ohm. cm.

5.7.7 The Moulds

The moulds used for the manufacture of polyester articles can range from extremely simple types and to elaborate and expensive ones. The great majority of work is carried out in the former and is the only one considered here.

A simple mould is sometimes available in an existing product. Thus a metal tank can be reproduced in polyester, the same applying to a porcelain cistern. If a special mould has to be made, however, then wood or plaster of paris will be perfectly adequate. In the former case, laminated blocks are usually employed, using methods employed by pattern makers.

The simplest material to use is plaster of paris, preferably of the "low expansion" type. Backing materials are normally employed to give strength, or the plaster can be reinforced with such fillers as sisal or jute. Various resins, particularly urea formaldehyde types, will give hardness, strength and water resistance. A suitable composition is:—

	Parts by weight
Plaster of paris	100
Urea resin	50
Hardener	5
Water	50

The resin, hardener and water are first mixed together, followed by the addition of plaster. This may then be used for the preparation of the mould.

Where wooden or plaster moulds are employed, the surfaces have to be prepared before use with polyester resins. This is because they are porous and it would be impossible to remove the mouldings from them. Similarly, even in the case of metal moulds, bonding will occur and mould lubricants are essential. In the case of the wood or plaster, a cellulose acetate or other lacquer should be employed to give a hard, smooth surface. The mould lubricant to be employed on top of the lacquer is a solution of polyvinyl alcohol in water. Most companies selling the resins sell suitable lubricants of this type. The entire surface of the mould must be covered with this lubricant every time the mould is used.

5.7.8   The Gel Coat

It was mentioned earlier that the article is made essentially by the use of a layer of resin followed by a layer of glass and so on. This is true but before the application of the materials used in the moulding, a coating of pure resin is applied. This is known as the gel coat.

It is advisable to employ a gel coat with all mouldings. The main functions which it performs are that:—

(1) It gives a continuous resin film on the outside which protects the glass and thus stops the ingress of moisture.
(2) Without the gel coat, the fibre pattern of the glass shows through; this is hidden by the gel coat.
(3) The gel coat can be employed for imparting the colour and giving special properties such as improved abrasion resistance.

A suitable gel coat composition based on Scott Bader products is:

	Parts by weight
Crystic Resin	60
Crystic Pregel 17	40
Catalyst Paste H	4
Accelerator E	4
Pigment Paste	4

The Crystic Pregel is added to a normal resin to increase the viscosity, which means that the gel coat will not flow so much on inclined surfaces. The proportion may be considerably reduced for horizontal surfaces. To avoid cracking, the coat should not exceed $0 \cdot 010$ in. in thickness and may be applied by brush, roller or special-type spray equipment.

5.7.9   The Moulding Proper

The basic moulding process is known as contact moulding or the "wet lay-up" process. The main point of this process is that the moulding can be laid-up by simple methods and cured in the cold without equipment if required. There are more complicated methods employing expensive equipment, but these are rarely used and are not considered here.

As mentioned previously, mould lubricants should be applied to the mould followed by the gel coat. The resin for the moulding itself should be applied as soon as possible after the gel coat has hardened so that there is good adhesion between the gel coat and the main body of the moulding. Before any laying-up begins, the chopped strand mat should be tailored to the correct size and shape.

The first process is to apply a liberal coat of resin with a brush or roller. The first layer of glass is then laid on this and it is immediately wetted by the resin. By stippling with a saturated brush, the glass mat readily takes the shape of the mould. The glass is now thoroughly impregnated with resin and then rolled to consolidate. Another layer of glass may then be applied followed by more resin and so on.

The assembly is now allowed to harden on the mould and this may take a few hours. It is then removed from the mould and allowed to mature at room temperature for a minimum period of 24 hours. If the whole curing process is to be undertaken at room temperature, then the process will take from two to four weeks. This is usually too long and the same degree of cure can be achieved in about three hours at 80°C.

5.7.10 Equipment and Suppliers

The resin compositions are best mixed in polythene utensils as this avoids adhesion between the composition and the vessel. Suitable items can be obtained from Vicsons, Ltd.

Obviously, any satisfactory type of brush may be employed, but special rollers are preferable. These may be obtained from K. and C. Mouldings (England) Ltd. or Paythem Engineering Co. Ltd.

The resin may be sprayed on, employing chopped glass fibre. Suitable spray equipment may be obtained from Metropolitan Plastics Ltd. or General Developments Ltd.

The urea resins mentioned may be obtained from Leicester, Lovell and Co. Ltd. Mixing equipment is available from the Daines Organization.

Some slight danger exists in that the materials used in the resins may cause irritation to the skin. The use of one of the well-known barrier creams is therefore strongly recommended. The catalysts employed are very irritating to the skin and will cause burns if not washed off immediately. They may also ignite combustible materials if they are sprayed on to them after standing for some time. Care must obviously be exercised in such matters. No special ventilation requirements are necessary provided workshops are roomy and adequately ventilated in the normal way.

5.7.11 Machining

After the moulding is fully cured, it will need to be trimmed. The edges are usually rough and ragged because of the glass fibres.

Abrasive discs and wheels are recommended for cutting wherever possible. This is because mouldings are not easy to cut or machine and will quickly blunt most of the usual steel tools. For this reason, carbide tipped tools should always be used. In machining the laminated plastics, care should be taken to clamp them tightly as close to the cutting line as possible. If this is not done, a certain amount of delamination may occur. Water is not recommended as a lubricant and over-heating must be avoided by regulating machining speeds.

Holes up to about $\frac{3}{8}$ in. diameter can be drilled with twist drills but above this size cutters are recommended. The drilling should be started on the gel coat side. There should be efficient dust extraction as the dust may be injurious to the health of the operator.

In general, it may be assumed that the polyester laminates will be much the same as metals in their working characteristics. The appropriate equipment and spacing of holes etc. should therefore be chosen on this principle.

5.7.12   Chemical Properties

It should be stressed that the resistance of polyester resins to chemicals will depend on the degree of cure, the type of resin and filler. In addition, the higher the temperature, the greater the rate of attack. The figures given in the following Table, therefore, may be taken to be very general in nature.

Before giving these figures, it may be stated that the resins are quite unaffected by water. This is irrespective of whether it is distilled, tap or sea water. These statements apply whether the temperature is 20°C. or 50°C. It is useful to know that detergents do not affect the resins.

Material	Degree of Attack	
	20°C.	50°C.
Acetic acid concentrated	2	2
Acetone	3	—
Ammonium hydroxide	3	—
Benzene	2	—
Carbon tetrachloride	0	—
Ethyl alcohol	1	2
Ethylene glycol	1	2
Formaldehyde	1	—
Hydrochloric acid concentrated	1	2
Lactic acid	0	—
Methyl ethyl ketone	3	—
Nitric acid (25%)	2	2
Paraffin	0	—
Petroleum ether	0	—
Potassium hydroxide	3	—
Sodium hydoxide 20%	2	3
Sulphuric acid (up to 30%)	0	—
Sodium hypochlorite	1	—
White spirit	0	—
Toluene	0	—
Zinc chloride solution	0	—
Photographic solution	1	—

0 = No attack for indefinite use. 1 = Slight surface attack or discoloration but will probably last for some years. 2 = More serious attack so that the product cannot be used for long periods. 3 = Severe attack and is unsatisfactory for use.

5.7.13   Conclusions

The details given for the manufacture of articles from polyester plastics on a small scale will show that the process is relatively simple. If, however, large-scale manufacture is attempted, additional refinements will be required and details should be obtained from the manufacturers already mentioned.

Once having established the process, the manufacturer may use his ingenuity in devising new techniques. For example, a mould would be made as already described for the manufacture of a cistern. The same process, however, can be employed for making a polyester pipe of any diameter. In this case, it is sufficient to take a cast-iron pipe, clean the surface, apply a mould release lubricant, apply a gel coat and then resin, followed by wrapping glass round the pipe with more resin and so on. In this way, a perfectly satisfactory and highly chemical-resistant plastic pipe can be made.

Manufacturers

The following are some of the firms who manufacture polyester-glass products for the plumbing trade:

Osma Plastics Ltd. (Tanks and rainwater goods);

Shanks and Co. Ltd. (Panels to match baths);

Elsy and Gibbons Ltd. (Tanks);

Wembley Fibreglass and Plastics Ltd. (Tanks, pipes, bath panels, etc.);

Fibreglass Reinforced Plastics Ltd.;

B.T.R. Industries Ltd. (Tanks);

Thermotank Plastics Ltd. (Shower cabinets).

The Osma 10-gallon glass fibre tank. Free from corrosion, rust and fungus growth and weighing only 5 lb., it is ideal for storage of most organic and inorganic acids and has excellent resistance to oils, solutions and solvents. It carries a 10-year guarantee (*Osma Plastics Ltd*)

Some details of the tanks made by Osma Plastics Ltd., are given in Section 5.4.

Prodorite Ltd. fabricate pipes and tanks from Orglas resin/glass laminates.

5.8   Miscellaneous

5.8.1   Protecting Tanks

Plastics can be used in a number of ways to protect metal tanks from corrosion. One of the most common is the use of a rigid pvc liner which is "welded" into a continuous covering. Another method is to dip in pvc pastes

(Section 5.3.13) and yet another is to paint with special resins, particularly epoxy and polyester types. As far as epoxy types are concerned (see also Sections 1.3.6 and 2.4) a specific example of an installation will illustrate the principles involved.

Access to aluminium fuel tanks in marine craft and their frequent inspection is usually difficult. In certain climatic conditions condensation and salt air will often penetrate the normal protective film covering the tanks and cause corrosion. A situation such as this was experienced with the aluminium fuel tanks installed in Royal Air Force rescue-target-towing launches, particularly those located with overseas units.

To solve the problem, work was undertaken on behalf of the Air Ministry by Vospers Ltd. and Leicester, Lovell and Co. Ltd., resulting in the development of a lightweight sheathing using epoxide resin and glass cloth. Complete sets of new tanks have been covered by Vospers Ltd. with this lightweight sheathing, and kits of these materials have also been made up and despatched by the Air Ministry to their overseas R.A.F. marine craft units for the sheathing of fuel tanks already installed in operational craft. The fact that kits of resin components can be made up in this way illustrates how versatile and relatively simple the process is. It can also be carried out on site if necessary.

A stage in the sheathing of an aluminium tank. Note the glass cloth being draped over on the left and the difference in colour between the first and second coats of epoxide resin (*Leicester Lovell & Co Ltd*)

The severity of the problem can be judged by the fact that the tanks measured approximately $6\frac{1}{2} \times 6 \times 3$ ft. and had a capacity of 640 gallons of 110–130 high-octane petroleum spirit. They are of welded construction in Grade N.S.3 aluminium. Corrosion appears to occur when the tanks are exposed to ambient temperatures of between 32°C. and 38°C. and in the worst condition, a third of the thickness of the aluminium may be eaten away.

A number of these fuel tanks are in service in various parts of the world and the two companies mentioned developed an efficient surface coating that could be applied with comparative ease by non-specialist personnel. Air Ministry specifications also required a surface coating that could withstand the considerable vibrations that occurs when launches are propelled at high speed.

The plastic used was epoxide resin, Epophen 1318, used with a low-viscosity hardener and reinforced with a glass cloth having a wide mesh size (MRGLAS 113S/P703). The low viscosity of the hardener ensures ease of application and helps to overcome any tendency for the resin to flow on vertical surfaces and cause wrinkling. The wide mesh of the glass cloth enables it to be draped around complex curvatures without rucking.

In the process, the tank is first etched, primed with "Double One" primer supplied by Docker Bros. Ltd. and this is followed by a single coat of resin. When this has set, the surface is "scuffed" with sandpaper. A second coat of resin is then applied and on to this is laid the glass cloth which is thoroughly impregnated with a third coat of resin. This completes the operation. The second and third coats of resin are pigmented black which assists visual determination that painting has been complete over the whole surface. It also enhances the finished appearance.

In the case of plastic liners, Plastic Liners Ltd. manufacture suitable products. These are welded as already mentioned and the liners have been tested and passed by the British Waterworks Association and many other building and water authorities. Sizes include those for 40, 50, 60, 70, 80 and 100 gallon containers.

There are a number of plastics which can be used for lining purposes and one of these is "Saran" (polyvinylidene chloride). Pipes, fittings, valves and pumps are lined with the material to give exceptional chemical resistance. One company doing this is:

J. and T. Lawrie Ltd.

5.8.2   PTFE for Jointing

This remarkable development has really revolutionized pipe jointing. Although the material is thermoplastic it has a wide temperature range, is the most inert substance known, and has a low coefficient of friction which is very valuable for screwing up and unscrewing joints which can be accomplished no matter how old the joint.

The tape is wrapped round the screw threads of any steam, gas (oxygen excluded in the case of certain tapes), chemical or water system and, on pressure exerted by the thread, forms a permanent seal. The following are some of the manufacturers:

Turner Brothers Asbestos Co. Ltd.;	Henry Crossley Packings, Ltd.; James Walker and Co. Ltd.
Uni-Tubes Ltd.;	

The following particulars refer to the PTFE tape known as "Kopex" manufactured by Uni-Tubes Ltd.

(1) Threads and joints can be effectively sealed in a matter of seconds without any mess, fuss or danger of contamination by toxic compounds.

(2) In use, the joint is completely sealed, unaffected by all the chemicals, gases, acids and solvents to which "Kopex" PTFE tape is resistant.

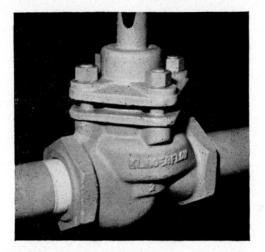

Using PTFE tape for sealing pipe threads (*Richard Klinger Ltd*)

(3) The joint can withstand the same temperature range as the PTFE material—
−60°C. to +250°C.

(4) Because of its unsintered nature, "Kopex" tape will mould itself to any thread
material, large or small in section or diameter.

(5) The low coefficient of friction is such that joints are seizure-proof during
connection and can withstand pressures of many thousands of p.s.i. if need be.

(6) After lengthy periods of constant use, joints can easily be broken and the tape
used again and again.

(7) The tape is just as effective on imperfect threads and can be used with all types
of materials, including steel, stainless steel, aluminium, copper, brass, ceramics
or plastic piping whether flexible or rigid.

It is proving particularly useful in the chemical, aircraft, and missile fields
where corrosive or contaminated materials, plus extremes of temperatures,
present problems that hitherto have been unsolvable with other materials.

The tape is manufactured in the following widths and thicknesses: Widths
from 0·25 to 1·5 in.; thicknesses from 0·003 to 0·010 in.

A simple hand dispenser, which can be kept in a tool kit, is usually employed
to carry this tape.

Part 6

INTERIOR FITTINGS

CONTENTS

6.1 **"Perspex" Lighting Fittings**

6.2 **"Perspex" Signs and Displays**

6.3 **Electrical Fittings**

6.4 **Miscellaneous Accessories**
  6.4.1 Door Furniture and Shutter Knobs ("Perspex")
  6.4.2 "Perspex" Ventilators
  6.4.3 Door and Lock Mechanisms (Nylon)
  6.4.4 Other Nylon Products

6.5 **Kitchen and Bathroom Furniture**

6.6 **PVC Handrails**

6.7 **Ventilation Systems**
  6.7.1 Chemical Resistance of Rigid PVC
  6.7.2 Design and Installation

6.8 **Telephone Kiosks**

Part 6

INTERIOR FITTINGS

Interior fittings, based on plastics, range from light switches to ventilation ducting and some of the products, particularly signs and displays, are also suitable for use out-of-doors.

The following are the sections in Part 6:

6.1 "Perspex" Lighting Fittings
6.2 "Perspex" Signs and Displays
6.3 Electrical Fittings
6.4 Miscellaneous Accessories
6.5 Kitchen and Bathroom Furniture
6.7 Ventilation Systems
6.8 Telephone Kiosks

6.1 "Perspex" Lighting Fittings

The excellent optical properties of "Perspex" is discussed in some detail in Section 4.2.1. More information is given in Section 6.2.

In industry, "Perspex", with its range of reflecting and transmitting opals, has led to its wide use for reflectors and diffusers for both fluorescent and metal filament fittings. The material does not chip or discolour in service and is unlikely to be broken in installation and maintenance. It particularly assists with the upward deflection of light on the ceilings and roofs. With opal "Perspex" reflectors, the upward component of light is uniformly diffused and contrast glare at the edge of the fittings is eliminated.

Fluorescent tube lighting is now widely used in offices, factories and show-rooms and to a lesser degree in dwelling houses and flats. A number of plastic fittings are available for these, including urea and melamine formaldehyde types, but "Perspex" is pre-eminent. There are simple inverted trough reflectors, decorative diffusing enclosing bowls and many others, since the ease with which the material may be shaped enables products of almost any design to be made.

Individual fittings are now giving way to built-in lighting systems and "Perspex" offers many advantages for these. They are light in weight thus simplifying installation, the optical consistency eliminates irregularity in appearance and in even the largest area there is adequate diffusion without loss of illumination. Panels can be supplied in a variety of shapes and designs and they are easy to clean. The material requires no framing and can be drilled for fixing which presents designers with great opportunities for exercising their skill.

The following is a selected, but by no means comprehensive, list of suppliers of commercial and industrial fluorescent lighting fittings:

Arrow Plastics Ltd.,
Richard Daleman Ltd.,
R. Denny and Co. Ltd.,

Revo Electric Co. Ltd.,
R. A. and G. Crosland Ltd.,
Clarke, Chapman and Co. Ltd.,

General Plastics Ltd.,
Suntex Safety Glass Industries Ltd.,
Thermo Plastics Ltd.,
Wokingham Plastics Ltd.,
Splintex Ltd.,
S. C. Errington (Hanwell) Ltd.,
Moon Aircraft Ltd.,
A.E.I. Lamp and Lighting Ltd.,
G.E.C. Lighting Equipment Ltd.,
Harris and Sheldon Display Ltd.,

Milton Engineering Co. Ltd.,
Northern Plastics Ltd.,
Orbex Ltd.,
Arnoplast Ltd.,
Thorn Electrical Industries Ltd.,
Atlas Lighting Ltd.,
Courtenay Pope Ltd.,
Crompton Parkinson Ltd.,
W. J. Cox (Sales) Ltd.,
Merchant Adventurers Ltd.

Suppliers of domestic lighting fittings are:

X-Lon Products (Proprietors: Pan-Ocean Ltd.),
Clearex Products Ltd.,
Plus Lighting Ltd.,
Knightshades Ltd.,
Troughton and Young (Lighting) Ltd.,
Oswald Hollman Ltd.,
Falks Ltd.,
Linolite Ltd.,
Fulford Brown Bros. Ltd.,

Maison Fittings,
Wraithe Bros. Ltd.,
Thorn Electrical Industries Ltd.,
Knight Electrics (Neon) Ltd.,
Cabot Signs Ltd.,
Kings Plastics Ltd.,
Austin Walters & Son Ltd.,
Ward and Co. (Lathes) Ltd.,
Acrylic Industries Ltd.,
Pearce Signs Ltd.

6.2   "Perspex" Signs and Displays

The use of "Perspex" for signs (illuminated and otherwise) is based on its unusual optical characteristics. It lends itself to the exploitation of the phenomenon of total internal reflection. The critical angle for a "Perspex"-air boundary is approximately 42°, so that quite a wide beam of light can be accepted and efficiently transmitted through long lengths of solid "Perspex". Light can be "piped" in this way around curves, but to prevent excessive light loss the radius of curvature should not be less than three times the thickness of the sheet or diameter of the rod. It is important that the surface be highly polished and free from scratches or surface defects as these will cause scattering of the light and reduce the efficiency of the system.

In practice, this means that if a sheet of "Perspex" has a design etched on its surface and light is piped into an *edge* then the design will glow. Alternatively, pressed "Perspex" letters may be cemented on to an opal "Perspex" background. Some examples of use are as follow:

(1) A Marks and Spencer sign with "Perspex" letters and metallized on the inside.

(2) Box letters of the word "Coca-Cola" in Piccadilly Circus are fabricated by bending and sticking Opal 040 "Perspex". The "C's" are about 10 ft. high.

(3) Many directional signs illuminated from below such as "cashier", "toilets", etc.

Manufacturers include:

The London Sand Blast Decorative Glass Works Ltd.

William J. Cox (Sales) Ltd.

6.3 Electrical Fittings

The best known electrical goods are moulded switches, plugs, sockets, lighting fittings, fuse boxes and the like. These are usually made from phenolics (dark colours), or urea or melamine formaldehyde plastics. The latter are worth noting by the architect as they can be made in almost any colour, although cream is common. These thermosetting plastics have good electrical properties, with adequate mechanical strength, low moisture absorption and of attractive design.

Electrical fittings made in plastics are supplied by the following companies:

Ashley Accessories Ltd.,
G. H. Scholes and Co. Ltd.,
J. A. Crabtree and Co. Ltd.,
Raydex Ltd.,
Henry Allday and Son (1922), Ltd.,
Charlesworth Mouldings Ltd.,
Adie Manufacturing Co. Ltd.,
Crater Products Ltd.,
M. K. Electric Ltd.,
Marbourn Ltd.,

F. W. Maul and Son Ltd.,
Monogram Electric,
Ranton and Co. Ltd.,
W. J. Sharplin Ltd.,
Smith Meters Ltd.,
J. G. Statter and Co. Ltd.,
S. G. Young (Rolls Switches),
A.E.I. (Woolwich) Ltd.,
Midland Electric Manufacturing
    Co. Ltd.

There is an increasing tendency to use pvc pipes and fittings for electrical conduit in spite of the fact that such pipes cannot be used for earthing.

Manufacturers are Falks Ltd. and Ega Electric Ltd.

6.4 Miscellaneous Accessories

The few products described in this section will serve to illustrate the versatility in the application of plastics.

6.4.1 Door Furniture and Shutter Knobs ("Perspex")

These are usually made in transparent "Perspex", because of its attractiveness and robustness. Various cut shapes and designs give a most pleasing appearance. The objects include handles (for mortice or rim locks), pulls, drawer and shutter knobs and finger plates.

Suppliers include Evered and Co. Ltd., William J. Cox (Sales) Ltd. and Albion Crystalcut Ltd.

6.4.2 "Perspex" Ventilators

These ventilators have an attractive appearance and high light transmission. Their low weight means that they can be fixed during glazing to frames without additional pinning. The ventilators are made in sizes to suit window frames and are usually in clear material although colours (transparent and translucent) are also supplied. Such ventilators are, of course, much stronger than glass.

A typical supplier is Plastic Designers Ltd.

Glass fibre roof extract units are made by Fenton Byrn and Co. Ltd.

16

6.4.3   Door and Lock Mechanisms (Nylon)

The properties which allow nylon to replace metals for certain applications are: great strength and stiffness, low coefficient of friction, good wearing resistance and silent action.

Articles manufactured from nylon include lock mechanisms (catch-bolt, dead-bolt and key), window hinge bearing faces, handles, wheels for garage sliding doors and runners of all kinds.

Suppliers include Yale and Tourne Ltd., Harrison (Birmingham) Brass Foundry Ltd. and Chubb and Sons Ltd.

Various moulded door fittings are available from Healey Mouldings Ltd.

6.4.4   Other Nylon Products

These include inserts for nuts to grip the bold thread (Plastic Engineers Ltd.), and nylon nuts and screws (Guest, Keen and Nettlefold Ltd.).

6.5   Kitchen and Bathroom Furniture

The only furniture referred to here is the type required by builders for fitted kitchens and perhaps bathrooms. As far as plastics are concerned, their main application is in working tops and the fronts of sliding doors to cabinets. Colour and durability are two outstanding reasons for using plastics, which are normally the decorative laminate type or polyesters. Some examples are given below.

North British Plastics Ltd.

Manufacturers of "Panax" decorative melamine laminate particularly suitable for kitchens and bathroom fittings. Sizes, in feet, are: 9 × 4; 8 × 4; 4 × 3 and 3 × 2.

For use in bathrooms the colours available are: Z504 dark green zamba, C104 grey coarse linen, F153 green fine linen.

For kitchens: Z501 red zamba, F152 blue fine linen, Z503 blue zamba, F151 buff fine linen.

Tayanbee Joinery Ltd.

Manufacturers of wall cupboards, floor cupboards, sliding door cabinets and shelf units. Facings are normal or plastic.

Hygena Ltd.

Responsible for a wide range of attractive kitchen furniture, with "Formica" used as the working top. The following are the standard "Formica" colours:

Suntone yellow softglow; dove grey softglow; charcoal capri; chicory green; polar white; wedgwood blue.

Additional colours will be provided at a slight premium, and at a further increase it is possible to have the material L-shaped or for corner tops.

Blue Gate Products Ltd.

This company supplies various floor units ("Cresta") faced with polyester. A kitchen unit employing the same material is also supplied to the following specifications:

Colours: Drawers white unless otherwise specified. Doors in white, primrose, blue, red, mist-brown or grey. Cream or green is not supplied in polyester but can be supplied in cellulose. *Carcase Colours:* Painted white or cream inside and outside of units. Other colours can be supplied at extra charge. *Tops:* Laminated melamine plastic in grey, mahogany woodgrain, yellow tuscany, red or blue romany. Other colours and continuous working tops over two or more units can be supplied for an extra charge. Extension tops to go over washing machines or other units are available and all tops are fitted with a plastic back-splash. Where continuous work tops are not required for floor units, a black plastic strip is available to seal the joint between two units.

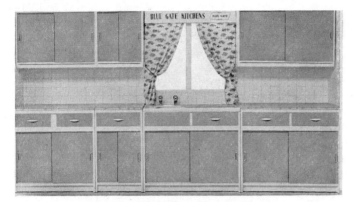

Kitchen furniture topped with laminated melamine (*Blue Gate Products Ltd*)

Prestige Furniture Ltd.

Manufacturer of "Prestige" kitchen furniture which uses plastic laminates (fully edged) in grey, blue, yellow or red.

W. H. Paul Ltd.

This company manufactures "Derby" kitchen units. The working tops of the floor cabinets are in "Formica" or "Warerite". The cabinets are finished both inside and outside with a sprayed-on "Granyte" plastic coating—a beautiful surface which is easy to keep clean and is virtually scratchproof and highly resistant to the effects of detergents, boiling water, fats, greases and the everyday alkalis and acids encountered in the modern kitchen. This hard-wearing finish will not chip or peel in a humid atmosphere.

Other Suppliers

Among other concerns in this field are:—

W. and G. Sissons Ltd. ("Formica" and "Warerite" worktops);
Eastham Thomas and Co. Ltd. (Kitchen cabinet with polystyrene interior);
F. Hills and Sons Ltd. (Toilet cubicles—faced melamine boards);
Ekco Plastics Ltd. (Sink-drainer in polypropylene);
English Rose Kitchens Ltd. (Worktops and cabinet surfaces in "Arborite");
Easiclene Porcelain Enamel (1938) Ltd. (Kitchen units topped with "Formica");
Home Woodworkers Ltd.;

Austins of East Ham Ltd.;
Ever-Tidy Kitchen Cabinets Ltd.;
Dennis and Robinson Ltd. (Laminated tops);
County Furniture (London) Ltd. ("Fablonite" tops);
W. Lusty and Sons Ltd. (Laminate tops);
J. T. Ellis and Co. Ltd. ("Formica" tops);
Grovewood Co. (pvc-faced products);
Dahl Brothers Ltd. ("Formica" tops).

6.6   PVC Handrails

Plastic handrails have a number of advantages over conventional types of which the following are the more important:—
Absolute smoothness—no danger of splinters.
Indefinite length possible (because of invisible welding).
Wide range of inherent colours.
The rails can be turned in any direction without using different sections, i.e. the rail can be shaped by the application of heat.
Ease of cleaning and thus hygienic.

"Osmarail," a tough PVC handrail is available in 14 contemporary colours. It is designed to fit the three main standard sizes of metal core rail and will give trouble-free service (*Osma Plastics Ltd*)

Examples of such products are as follow:

Semtex Ltd.

Semtex pvc handrail accommodates all bends without jointing and is made to fit rectangular core rails, wood or metal, of 2 in. $\times$ $\frac{3}{8}$ in., 2 in. $\times$ $\frac{1}{4}$ in., $1\frac{1}{2}$ in. $\times$ $\frac{3}{8}$ in., and $1\frac{1}{2}$ in. $\times$ $\frac{1}{4}$ in. sections. Semtex handrail is supplied in rolls of 60 ft. in a choice of six colours and offers an attractive new note for blocks of flats, houses, offices, stores or wherever a handrail is employed.

The Marley Tile Co. Ltd.

"Marleyrail", a vinyl handrail, leads up to new thoughts in staircase and balustrade design. Architects and designers are able to conceive curves and end finishes that have been hitherto impossible. In multi-storey blocks and small private homes "Marleyrail" is negotiating wreaths and bends of every type without jointing as it is flexible.

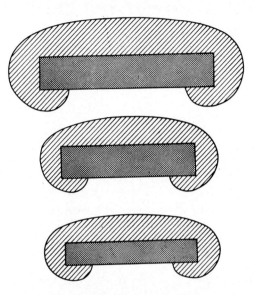

PVC "**Marleyrails**" (*The Marley Tile Co Ltd*)

Colours available are: Metallic blue MR.8; bronze MR.1; metallic green MR.6; pewter MR.3; red MR.4; brown MR.7; grey MR.5; black MR.2.

"Marleyrail" is supplied in 60-ft. rolls but greater lengths are made possible by invisible welding. The three sizes of "Marleyrail" are made to fit rectangular metallic or wooden core rails of 2 in. by $\frac{3}{8}$ in., 2 in. $\times \frac{1}{4}$ in., $1\frac{1}{2}$ in. $\times \frac{3}{8}$ in. and $1\frac{1}{2}$ in. $\times \frac{1}{4}$ in.

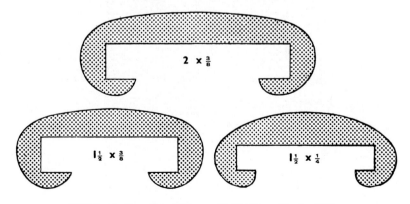

PVC handrail sections ("**Osmarails**") (*Osma Plastics Ltd*)

Osma Plastics Ltd.

The pvc handrail is supplied on $1\frac{1}{2} \times \frac{1}{4}$ in. stove-enamelled steel core rail. It is available in lengths (at 1 ft. intervals) from 3 to 15 ft. with ends capped and slightly dipped to enhance its appearance.

Sizes in inches (inside): $2 \times \frac{3}{8}$; $1\frac{1}{2} \times \frac{3}{8}$ and $1\frac{1}{2} \times \frac{1}{4}$. Colours: Black, grey, grott blue, saxe blue, quartz green, russet green, scarlet red, orange rust. Supplementary colours: Mid grey, gold, red, metallic blue, metallic green, metallic silver.

Other Suppliers

Other suppliers of pvc handrails are:

The Safety Tread Ltd. (This company manufactures "End-urail" in nine colours with end caps to match or contrast).

The Birmingham Guild Ltd.
Garland Ltd.
Holmsund Flooring Ltd.

6.7 Ventilation Systems

Ventilation systems based on pvc offer a number of important advantages over conventional systems of which the most important are lightness (for suspension overhead), chemical resistance, quietness, thermal properties and flexibility of the products and their ease of installation.

An example of the system is the use of I.C.I.'s "Darvic" and "Corvic" brands of pvc as used by A. B. Plastics Ltd. (Burn Brothers), in their well-known "Terrain" system.

Detailed view of the extraction system ducting fabricated from "Darvic" PVC sheet by Man Mill Plastics Ltd for Brightside Heating & Engineering Co Ltd and installed in Hide Tower, a 23-storey block of flats in Hide Place, Westminster, built for the Westminster City Council (*Imperial Chemical Industries Ltd*)

PVC was specified for the extract hood and ducting for the Chemistry Laboratories of Wilson Grammar School at Camberwell.

The use of this material, together with the inherent flexibility of the "Terrain" system, enabled several original features to be incorporated. These included sliding shutters in each fume cupboard, enabling the rate of extraction from the low-level high-velocity slot and the top of the hood to be balanced against the high-level extraction point, and clear panels to be incorporated in the side of the hood to provide illumination to the interior of the cupboard by means of lights installed outside the air stream.

"Terrain" ducting was specified for the low-velocity warm-air system recently installed at the council offices at Orpington, Kent. The ducting had to be installed in light steel-trussed roofs, mostly above suspended ceilings. The light weight of the ducting enabled it to be carried on the suspended frame of the false ceiling and no additional bracing was required. The lightness also assisted in the handling and installation of the sections of ducting in the restricted spaces between the roof trusses.

The installation was carried out during normal working hours, while the office staff were in occupation.

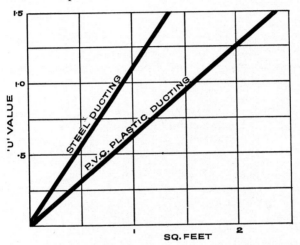

Comparative "U" value between steel and plastic (*AB Plastics Ltd*)

The good thermal properties of pvc ducting (K value 1·4), considerably reduce heat losses in warm-air systems, being equivalent in this respect to metal ducting with approximately ½ in. of insulation. A comparative installation having large mains passing through a roof space requiring insulation, could possibly have the cost reduced by approximately 50%, dependent upon the "U" value of the insulating medium.

This insulation effect of pvc also assists in the prevention of condensation, internally or externally, on the ducting where temperature differentials and high moisture conditions are involved. This has particular application in kitchen and canteen hoods and vat extraction installations.

PVC has a considerably lower coefficient of friction than galvanized steel and experiments have shown that it is considerably smoother. This gives a reduction in the resistance to air flow which can result in an appreciable saving in power consumption over a long running period.

The plastic sheet, being homogeneous and resistant to corrosion, does not flake or become rough on the surface; thus the original design conditions can be maintained, which is important when the specification is set within fine limits.

"Terrain" ducting is manufactured from sheet and extrusions of unplasticized unmodified polyvinyl chloride (i.e. rigid) supplied by Imperial Chemical Industries Ltd.

It is resistant to strong acids, strong alkalis, aqueous solutions and moist gases.

Although there may be come superficial attack on the pvc by high concentrations of some chemicals, such as chlorine and mixed oxides of nitrogen, it has a longer life than most alternatives. It may successfully be used with many organic liquids but should not be used with aromatic or chlorinated hydrocarbons.

6.7.1   Chemical Resistance of Rigid PVC

The following tables, derived from laboratory tests and published information, give the resistance of unplasticized pvc to various chemicals. These tables are intended to serve as a guide only, and potential users are advised to satisfy themselves that pvc will prove serviceable under their particular working conditions.

PVC is resistant to aqueous solutions of nearly all inorganic salts in all concentrations at temperatures up to 60°C. (140°F.). It is satisfactory in use up to 60°C. (140°F.) with the following chemicals:

Acetaldehyde 40%
Acetic acid (up to 60%)
Ammonia (dry gas)
Ammonium hydroxide (0·88)
Bleach lye
Butadiene
Carbon dioxide (dry)
Chromic acid (up to 50%)
Citric acid
    (cold sat. solution)
Developers (photographic)
Emulsions (photographic)
Fatty acids
Formaldehyde
Fruit pulp
Glycerine
Glycollic acid
Hydrobromic acid
    (up to 50%)
Hydrochloric acid
Hydrogen

Hydrogen peroxide
Hydrogen sulphide
Lactic acid (up to 10%)
Lead tetraethyl
Nitric acid (up to 50%)
Oils and fats
Oleic acid
Oxygen and ozone
Petrol
Phosphoric acid
Sea water
Soap solution
Sodium hydroxide
Stearic acid
Sulphur dioxide (dry)
Sulphuric acid 90%
Tartaric acid
    (sat. solution up to 30%)
Urea
Vinegar
Yeast

The following chemicals attack pvc at 60°C. (140°F.) although the material can be used with them at 20°C. (68°F.):

Ammonia (100% liquid)
*Arsenic acid (80% solution)
*Benzoic acid
*Butyl alcohol
*Butyric acid (20%)
*Carbon dioxide (wet)
*Chloracetic acid (100%)
*Chloric acid (up to 20% aqueous
   solution)
*Chlorine (dry)
*Chlorine water

*Ethyl alcohol
*Formic acid (up to 50%)
 Formic acid (up to 100%)
*Hydrofluoric acid (40%)
*Maleic acid (sat. solution)
*Methyl alcohol
*Perchloric acid
*Phenol
*Sodium benzoate (35% solution)
*Sulphur dioxide (moist 100%)

*Only slight attack at 60°C. (140°F.).

PVC is attacked by the following chemicals:

Acetaldehyde (100%)
Acetone
*Acetic acid (80–110%)
Aniline and aniline hydrochloride
*Benzaldehyde (0·1% aqueous
   solution)
Benzene
Bromine
Butyl acetate
Butyric acid (conc.)
*Carbon tetrachloride
*Cresol
Crotonaldehyde
Cyclohexanol
Cyclohexanone

Ethyl acetate
Ethyl acrylate
Lactic acid
Methyl chloride
Methyl methacrylate
Methylene chloride
Nitric acid (98%)
Petrol benzene (80–20)
Phenylhydrazine
Phosphorous trichloride
*Sulphur dioxide (liquid)
Toluene
Trichlorethylene
Vinyl acetate

*These chemicals attack the material only slightly at 20°C. (68°F.) and it can be used where alternative materials are unsatisfactory and where a limited life is permissible.

6.7.2   Design and Installation

A.B. Plastics Ltd. have developed important features of design and installation of which a few details are here given. The colour is usually grey, but others can be supplied on request.

Fixing—The light weight of the ducting requires only the lightest hangers or brackets, which can be fixed in position beforehand. The flange of the ducting is then fixed by means of rivets. By virtue of its method of prefabrication and assembly, the cost of installation time together with on-site labour and site occupation are reduced to a minimum.

Jointing—Extruded sections attached by cold solvent welding to one end of the duct provide a sleeve socket into which the plain end of the adjacent duct is inserted. The joint is made air tight by a plastic foam packing. This joint also accommodates the thermal expansion of the duct, preventing overall movement and displacement. The rib on the side of the sleeve serves to stiffen the ducting and provides an attachment point for brackets or hangers.

Branches and Tees—These are formed with angle sections fitted into the side of the main run, giving a sleeve joint into which the main duct fits. The section also allows for the fitting of a guide vane and control damper. These are similar to branches but have guide baffles to direct the air flow. They retain the clean symmetrical outside appearance of the branch.

Bends and Offsets—These can be formed with sharp external angles and fitted with streamlining baffles internally; on the larger sections, swept configurations are used.

Dampers—These are made to an efficient aero-dynamic shape, and have no projecting stiffening edges. When fully open the minimum resistance to air flow is presented.

Inspection Doors—These can be supplied as a sliding shutter or, where insulation is required, a bolted panel is used. They are clean in appearance and provide quick, easy access to the duct.

Diffusers and Grills—These can be supplied in pvc with adjustable or fixed louvres, and being free from corrosion retain their neat appearance and may be easily cleaned.

Other manufacturers of I.C.I.'s "Darvic" ventilation ducting, tank linings, etc. include:

Tanks and Linings Ltd.;	Prodorite Ltd.;
Chemidus Plastics Ltd.;	ManMil Plastics Ltd.;
Tough Plastics Ltd.;	Acalor (1948) Ltd.;
Extrudex Ltd.;	Turner and Brown Ltd.

Ducting can, of course, be made in other materials and glass-reinforced/polyester products are obvious examples.

Manufacturers are:

Wembley Fibreglass and Plastics Ltd.

Fibreglass Reinforced Plastics Ltd.

6.8 Telephone Kiosks

W. J. Cox manufacture such a product from clear "Perspex". The Cox phonedome presents a simple and attractive method of increasing the audibility of a telephone conversation within noisy surroundings. The shape of the unit magnifies the sound of speech within and deflects much of the extraneous sounds from without. The cut-out section is tailored to the shape of the head and shoulders, the edge being protected by an extruded section of white pvc. The unit is light and is easily installed by use of the holes provided in the flange. No maintenance or redecoration is required.

Part 7

PLASTICS ON BUILDING SITES

CONTENTS

7.1 Scope
  7.1.1 Properties of Polythene Film
  7.1.2 Suppliers of Sheet or Film

7.2 Plastics for Temporary Weather Protection

7.3 Plastics in Concrete Work

7.4 Plastics in Shuttering

7.5 Hose Pipes

Part 7

PLASTICS ON BUILDING SITES

7.1 Scope

Quite apart from the number of plastics which find their way into the final structure, there are a number of materials which are in use only while the building is being constructed. They are normally employed because they are time saving, economical and have properties possessed by no other materials, at least at a comparable cost.

The places where plastics are used on building sites are:

    7.2   Plastics for Temporary Weather Protection
    7.3   Plastics in Concrete Work
    7.4   Plastics in Shuttering
    7.5   Hose Pipes

7.1.1 Properties of Polythene Film

In the case of the first two uses, polythene film is much employed. It is opportune, therefore, to comment on its properties, further details being given in Sections 1.3.3 and 5.3.5. Considering the thickness employed, polythene film is quite tough, it is impervious to water, resistant to chemicals likely to be encountered on building sites, and it is light enough for ready erection almost anywhere.

The material is available in widths of up to 30 ft. and even this can be increased (at special request) by heat sealing or the use of special adhesives. Heat sealing is best carried out by specialists. Temporary sealing can be effected by using such sealing compounds as "Seelastik," "Bostik" or "Asbestumen". Most stockists also sell adhesives for giving permanent bonds.

Polythene is often sold in terms of gauges instead of thicknesses, the equivalents being:

Gauge	Thickness (in.)
20	0·0002
150	0·0015
250	0·0025
500	0·005
1,000	0·01

7.1.2 Suppliers of Sheet or Film

Suppliers of pvc sheet are given in Section 3.2.1 and a supplier of polystyrene sheet is Monsanto Chemical Co. Ltd.

Polythene sheet or film can be obtained from the following companies:—

British Visqueen Ltd.,
BX Plastics Ltd.,
British Cellophane Ltd.,
Cascelloid (Division of British
    Xylonite Co. Ltd.),

Peter Dixon and Son Ltd.,
Albert Green (Plastics) Ltd.,
Hughes Brushes Ltd.,
Henry Jackson (Liverpool) Ltd.,
The Metal Box Co. Ltd.,

Chiltern Hunt Ltd.,   Rollene Plastics Ltd.,
Colodense Ltd.,   Smith and Nephew Ltd.,
Commercial Plastics Ltd.,   Venus Packaging Ltd.
Fablon Ltd.,

Some very detailed information on the use of polythene sheet in building
is given by British Visqueen Ltd., particularly their Building Technical
Bulletins Nos. 1 and 2 ("Visqueen for use in concreting and weather
protection").

7.2   Plastics for Temporary Weather Protection

Much building time has been lost in the U.K. due to the weather and many
materials have deteriorated or been lost, or expensive temporary storage has
had to be provided. This particularly applies to cement. It is thus desirable to
devise a means of affording temporary protection so that work can proceed
in all weathers. Obviously the system must be cheap.

Polythene film fulfils all the necessary requirements. The simplest method
is to take advantage of existing scaffolding. Polythene sheet may be nailed or
stuck to this to give full protection without any loss of daylight. It is best,
however, to secure the film to the scaffold boards with light wooden laths
which should not be more than 4 ft. apart. A better method, and one which
will allow the polythene to be used again (moving from one part of a large
building to another), is to fix the polythene to a light wooden frame which can
be hooked to the scaffolding and thus moved when required. It would probably be advisable to use 1,000-gauge polythene for such work.

Alternatively, it is possible to build a polythene tent using poles etc., the
film being secured at ground level with ropes, pegs or battens. For light work,
500-gauge may be necessary.

Another useful technique is to employ polythene sheet for temporary glazing. This will allow plastering and other work to be undertaken in a building
where only the shell is completed. The film is best used by securing it to
wooden battens and fixing these over the windows. Light sheet (250 gauge),
can often be used for the purpose. Double glazing can also be used in a similar
way, the same method being used for ceilings. The sheet (whether as glazing
or partitions) can also be employed as a dust or draught excluder.

A more interesting development is the blowing of a "bubble" over a building site. A continuous sheet of polythene is used for the purpose and is anchor-
ed round the edges, being blown up by means of a low-pressure compressor.
This is kept running continuously. Air locks are provided for entering or
leaving so that escape of air is not too rapid. If it is required to keep such a
structure for long periods then reinforced films are best employed such as
"Terylene"-reinforced transparent pvc film. Apart from use in building construction, the method can be adopted for providing temporary stores.

Polythene sheet can also be employed as a tarpaulin and, as light transmission is not required, black film can be used. It will normally be held in
place by means of, say, bricks or timber. The material can be eyeletted but
reinforcement of the eyelets is essential.

7.3 Plastics in Concrete Work

Polythene sheet can be used in a number of ways in laying concrete and results in a number of advantages. For example, where reinforced concrete is laid on a concrete base, the use of polythene film between the two markedly reduces stress cracking. The two slabs of concrete can move readily relative to one another and thus allow the number of expansion joints to be reduced. The method has been used in the construction of roads and runways.

The sheet can also be used as a concrete underlay. It prevents moisture draining out of the mix during curing and it protects concrete rafts and slabs from attacks by sulphates and aqueous salt solutions. In most cases 150-gauge material is suitable although under more severe conditions it may be desirable to use a little thicker sheet.

In using a polythene film as an underlay it can also be employed as a damp-proof course, in which case 500-gauge material should be used. Some care is required in the preparation of the subfloor to prevent puncturing of the polythene. The main point is to lay a $1\frac{1}{2}$–2 in. sand binding on top of the hardcore. The sheeting is usually incorporated with the walls (including party walls) at damp-course level. Joins between sheets of polythene can be made by overlapping by at least 6 in. or by making a welt-type of fold. No adhesive is necessary. Polythene sheet can be used as a damp course on walls and ceilings, usually in wooden building construction or in cold-storage establishments. The sheet is fixed by adhesive on the warm side of the wall and excludes moisture and draughts.

Yet a further use in concrete work is an aid to curing. Usually, the surface of the concrete has to be continually sprayed to prevent too rapid drying. Another method is to employ wet hessian or tarpaulins. Polythene sheet is now used and is laid as soon as pouring is completed. The film has low moisture permeability and prevents rapid loss of moisture so that the curing process is a slow and steady one. This not only eliminates cracking and spalling, but tests have shown that the concrete has considerably better abrasion resistance when this method is employed than when damp sacking or air-curing is used. Similarly and for the same reasons, polythene sheet can be used when concrete foundations are to be poured.

7.4 Plastics in Shuttering

The main purpose in using plastics in shuttering is to improve the surface finish of the concrete although other advantages do result. The technique may be employed whether making precast units or casting *in situ*.

It is possible not only to improve the surface finish but to give the concrete a pattern. This is achieved by using a plastic which, itself, has been given a pattern by the vacuum forming process. In this, a sheet of plastic is softened by heat, laid on a mould shaped to the desired pattern, when vacuum is applied to the under surface. The softened plastic is thereby pulled down into the shape on the mould. The plastics normally employed in the process are pvc (I.C.I.'s "Flovic") and polystyrene. Some firms making sheet for vacuum forming are: I.C.I. Ltd.; Monsanto Chemical Co. Ltd.; British Celanese Ltd.; Commercial Plastics Ltd.; Erinoid Ltd. and Saro Laminated Products Ltd.

Sheets of pvc have been employed very successfully by the Cement and Concrete Association.

In the case of large timber moulds used in concrete work, it is usual to line them with metal, plywood or hardboard, the idea being to give a smooth surface. Plastics have been used with success for this purpose although, for economic reasons, only a thin sheet can be employed. Naturally, in using such methods, the usual concrete casting techniques must be followed to give satisfactory results, that is, joints must be kept watertight.

A big advantage in using a plastic sheet is the ease of stripping. Normally, as the shuttering is dismantled, the panels will fall away from the concrete. The plastic sheets can be re-used after wiping clean. The use of mould lubricants (release agents or mould oil) is unnecessary with plastic sheets which is an obvious saving not only in material and time, but the concrete which is produced is cleaner and requires no subsequent cleaning.

The plastic sheet is quite resistant to any of the chemicals likely to be found in concrete work. It will therefore have a long life and using "Flovic", over 130 castings have been obtained without deterioration of the material.

In using sheets with patterns in the surface, some instructions should be noted. The size of grooves in a pattern will depend on whether the concrete is precast or cast on site. With precast slabs cast face downwards, only 3–4 in. thickness of concrete may be used, but with on site cast the concrete may be 3–4 ft. deep. Generally, patterns with grooves 2–3 in. diameter and 1–2 in. deep are satisfactory without support underneath but above these dimensions some support may be necessary.

The plastic sheets can be bonded to the wood shuttering by means of adhesives. Adhesives based on water emulsions are best and after bonding the sheets should be left for 24 hours before use. The wood-plastic laminate can be handled in the same way as wood after this period, i.e. it can be sawn without stripping off the plastic. The latter can be removed if required by heating with a blow lamp (which destroys the plastic) or soaking in water for two days.

Polythene film has also been used for shuttering to give a smooth surface and to render shutter "striking" easier. It is difficult, however, to avoid wrinkles in the surface of the concrete (due to trapped air under the film) and when striking, tearing often results. The materials described previously are the best ones to use.

Glass-reinforced polyester moulds are sometimes used for casting concrete products. After the initial expense they may be employed many times, this being due to their great strength. Wembley Fibreglass and Plastics Ltd. is prepared to make this type of product.

An interesting development in the use of plastics in concrete work is the addition of water-soluble cellulose ethers. These are added to lime mortars, cements, tile adhesives and cements, plasters, crackfilling and grouting compounds and cement-based paints. The materials are made by British Celanese Ltd. and sold by J. M. Steel and Co. Ltd. from whom further details can be obtained.

The "Celacol" range of cellulose ethers includes types specially developed for the building industry. These grades form viscous solutions in water and thereby control additions of water made to mortars and cements. "Celacol" is available in a number of physical forms designed to give easy handling under the various conditions of use.

The principal advantage of its use is improved water retention—a factor particularly necessary when building or finishing high suction materials. This results in improved workability. Also, increased control over water additions to mortars and cements can reduce the possibilities of hair-cracking and frost damage. The chance of segregation is also reduced.

Croid Ltd. use PVA (polyvinyl alcohol) as a bond coat to avoid hacking and as an additive to upgrade screeds and renderings. The material increases the bond strength $2\frac{1}{2}$ times on brick and makes direct rendering over glazed surfaces a practical proposition.

Tragacine Adhesives also employ pva in their Flexibond AAL for adding to cement-like mixes to confer resiliency, impact and abrasion resistance. Such additions are worth investigating with great care.

7.5 Hose Pipes

The old type rubber hose used on building sites perished quite rapidly. Transparent and flexible pvc is much better and is now available from most stockists. Some manufacturers are as follow:

Bardex (Plastics) Ltd.,	C. and C. Marshall Ltd.,
Duratube and Wire Ltd.,	Melwood Thermoplastics Ltd.,
Albert Green (Plastics) Ltd.,	H. P. Muntz and Barwell Ltd.,
Greengate and Irwell Rubber Co. Ltd.,	Tenaplas Ltd.,
V. and N. Hartley Ltd.,	Wragby Plastics Ltd.

Oil-resistant synthetic rubber hose is available from the following:

S. Smith and Sons (England) Ltd.,	Leyland and Birmingham Rubber
John Bull Rubber Co. Ltd.,	Co. Ltd.,
Dunlop Rubber Co. Ltd.,	BTR Industries Ltd.
Dunlop Rubber Co. Ltd., Hose Division,	

17

Part 8

ADHESIVES, SEALING COMPOUNDS AND FINISHES

CONTENTS

8.1 Introduction

8.2 Plastic Finishes
  8.2.1 *Epoxy Paints*
  8.2.2 *Polyester Finishes*
  8.2.3 *Silicone Treatment for Water Repellancy*
  8.2.4 *Treatment of Plastic Floors*

8.3 Sealing Compounds
  8.3.1 *Synthetic Sealing Compounds*
  8.3.2 *Floor Sealants*
  8.3.4 *Waterstops*

8.4 Adhesives for Plastics
  8.4.1 *Suppliers and Their Products*
  8.4.2 *Bonding Foamed Products*
  8.4.3 *Bonding Laminated Plastics*
  8.4.4 *Bonding Boards*
  8.4.5 *Bonding Acoustic Tiles*
  8.4.6 *Bonding Flooring Products*
  8.4.7 *Bonding Flexible PVC*

Part 8

ADHESIVES, SEALING COMPOUNDS AND FINISHES

8.1 Introduction

Some of the plastics used in the building industry are obvious because they can be seen. There are a number, however, which are either plastics (more correctly polymers, the basis of plastics) or for use with plastics, which cannot be seen. Nevertheless, they perform a very useful function.

The products concerned are surface finishes, sealing compounds and adhesives. The first of these are various kinds of plastics which could be loosely called paints, although the epoxy types are definitely sold as paints and varnishes. All products of this type give special protection in one form or another.

The sealing compounds to be discussed are based on polymers and frequently on various types of synthetic rubbers. The adhesives, although often based on plastics or rubbers, need not necessarily be so since the types described are for bonding plastics to other things. As many millions of tiles are stuck to floors and much hardboard and laminates are stuck to walls and ceilings as well as to furniture, the importance of the subject will be appreciated.

The sections are therefore:

8.2 Plastic Finishes
8.3 Sealing Compounds
8.4 Adhesives for Plastics

8.2 Plastic Finishes

Many of the conventional paints and varnishes have certain limitations and, in particular, need replacing at fairly regular intervals. There have been improvements in recent years but these have usually been due to the introduction of polymers into the paints in one form or another.

Certain plastics, when used in paint or varnish form, have exceptional durability and longevity. In particular, the epoxy resins have given remarkable results. Polyester resins are also being employed but to a much lesser extent.

Tough polyurethane lacquers are also acquiring some prominence (see products of British Paints Ltd. and The Wall Paper Manufacturers Ltd. for example).

The silicones are in rather a different category. They are not paints or varnishes but are employed to confer water repellancy. The results are nevertheless impressive and will be described.

Information is also given on the protection of plastic floors. The subsections are therefore as follow:

8.2.1 Epoxy Paints
8.2.2 Polyester Finishes
8.2.3 Silicone Treatment for Water Repellency
8.2.4 Treatment of Plastic Floors

8.2.1 Epoxy Paints

Epoxy paints are remarkable products which have so far been neglected by the domestic side of the painting industry. Whether this is due to conservatism, the inability of suppliers to publicize the products, or resistance to the use of two-part paints is difficult to say. Whatever the reasons, the materials are too valuable to ignore and must be seriously considered by painters and decorators.

The outstanding features of the paints are their adhesion properties, and abrasion and chemical resistance. As far as adhesion is concerned, epoxy paints can be applied to metals, wood, concrete, plaster and other building surfaces to give extremely good bonds. There is no danger of lifting previous coats and no possibility of chipping. The same materials are used for making adhesives for bonding metal to metal and glass to glass, etc. They are used for marking out zebra crossings.

As far as abrasion resistance is concerned, epoxy screeds have 10 times the resistance of concrete. Carson's "Ultravar" on the Rocker Hardness Test gives a figure of over 31 compared with only 13 for a high-grade conventional varnish. The materials are, therefore, ideal for use as a protective finish on wood floors, handrails, skirtings, counters and doors, whether exterior or interior.

The epoxy resins are the biggest development in the paint industry since the alkyds, and will undoubtedly become widely adopted in due course. It is true that the paints are two-part compositions so that some preparation is necessary, but as manufacturers usually supply in pre-weighed packages, this is not all that difficult.

Nature of Epoxy Resins

Epoxy resins are described in Section 2.4. Some are liquids and some low-melting point solids but all dissolve in various solvents to form paints and varnishes.

The resins themselves are thermoplastic. When they are mixed with hardeners, a chemical reaction at once begins which converts the thermoplastic resins into hard infusible products.

This reaction explains why all epoxy paints and varnishes are supplied in two parts. A definite proportion of each has to be used, and as there are many different resins and hardeners, each paint supplier will recommend the amounts to use. Some suppliers sell, say, a one-gallon can or drum with sufficient space in it to allow the hardener to be added. Thus the can itself can be used for the mixing process.

Suppliers

There are only few suppliers of basic resins in the country and these have been given in Section 1.3.6.

Apart from epoxy, the materials are also called epoxide, ethoxyline or epichlorhydrin resins, names which might be given in connection with epoxy paints. A number of paint suppliers make paints and varnishes based on epoxy resins, some of which are:—

British Paints Ltd.; Walter Carson and Sons Ltd.; Coates Bros. Paints Ltd.; I.C.I. Ltd.; International Paints Ltd.; Jenson and Nicholson Ltd.; Pinchin, Johnson and Co. Ltd.; The Wallpaper Manufacturers Ltd.

It should be stressed that these firms do not necessarily make the products for the domestic field, but many of the existing paints could be used as such for the purposes already described. For example, the paints designed for the hulls of ships, whether wood or metal, would do very well for outdoor woodwork in coastal or other exposed areas. This sort of thinking is necessary to allow these valuable materials to establish their correct place in the paint field. Another example is the painting of garage floors and concrete.

At the moment, the materials are available only in a limited range of colours. The varnishes are available as transparent materials or with an egg-shell finish where gloss is not required. Although not necessarily designed for domestic purposes such colours as white, red oxide, grey and porcelain blue are made. Some of the materials require primers (usually on metals) but in most cases it is satisfactory to apply two coats of the same material.

Preparing the Paints

The correct proportions of resin and hardener must be well mixed. Mechanical stirring is to be preferred but vigorous hand stirring is satisfactory. Once mixed, the chemical reaction begins. After maturing for about 30 minutes, therefore, the material must be used within a few hours, the pot life being stipulated by the manufacturer. For this reason only enough material required for immediate purposes should be mixed.

Although the epoxy materials cure very quickly when blended, they have a long storage life before mixing. However, they should preferably be stored in a cool place.

The epoxy paints do not have the same solution characteristics as other resins. True solvents for them include methyl ethyl ketone (MEK), Oxitol, butyl Oxitol, Oxitol acetate, diacetone alcohol and methyl cyclohexanone.

These are thus the best materials for cleaning brushes and spray guns. However, although not true solvents, alcohols and some aromatic hydro-carbons can be used as thinners to a limited extent. Some paints will even tolerate a certain amount of white spirit or turps substitute. It is best, nevertheless, to use the special thinners and brush-cleaning liquids sold by the paint suppliers.

Brushes and paint guns must be cleaned immediately after use. If not, they will become useless as the epoxy resins, as adhesives, cannot be removed, except by such drastic treatment as burning.

If paint has started to thicken up, this means that it is beginning to cure. On no account add fresh paint to it or attempt to make it re-useable by adding thinners.

Application

As with any other paints, the surfaces to be treated should be carefully prepared. They need to be dry but it does not matter if they are alkaline. Metal is preferably shot-blasted or even flame cleaned or wirebrushed. Con-

crete is wirebrushed and freed of loose particles. Paint, or other deposits, is
cleaned off wood and sanded. With any surface, the main rules are cleanliness,
roughness and dryness.

Paints are usually supplied with a consistency suitable for brushing. Some
of them can be supplied as thixotropic materials. The undercoat is best
brushed on to ensure proper coverage of the surface. The top coat or subsequent coats may be applied by brush, spray or roller. Some of the paints are
available in different colours for primer and top coat to ensure that full
coverage with the second coat has been given. Coverage figures vary a great
deal depending on the surface and the material. Paints may only cover about
30 sq. yd. per gallon but some varnishes will cover as much as 100 sq. yd. per
gallon. The first coat can often be thinned, a typical example being four of
varnish to one of white spirit. It will be noted that only a small quantity of
thinner is required.

These swimming baths have been lined and decorated with Plastics and
Resins "Pallidux". In addition to fresh water this material is corrosion
resistant against sea water (*Plastics and Resins Ltd*)

There is an approximate time sequence for each operation which should be
carefully followed. An average schedule is:
(1) Pot life: From 8 hours to 3 days, usually the former.
(2) Surface dry: 1–2 hours at room temperature.
(3) Hard dry: About 24 hours.
(4) Re-coating time: At least 16 hours, preferably 24 hours.
(5) Fully cured: Nearly cured in 48 hours, but fully cured in 7 days.
    Treated floors can usually be walked on in 24 hours but excessive
    pressures should not be exerted.
If it is possible to do it, a cure at an elevated temperature is much quicker.
Stoving for 30 minutes at 120°C. gives a complete cure. Heaters placed opposite a wall will achieve the same sort of result.

The paints and varnishes should be applied in well-ventilated places. If
they are not, curing and properties might be impaired. More important, however, is that it is essential for the health and comfort of the operators. Barrier
creams are best employed on hands.

Some Examples of Epoxy Paints

Walter Carson and Sons, Ltd. produce No. 81 "Ultravar" transparent varnish and No. 82 "Ultravar" eggshell varnish. Both are for household use, the former as a floor varnish and for handrails, skirtings, counters, tables and the like. It is far more hard wearing than traditional French polish. The No. 82 is for use on skirtings and doors where a soft sheen is more suitable than a full gloss. The materials are available in the usual tin sizes from ½ pint to 1 gallon.

Coates "Epigloss" floor paint is for all types of floors and concrete surfaces and is available in a limited range of colours. It is satisfactory over asphalt and hard bituminous surfaces. "Epigloss" Type "O" is specially for chemical resistance, particularly painting steel and chemical plant. "Epigloss" Type "A" is an air-drying brushing quality which has been found useful in bakeries, breweries, laundries, dry-cleaning plant and the protection of machinery.

International Paints Ltd. makes a series which is largely for industrial purposes, although it could no doubt be developed for use elsewhere. "International Intergard" is for lining tanks of cargo vessels. "Intertar", a coal-tar epoxide composition (which hardens up unlike normal coal-tar formulations) is also used for tankers, in the oil industry and for plant protection in exposed conditions. "International" Group 37 is similar but has been used for more domestic purposes, the clear finish, for example, as a floor varnish. Other epoxy paints are also made.

Chemical Resistance

The chemical resistance will vary according to the type of paint, but all of them are fairly good. Some examples of materials which epoxy paints resist are:

Acetic acid (and vinegar)	Benzene
Sulphuric acid (40%)	Toluene
Phosphoric acid (10%)	Ethyl alcohol (beer, etc.)
Caustic soda solution	Butyl alcohol
Sodium hypochlorite solution	Petroleum
Hydrochloric acid (20%)	Turpentine
Fruit juices (not pineapple)	Wines
Cosmetics	Mustard
Oil	Tomato juice

The range is fairly wide which means that the epoxy coatings can be used in a variety of applications.

8.2.2 Polyester Finishes

A considerable amount of information has already been given on polyester plastics and their various uses in building in Sections 1.3.7 and 5.7.

8.2.3 Silicone Treatment for Water Repellency

The silicones are members of the plastics family and have a number of valuable properties. One of the most important of these is water repellency which property is retained for years when applied to masonry surfaces. They are thus forming an important addition to the decorator's standard range of products.

There are, of course, a number of other waterproofing treatments using wax emulsions, stearates and the like. Silicones have advantages over these for a number of reasons. They have a lower surface tension and, therefore, flow more easily into minute pores which normally act as capillaries. Depth of penetration is greater and varies from $\frac{1}{16}$ in. to $\frac{1}{4}$ in. depending on the porosity of the surface. The pores in the masonry are not clogged so that the material treated can still breathe and thus any water trapped at the time of treatment can escape. Silicones do not adversely affect the treated surfaces, particularly from the point of view of colour, appearance or texture, where no difference can be detected.

Water rolls off walls treated with I.C.I. silicone water repellents
(Imperial Chemical Industries Ltd)

Most above-ground masonry surfaces can be treated with silicones. They include concrete, stone, brick, cinder block, stucco, reconstructed stone or other materials provided there is no excessive water pressure. The only two masonry surfaces which should not be treated are gypsum and limestone.

Available Materials

There are only two manufacturers of the basic materials in the U.K. and these are I.C.I. Ltd. and Midland Silicones Ltd. I.C.I. refer to their products as R.220 and R.221, and Midland Silicones as Dri-Sil 29.

It is possible to buy the materials direct from these suppliers. Many companies, however, prefer to purchase proprietary materials ready for use and some examples are here given:

Company	Trade Name
Associated Building Products Ltd.	Hydralex;
C. R. Averill Ltd.	"Colorshield" No. 5 silicone water-proofer;
Berry Wiggins and Co. Ltd.	Aquaseal No. 66 colourless silicone water repellent;
Craig and Rose Ltd.	Silicone C. and R.;
Evode Ltd.	"Evosil";
Liverpool Borax Co. Ltd.	"Romanite" WR.;
Smith and Walton Ltd.	Masonry water repellent;
Solignum Ltd.	"Impervion" silicone water repeller;
Tretol Associated Products Ltd.	"Tretol" silicone waterproofer.

One typical example of a proprietary material may be given to illustrate what is available. ("Tretol" silicone waterproofer is ready to use, may be applied by brush or spray and has a coverage of 15–25 sq. yd. per gallon, depending on the porosity of the surface. The material contains a fugitive dye which enables the decorator to tell which parts of the surface he has already treated. The dye disappears after a few days' exposure to sunlight. Most other products manufactured by other companies have similar features.

Typical Formulations

For those manufacturers who wish to make up their own products, some detailed formulation techniques may be given.

Resin R.220 is solvent based and contains 10% silicones. It may be diluted with such thinners as toluene, xylene or white spirit but the flash point should be kept above 75°F. A working concentration of 2% is satisfactory so that it must be diluted with four parts by volume of solvent. This may be spirit if the solution is to be used in a matter of weeks, but for longer periods one quarter of the white spirit should be replaced with toluene or xylene.

Resin R.221 is supplied as a 70% solution and should be diluted to 5% by weight with white spirit or Esso Distillate although the latter gives slightly longer drying times. When diluting by weight, 13 lb. of diluent should be added to 1 lb. of R.221. For dilution by volume one gallon of R.221 should be diluted with 17·5 gallons of white spirit.

No difficult handling precautions are necessary compared with any other surface coating material containing large quantities of organic solvent. The precautions include care against fire and avoiding breathing large quantities of vapour. While spraying, an adjustment to give maximum flooding and minimum misting will give best application results. Storage of concentrated and diluted resins should be in a dry atmosphere and dry containers should be employed. The containers should be tin-lined or lacquered but should not have internally soldered seams. If these precautions are not taken then precipitation of the resin may take place. If the materials thicken up during storage it will probably be possible to return them to their original condition by keeping in a warm room.

Surface Preparation and Application

The following procedure is required to treat surfaces and apply silicone water repellents:—

(1) All cracks should be filled up and any defective pointing should be repaired, preferably using a waterproof sand-and-cement mortar a day or two before treatment is to take place. The repellents will reduce penetration only through normal pores of masonry.

(2) All loose particles and dirt should be cleaned off. In cleaning, however, care should be taken to avoid the use of water with detergents otherwise the stain left behind may affect repellency.

(3) The silicone solutions should be applied on dry days. Two or three days dry weather and the expectation of a few hours dry weather after application are preferable. It is not impossible to apply the materials if there is any dampness, but best results are obtained if everything is dry.

(4) The solution should now be applied by means of a soft brush or spray. The masonry surface should be flooded with at least a six-inch run down of silicone and should not be brushed out. A low pressure should be employed and the material should emerge from the gun in an easy stream. Painted woodwork and plants should be protected during the spraying.

(5) Normally, unless the surface is particularly porous, only one coating is necessary and it will last for years. If a very porous surface is encountered, however, it may be given two coatings. The first coating should be allowed to dry thoroughly before the application of the second and this should take about eight hours on a normal day. Application should be avoided, however, if it is very cold or likely to become so soon after the application of a coat.

(6) The coverage power of the above quantities of solutions will obviously depend on the porosity but will vary between about 100 sq. ft. and 200–250 sq. ft. The amount to be used must be left to the discretion of the individual decorator who will use the lower figure if he considers the walls to be exceptionally porous.

(7) It is best to use solutions with fugitive dyes as the area covered can easily be seen. If this is not done, it should be remembered that the solvent soon dries off to leave a transparent coat so that the part painted is indistinguishable from an untreated wall.

(8) Generally speaking, the silicone coatings, after drying, can be painted. This, however, will depend on the resin used, or the type of formulation purchased, and details should be obtained from suppliers. Generally, however, *any* solvent-based paint can be overpainted on the silicone-treated surface. Some proprietary materials specifically exclude the use of water or emulsion paints on newly painted silicone surfaces, although there is no difficulty after a few months. I.C.I. claim, however, that their R.220 can be used under emulsion paints and the life of such paints is extended. The technique is also permissible with cement-based paints, but in this case it is preferable to apply the silicone over the paint. Generally, R.221 should be used only with solvent-based paints.

Some Results of Applications

It is quite clear that the weather resistance of walls can be considerably improved by the application of silicones and this applies whether more normal painting is to take place or not. Water penetration of walls is likely to cause efflorescence, frost spalling and cracking, peeling and flaking of paint on interior and exterior walls and the absorption of dirt and soot. Silicones will minimize these troubles.

In addition, in industrial areas, water carries sulphurous fumes with it and thus causes pronounced erosive action. Even in rural areas, soft rainwater can cause trouble by dissolving out cementitious material in stonework. The use of silicones will overcome all these troubles.

The lower brick has been treated with a water repellent based on I.C.I. silicones. Water does not penetrate the treated surface. Water soaks in rapidly to the untreated brick (*Imperial Chemical Industries Ltd*)

A typical test carried out by I.C.I. will illustrate the benefits of the process. Two bricks were taken from a batch and one was silicone treated and the other left untreated. They were then aged out-of-doors for one year. After this they were treated in the laboratory to the equivalent of 24 hours continuous rain in a 15 m.p.h. wind. The moisture absorption was checked after the test and found to be 20% for the untreated brick and only 1·8% for the treated brick. A typical waterproofing solution, not based on silicones, had an absorption of 20%. The material used here was a 12% wax emulsion, but a 44% aluminium stearate was no better. These materials provided some protection for only a few days after treatment, the 12% wax giving a figure of 7·0% water absorption, and the silicones only 0·3% in the same time.

Similar tests were carried out by using Red Leicester brick with the following results:

Treatment	Initial	Water Absorption 10 months exposure	18 months
2% R.220	0·17	0·18	0·24
5% R.221	0·15	0·18	0·19

There is no doubt at all that, at the present time, the best materials known for waterproofing walls are the silicones.

8.2.4 Treatment of Plastic Floors

A number of proprietary polishes may be purchased to maintain vinyl and similar type floors. The technique to be used is summarized by that recommended by Semtex Ltd. for their vinyl floors.

For the first two weeks after installation, sweep and wipe the floor with a damp cloth if necessary. Use water sparingly to permit the adhesive to dry out thoroughly. Wash the floor regularly, using Semtex CX cleaner or good soda-free soap. Do not use strong soaps, harsh cleaning powders, pastes containing abrasives or solvents such as paraffin, turpentine etc. To remove rubber heel marks, cigarette scars and similar stains, sprinkle dry Semtex CX cleaner on the defective spots and rub lightly with fine steel wool, dampened with water.

Apply a thin, even film of Semtex "Safeshine" or Semtex "Non-Slip" polish or any other good water-emulsion polish, with a clean mop or cloth and leave to dry. "Safeshine" shines as it dries. Paste polishes may be used if preferred. Liquid polishes containing turpentine, white spirit or similar solvents are not recommended.

Once the floor has been cleaned and a glossy surface built up, just sweep it daily and wipe over with a slightly dampened mop or cloth. Apply "Safeshine" or "Non-Slip" polish occasionally to preserve a fresh, bright appearance. Areas subjected to heavy traffic may be scrubbed by hand or machine as often as desired.

8.3 Sealing Compounds

The sealing compounds to be mainly dealt with in this section are plastic or synthetic-rubber compounds for filling joints, cracks and the like. Brief mention is also made of a liquid sealant for floors and various waterstops. The sub-sections are therefore as follow:

    8.3.1   Synthetic Sealing Compounds
    8.3.2   Floor Sealants
    8.3.4   Waterstops

8.3.1 Synthetic Sealing Compounds

Compounds of this type are made by the following companies: Evode Ltd. ("Evostik" Sealing Compound No. 723); Farmiloe Sealants Ltd. ("Farocaulk" etc.); Secomastic Ltd. ("Secoseal"); Tretol-Serviced Ltd. ("Vertiseal"); British Paints Ltd. (polysulphide type sealing, jointing and glazing materials); Sealocrete Products Ltd. ("Calktite" polysulphide); Stuart B. Dickens Ltd.

"Evostik" Sealing Compound No. 723

The material is a heavy off-white synthetic rubber compound, which when dry remains resilient throughout its long life, with strong adhesive qualities to metal, concrete and most other components. It is water and oil-proof, acid and alkali resistant, and immune to extremes of temperature. It is available for large constructional purposes, such as the installation of metal framing, in 28-lb. or 12-lb. containers and is also available in extruding tubes for bench or repair work.

Application

As a sealing compound: All surfaces to be thoroughly clean and dry. In assembly of large metal components apply by putty knife or trowel to one surface, and within 10–20 minutes bolt adjoining component in position so that the sealing compound is forced into all existing apertures to seal the joint completely. The surplus compound that has been squeezed out can subsequently be removed after 24 hours by cutting with a wet knife.

For sealing smaller components, the extruder tube with nozzle should be used. After removing the plastic cap, place the nozzle lightly on to the area to be sealed, and while firmly pressing the bottom of the tube, draw it slowly towards the body. By this means any cavity up to the width of the nozzle can be filled and a clean finish created by the movement of the tip of the nozzle.   Right-angle and "U"-shaped joints should have the extruder nozzle inserted in the angle and, while the sealing compound is still wet, the second unit, say a glass or similar panel, should be placed in position.   Another extrusion of the sealing compound to the second unit is necessary if a cover strip is used, and after bolting both components home, surplus material should be removed as described. If necessary, an external fillet can be applied at the top joint in a similar manner. For sealing and water-proofing joints in floor covering, such as in pvc flooring, apply an extrusion from the tube on to the floor, and within 10 minutes press the edges of the floor covering down so that a quantity is forced up into the joint. Remove excess immediately.

As an adhesive: Where the components are rough, for example asbestos insulation cloth, spread a liberal quantity on to the metal frame and, while this is still tacky, place asbestos strip on top of the adhesive, pressing firmly home. The strength of the semi-dry adhesive will keep this firmly in position during its subsequent drying—approximately one hour. This is useful where a certain amount of gap filling is necessary. Evostik Cleaner No. 185 should be used for cleaning purposes.

Farmiloe Sealants

These compounds are based on the synthetic butyl rubber and have the following claimed properties:

(a) Excellent resistance to ozone, sunlight, heat and corrosion.
(b) High flexibility—non-hardening.
(c) Excellent shock absorption and vibration isolation properties.
(d) Impermeability to gases, moisture vapour.
(e) Very low water absorption.
(f) Outstanding thermal and electrical properties, hence excellent insulation.
The range of Farmiloe Sealants is as follows:

"Farocaulk" —non-hardening mastic in brush, knife, trowel and gun grades.
"Farostrip" —soft compression adhesive laminate for glazing and sealing applications.

"Farofoam" —soft compression adhesive seal based on a laminated dense or open cell sponge for glazing or expansion joints.

"Faroform" —gaskets and extrusions for weather seals.

"Farosheet" —sheeting with adhesive surfaces for cladding, tanking or roofing.

"Faroled" —lead-butyl laminates for conventional and new style roofing and flashings.

"Farobase" —solvent based primers for developing adhesion between Faro products and porous building materials.

"Faroflor" —floor tiles and sheeting offering chemical resistance and high sound insulation for industrial and domestic application.

"Secoseal"

Secomastic Ltd. advances some excellent reasons for adopting the use of its "Secoseal". Joints in many large curtain wall structures call for the use of sealants which possess exceptional extensibility yet are physically robust. The high degree of "stretchability" is necessary because of the large thermal movements to which joints in many curtain walls are subject, and toughness is required because the sealant is frequently exposed to weather erosion and to accidental mechanical damage such as can be caused when the facades are being cleaned.

These requirements have led to the development of cold curing rubber-like sealants, notably elastomeric sealants based on the polysulphide liquid polymers manufactured by the Thiokol Chemical Corp.

Secomastic Ltd. has for many years specialized in the production of gun-applied oleo-resinous sealants which have a long record of successful use in curtain walling extending over the greater part of a decade. These materials are, by their nature, soft and are therefore not normally used in exposed joints where physical damage could occur; in practice they are often protected by glazing beads or used as a bedding in conjunction with spacers. A further limitation of oleo-resinous sealants is their inability to accept continuous movement greater than a specific maximum (in the case of " Secomastic" joint sealing compound, 25% of the original joint width) and hence, where large movements are likely, joints must be designed to accommodate a relatively large body of mastic.

For aesthetic or technical reasons, this is not always desirable or possible and consequently the designer is sometimes faced with the problem of sealing a joint ¼ in. wide that may expand to ⅜ in. Such a joint calls for the use of an elastomeric sealant. Any high performance mastic sealant, formulated on scientific lines has of necessity to be a compromise between many different properties. Great extensibility is meaningless without adhesion or the ability to resist slump in vertical joints; resistance to erosion must be combined with good performance under ultra-violet light ageing. The processing of the basic polymer and its combination with other essential constituents designed to give the required all-round properties is dependent upon the skill and experience of the manufacturer. It is here that the architect must be guided by his assessment of the competence of the particular manufacturer and of his reputation in the specialized field of building sealants.

"Secoseal" Elastomeric Sealant is the outcome of research designed to complement the sealants available to the architect for solving the more exacting requirements of high-movement joints in modern building construction, and to overcome the far-from-easy technical difficulties of building curtain wall structures that remain permanently and completely weathertight without the need for periodic maintenance.

"Secoseal" is intended for use where joints may be expected to expand by as much as 50% or more of their original width—or in joints that will not accommodate a depth of sealant of more than $\frac{1}{4}$ in.

The main characteristics of "Secoseal" may be summarized as follows:

Colours: grey or black.

Working life after mixing: 2 to 4 hours at normal temperatures.

Slump before curing: Nil in joints up to $\frac{3}{4}$ in. $\times \frac{3}{4}$ in.

Extensibility: Minimum of 50% indefinitely.

Tensile strength: 150 lb./sq. in. at 67°F.

Adhesion: Excellent on properly prepared surfaces.

Services temperature range: −65°F. to +250°F.

Ageing and weathering resistance: Laboratory tests show that a minimum life of 30 years can be expected.

Resistance to oil, solvents and chemicals: Withstands petrol, oil and most organic solvents, weak acids and alkalis, but is not resistant to concentrated acids or to oxidizing chemicals such as chromic acid.

Application: "Secoseal" is supplied in tins and cartridges and is applied by hand or air-operated caulking gun. Each pack is complete with catalyst and simply mixed on the site with the aid of the "Secoseal" stirrer, which can be conveniently operated by use of a slow-speed drill.

Where the material is used from tins the guns may be loaded directly or the "Secoseal" may be loaded into cartridges and these charged into the guns. Care should be taken to ensure that surfaces to which "Secoseal" is to be applied are scrupulously clean and free from grease.

"Vertiseal"

"Vertiseal" (Tretol-Servicised Ltd.), is a cold-applied joint sealing compound. It is specially designed and formulated for positive sealing of critical vertical joints where properties are required which are outside the scope of normal building mastics. It is for use in vertical or sloping joints in concrete, brickwork, masonry, metal or any combination of these materials.

"Vertiseal" will provide a permanent seal which will retain its bond, resilience and toughness in spite of prolonged weathering, repeated expansion, contraction and movement, complete immersion in fresh and salt water and attack by most solvents and chemicals.

Application: "Vertiseal" is a trowel or gun applied grade of sealing compound supplied in the form of two separate components (base and reactor) that are mixed together immediately before use. The correct quantity of reactor is supplied with each container of "Vertiseal". A special primer is supplied for use with the material. It is available in black, brick red and stone grey.

Preparation of joint: Joints should be opened to a minimum width of $\frac{1}{4}$ in. and depth of 1 in., depth of joint at all times being as big as, or preferably greater than, the width. The joint should be cleaned free of any loose or foreign matter and must be completely dry at time of application of the primer.

Mixing instructions: Mixing is best achieved by using a $\frac{1}{2}$ in. slow-speed 450 r.p.m. electric drill with a 2 to 3 in. diameter propeller-type of blade on a long shaft. Add half of the curing agent to the base material in the can, commence stirring, then add remainder of curing agent and continue stirring until a consistent colour is obtained free from black or brown streaks. The entire operation should

18

occupy approximately 5 minutes and this period of time must not be exceeded unduly; extended mixing time will cause premature setting. As the compound sets very quickly, only enough material that can be used within one hour should be mixed at any one time.

If the curing agent comes into contact with the skin or clothing, it should be washed off immediately with soap and water. Empty curing agent containers should be destroyed.

Installation: After 5 hours but not more than 24 hours following application of the primer, the "Vertiseal" should be applied by trowel or caulking gun, commencing from the bottom and working upwards.

Trowel application: "Vertiseal" can be successfully applied by putty knife or spatula into joints ¾ in. or more in width. For best results, start at the bottom of the joint and work upwards. After filling 5 or 6 feet of joint, the "Vertiseal" may be held in position by damming with a timber batten, which should be brought upwards with the compound. Immediately prior to this, a strip of waxed paper should be applied over the face of the "Vertiseal" to avoid this sticking to the batten. The latter should be brought up tight against the "Vertiseal" to avoid slumping, and held in position for several days before removing.

Gun application: After proper mixing, use a trowel or putty knife to transfer to the open-end-type caulking gun. Gun application should begin at the bottom of the joint and work upward. Install wax paper and dam after each 5 or 6 feet of joint has been filled, as previously described.

Note:—For clean straight edges, masking tape should be applied to both sides of the opening before application. Primer application should be made at this point to the clean dry joint surface against which "Vertiseal" is to be bonded; allow it to dry for at least 5 hours (but not more than 24 hours) at normal temperature before application of "Vertiseal", and remove tape before the "Vertiseal" has completely cured.

Curing period: Seven days at least following the date of application must be allowed to elapse before "Vertiseal" is submitted to constant immersion in any form of liquid.

Storage: The material should be used within 6 months of delivery. No installations should be carried out at temperatures below 40°F. If the outside temperature is below 50°F., the material should be stored for some hours at about 70°F. before mixing.

"Vertiseal" solvent should be used to clean equipment.

Stuart B. Dickens Ltd.

This company has developed an unusual sealing and jointing compound. It is based on polyester resins and is known as "Certite." It is particularly important with concrete work and once the hardener has been added the material starts to set and in a short time is stronger than the concrete. Various concrete units can be readily jointed, enabling fixings of clamps, bolts, brackets and a wide range of other supporting units to be made. First-class concrete repairs can also be made.

Other manufacturers of sealants are:
Storey Witty and Co. Ltd.
The Expandite Group of Companies.

8.3.2 Floor Sealants

One of the problems of laying tiled floors where adhesives are involved is to have a completely dry sub-floor. Where the sub-floors are cement, for example, a waiting period as long as three months is often recommended.

Certain floor sealing compounds are claimed to avoid the necessity for this long wait as they exclude moisture. A typical example is "Structoplast".

Structoplast Ltd.

"Structoplast" can be applied to a new screed as early as three days after laying. Two days after application of the "Structoplast", the decorative floor finish can be laid with the conventional adhesives, thus showing a great saving in the time normally required before a finished floor can be brought into service. Thus, floor finishing need not be held up while waiting for the screed to dry out, as "Structoplast" will adhere to a screed which gives a reading on the Protimeter as high as 9.5 without any problem.

"Structoplast" is a liquid which can be squeegeed on to the screed, does not add any appreciable thickness to the floor level, and when hard, produces a firmly bonded waterproof membrane preventing any moisture from attacking the adhesive or the floor finish.

Other features claimed for "Structoplast" are:

(1) The material may be applied to an existing floor subject to rising damp.
(2) once cured, the material forms a firmly bonded waterproof membrane.
(3) the floor should be sound, free from oil and grease and there should be no hydrostatic pressure present.
(4) the material contains no bitumen.
(5) the treated floor is resistant to alkalis and will not soften at temperatures up to 95°C.
(6) if the surface is dusty or porous, a priming coat should be applied.
(7) the coverage of the material is approximately 2 sq. yd. per lb. dependent upon the texture of the surface treated. The material is supplied in a two-can pack, the contents of one being incorporated with the other just before application.
(8) floor finishes which require pinning cannot be satisfactorily laid over a "Structoplast"-treated surface.
(9) it is supplied in 2, 7 and 14 lb. tins complete with the requisite amount of hardener for incorporating on site.

8.3.4 Waterstops

Waterstops are made by the following companies: Tretol-Servicised Ltd. (pvc and rubber), Expandite Ltd. and Sealocrete Products Ltd.

The following comments on pvc waterstops are made by Tretol-Servicised Ltd. Claims made by the company are that: they provide a permanent, water-tight seal; easily joined on site; flexible and durable; resistant to most diluted acids, chemicals, petrol and oils etc.; have given effective service over a large number of years.

The waterstops are available in lengths of 50 ft. in the following sizes:

Type	Size	Web Thickness	End Bulb	Hollow Bulb
Flat	4 in.	$\frac{3}{16}$ in.	$\frac{1}{2}$ in.	—
Dumbell	6 in.	$\frac{3}{16}$ in.	$\frac{1}{2}$ in.	—
	9 in.	$\frac{3}{16}$ in.	$\frac{3}{4}$ in.	—

Type	Size	Web Thickness	End Bulb	Hollow Bulb
Centre	$5\frac{1}{2}$ in.	$\frac{3}{16}$ in.	$\frac{1}{2}$ in.	$\frac{5}{16}$ in.
Bulb	$7\frac{1}{2}$ in.	$\frac{3}{16}$ in.	$\frac{1}{2}$ in.	$\frac{3}{4}$ in.
	$9\frac{1}{2}$ in.	$\frac{3}{16}$ in.	$\frac{3}{4}$ in.	$\frac{1}{2}$ in.

Details of the Installation

Site jointing: To ease the problem of site jointing, Tretol-Servicised Ltd. have designed and produced a full range of junction pieces whereby it is only necessary to form butt-joints. These can be achieved by using Tretol-Servicised electrical pvc jig, a metal blade and a blow lamp.

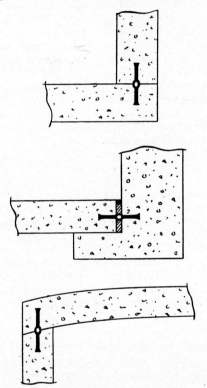

Positioning of PVC waterstops (*Expandite Ltd*)

Installation of pvc waterstop: The waterstop is placed in such a position that one bulb will be embedded in each of the two adjoining concrete slabs or walls. The waterstop shall be held firmly in place with a block or other suitable arrangement on the outside of the split form (away from the concrete which is being poured). After the concrete has set up, the split form and block may be removed, the extension board set in place, and the adjoining concrete poured. It is essential that the concrete be compacted around the pvc waterstop to ensure "honeycombing" does not take place. As the concrete sets up, the waterstop is subjected to tension, pulling the end bulbs against the concrete to effect a positive seal.

Details of "Expandite" Waterstops

The Expandite sizes of pvc stops are as follows:—

	Type D	Type E	Type F
Overall width, in.	4	6	9
Nominal web thickness, in.	$\frac{3}{16}$	$\frac{3}{16}$	$\frac{3}{16}$
Bulb diameter, in.	$\frac{1}{2}$	$\frac{1}{2}$	$\frac{3}{4}$
Weight per 100 ft. (approx.)	60 lb.	90 lb.	150 lb.

Expandite comment on their waterstops as follows:

(1) All flexible waterbars including those made of pvc can only be used in conjunction with in-situ concrete and are not appropriate for brickwork, precast concrete or other forms of construction.

(2) The principle on which these waterstops act is basically mechanical and does not depend upon adhesion of the pvc to the concrete, and the principle is that, when the concrete contracts due to hydration of the cement, the waterstop is placed in tension across the joint so that the end bulbs lock into the concrete and prevent the passage of water.

(3) PVC waterstops, if made to an appropriate specification with regard to physical and chemical properties, have adequate tensile strength and elongation of break of the order of 250% and are thus capable of accommodating all normal joint movement which is likely to occur in building structures. Waterstops with a central bulb will accommodate a reasonable amount of shear movement, certainly up to $\frac{1}{2}$ in.

(4) The width of waterstops is sometimes assumed to have a bearing on the maximum head of water which can be accommodated. However, this is not really the case and most waterstops, as long as good compaction is provided around the end bulbs, will withstand very high heads of water indeed.

(5) The width of waterstop, however, has a direct relationship to the thickness of the concrete slab and the maximum size of aggregate and a good rule-of-thumb guide for choice of width of waterstop is as follows:—

The size of waterstop which may be required for any particular structure is in the first instance dependent on three factors.

(*a*) The width of the waterstop must not be greater than the thickness of the slab.

(*b*) The distance between the waterstop and reinforcement should not be less than twice the size of the aggregate. Therefore, if $\frac{3}{4}$ in. aggregate is being used this distance should not be less than $1\frac{1}{2}$ in.

(*c*) Half the width of the waterstop should be at least three times the size of the aggregate, i.e. if $\frac{3}{4}$ in. aggregate is used then the waterstop should be at least $5\frac{1}{2}$ in. wide.

(6) The great advantage with pvc waterstop is the relative ease with which they may be jointed on site using simple welding techniques, and it is noteworthy that the welds made by these methods can be as strong as the material itself.

8.4 Adhesives for Plastics

There are now adhesives available for bonding nearly all plastics to almost any surface. However, it is unusual to employ a universal adhesive and certainly not advisable. For example, vinyl floors usually contain plasticizers and these can attack some of the adhesives thus destroying the bond.

Over the years, therefore, special types of adhesive have been developed for the different operations and–or materials and these should be employed. There are, of course, also preferred methods of laying floors, insulating walls and so on and manufacturers instructions must be followed. All of these matters are considered in this section which is therefore divided into the following sub-sections.

8.4.1   Suppliers and Their Products
8.4.2   Bonding Foamed Products
8.4.3   Bonding Laminated Plastics
8.4.4   Bonding Boards
8.4.5   Bonding Acoustic Tiles
8.4.6   Bonding Flooring Products
8.4.7   Bonding Flexible PVC

8.4.1   Suppliers and Their Products

The following table gives a list of some suppliers of adhesives together with their products and the uses to which they are put.

Evode Ltd.
"Evo-stik" Impact Adhesive 528.
   (For bonding laminated plastics and hardboard);
"Evotex" Adhesive S.L.820.
   (For bonding flexible pvc to walls and working tops);
"Evo-stik" Adhesive 873.
   (For bonding pvc and rubber tiles and sheeting);
"Evo-stik" Impact Adhesive S.H.100 and S.H.25;
   (For bonding pvc floor tiles);
"Evo-stik" Cement 5080.
   (For bonding hard and soft board, rubber tiles, nosings, treads, coverings etc.);
"Evo-stik" Adhesive 863.
   (For bonding expanded polystyrene);
"Evo-stik" Impact Adhesive 567.
   (For bonding cellular pvc and other foams).

Allweather Paints Ltd.
"Pitagrip" White Adhesive.
   (For bonding polystyrene foam).

Union Glue and Gelatine Co. Ltd.

"Styroglue" 600.
 (For bonding polystyrene foams).

National Adhesives Ltd.

"National" 7550.
 (For bonding polystyrene foam to boards, wood and porous surfaces);
"National" 31–343.
 (For bonding polystyrene foam to itself or to plaster, cement etc.)

Berry Wiggins and Co. Ltd.

"Aquaseal" No. 1975.
 (For cold bonding of polystyrene foam);
"Kingsworth" Compound No. 1983.
 (For hot bonding of polystyrene foam).

Bardens (Bury) Ltd.

"Polytak" 200.
 (For bonding polystyrene foam).

Plycol Ltd.

"Bitutherm" 840 Adhesive.
 (For bonding polystyrene foam);
"Bitutherm" Hot-Dip.
 (For bonding polystyrene foam).

The Liquitile Supply Co. Ltd.

"Unibond".
 (For bonding polystyrene foam);
"E-P-A."
 (For bonding polystyrene foam).

Tretol Associated Products Ltd.

"Tretobond" 404.
 (For bonding laminated plastics);
"Tretobond" 425.
 (For bonding insulation boards);
"Tretobond" AT.79.
 (For bonding lightweight acoustic tiles);
"Tretobond" 740.
 (For bonding polystyrene foam);
"Tretobonds" T.620 and T.621.
 (For bonding sheet type floors).

Leicester, Lovell and Co. Ltd.

"Cascoset" MT-3.
 (For bonding vinyl tiles and sheet flooring).

Expandite Adhesives Ltd.

Adhesive S.92.
 (For bonding laminates);

Adhesive L.210.
(For bonding polystyrene foam).

Bostik Ltd.
"Bostik" 3.
(For bonding laminated plastics).

Armstrong Cork Co. Ltd.
L.90 Adhesive.
(For bonding thermoplastic tiles);
L.128 Adhesive.
(For bonding rubber tiles, sheets and fibrous-backed pvc);
L.520.
(For bonding vinyl–cork tiles).

Croid Ltd.
Adhesives for pvc wall and ceiling coverings.
Tragacine adhesives (for bonding Formica, etc. to wood and plasterboard).

Dunlop Chemical Products Division
SF styrene foam. (For a bond to wood, concrete, plaster, hardboard, asbestos, brickwork, painted surfaces, etc.)

RF rubber flooring. (Suitable for under-floor heating, permanently secures sheet or tiles to metal, wood or concrete sub-floors).

PT plastic floor/wall tile. (Suitable for under-floor heating and all sub-floor screeds, immune to plasticiser migration).

LP laminated plastics. (Easy-to-use brushable contact adhesive for decorative laminates; excellent as a general purpose adhesive).

AT acoustic tile. (Mastic—for tiles up to 12 in. $\times$ 24 in. only 4–5 blobs needed. Adhesive—contact-type for larger tiles and panels).

Industrial Adhesives Ltd.
"Indasol" and "Indatex".

Expanded Rubber and Plastics Ltd.
"Polyzote" Adhesive Formula 20.
(For fixing expanded polystyrene boards and tiles).

Plus Products Ltd.
Synthetic Adhesive Plus 17/22.
(For fixing expanded polystyrene boards and tiles).

8.4.2 Bonding Foamed Products

There are different adhesives for the different types of foams and these are given here. Most work, however, has been devoted to polystyrene foam.

"Evo-stik" Adhesive 863

A white, heavy bodied, non-inflammable adhesive for bonding expanded polystyrene to wall and ceiling surfaces of plaster, cement, smooth concrete, hardboard, timber and flat asbestos sheeting etc. The entire surface of the polystyrene foam panels should be liberally coated with adhesive by serrated trowel and the panels should then be placed in their final position on the wall or ceiling surface. Firm hand pressure should then be applied to the foam panels to ensure overall contact of the surfaces. The initial tack of the adhesive is sufficient to hold the foam firmly in position without any sustained mechanical pressure, but if necessary slight adjustments can be made in the positioning of the panels while the adhesive is still wet.

One gallon is sufficient to coat approximately 8–10 sq. yd. of polystyrene foam.

"Evo-stik" Impact Adhesive 567

This adhesive has been specially developed to provide a strong, efficient bond for cellular pvc and micro-cellular foam without the need of applying the adhesive to its surface and is particularly suitable for honeycomb structures such as "Plasticell", "Polyzote", etc. and also many types of wool-backed pvc such as "Lanide".

Application is by brush to surfaces of the metal, wood, plaster or component to which the cellular construction panel is to be bonded, taking care that an even film of adhesive is spread overall. Allow this to dry for approximately 15 minutes. At this stage, a strong resin-tack commences and will stay tacky for two hours, during which time the other component should be pressed firmly on to the adhesive film using hand pressure for cellular construction panels and a light roller for wool or other backed pvc or similar materials.

"Pitagrip" White Adhesive

Seal the substrate to which foam is to be stuck with "Pitagrip" diluted with 2 parts of water to satisfy all the suction present. A full coat of "Pitagrip" is applied when the sealing coat is dry. The foam is pressed into place when the full coat is nearly dry and is beginning to set up.

Dunlop Chemical Products Division

SF styrene foam. This adhesive is for bonding foam products to wood, concrete, plaster, hardboard, asbestos, brickwork, painted surfaces, etc.

"Styroglue" 600

"Styroglue" 600 is an adhesive for bonding expanded polystyrene to itself or to other surfaces, such as wood, plaster, cement etc. This adhesive is not recommended for bonding to ceilings; for this work "Styroglue" 560 is to be preferred.

The advantages claimed for "Styroglue" 600 are:—Easy to spread; coated to one surface only; no solvent attack on polystyrene, even at elevated temperatures; resistance to heat superior to the melting-point of the polystyrene; easy removal of the panels or tiles if the position is not satisfactory; not affected by frost.

Directions for the use of "Styroglue" are summarized as follows:

(1) Surfaces to be bonded should be cleaned and free from dust. Metal surfaces should be degreased. New plaster should be left for at least 7 days before bonding, and oil-based paints should be keyed with a wire brush. When working in an area with high humidity, such as in a cold store, the surface moisture must be wiped away just prior to bonding.

(2) The adhesive should be well stirred before use.

(3) For porous bases the adhesive should be applied with a thin film to the base
with a brush or with a spatula and the expanded polystyrene placed immediately into position and pressed down.

For working large surfaces the open time will vary according to the porosity
of the base. As a guide, the open time for bonding to plaster is about 3–5 minutes
at 65°F, for wood 5–8 minutes, for cement 8-12 minutes.

For non-porous surfaces or for bonding polystyrene to itself, the application
of the adhesive to both surfaces is recommended; the open time will vary between
10–40 minutes at 65°F.

"National" 7550

This adhesive is for bonding "Flamingo" foam expanded polystyrene to plaster
board, hardboard, porous wall and ceiling surfaces, and wood. The adhesive should
be applied by brush to the substrate only. The average coverage is 150 sq. ft. per
gallon (10 lb. adhesive) although on dense, smooth, less absorbent surfaces 200 sq.
ft. per gallon (10 lb. adhesive) is possible. "National" 7550 is not recommended
for use where any dampness is likely to occur.

"National" 31-343

For bonding "Flamingo" foam expanded polystyrene to itself, plaster, cement,
concrete, hardboard and wood. Can be based on aluminium strip construction—
pipe shell lagging.

"Aquaseal" No. 1975

This is a bitumen–rubber emulsion adhesive of the contact type specially
intended for erecting "Flamingo" foam expanded polystyrene. It is for brush
application, but may also be applied by notched trowel. When applied by the
latter the material should be spread horizontally on to the polystyrene and vertically
on to the wall. This method of application ensures maximum contact area.

"Aquaseal" No. 1975 is applied to both surfaces at the rate of 90–100 sq. ft.
per gallon and allowed to dry for approximately one hour before the two surfaces
are fixed together. This covering capacity gives a wet-coat thickness of approximately $\frac{1}{24}$ in. and a dry thickness of approximately $\frac{1}{40}$ in.

Where this adhesive is used on inverted surfaces, additional mechanical support
should be provided. (See "British Standard Code of Practice CP.406/1952", page
32/Section 3-304.)

When fixing a second layer of insulation, in addition to the adhesive, it will be
skewered to the first layer in the normal manner.

"Kingsnorth" Compound No. 1983

A solid bitumen compound for erecting "Flamingo" foam expanded polystyrene.
The recommended working temperature for the material is 160–175°F. and its
heat resistance—Tombstone Mould Test—is over 100°F. The working temperature
will require careful control for, if the material is not hot enough it will be too
viscous for dipping, whereas if it is too hot, the insulation may be affected.

Dip the slabs in molten Compound No. 1983 heated to a temperature of 160–
180°F. and apply slabs to surface while the compound is still hot and sticky and
press firmly in position.

Where these adhesives are used in inverted surfaces, additional mechanical
support should be provided.

Covering capacity is 560 sq. ft. per cwt.

"Polytak" 200 and "Polytak" 860

These products are also for bonding "Flamingo" foam expanded polystyrene. The materials to which bonding can be effected are:

Asbestos board (hard); asbestos board (soft); brick; cardboard; plastics (some); wood; cement; hardboard; glass and metals; painted surfaces; plywood; polystyrene foam; plaster.

Application is by brush, spreader or spray, the covering capacity being approximately 270 sq. ft. per gal. (*per one surface*). This grade, which is water "white", provides a permanent and superior bond with most materials but, being rather thin needs care in application. Where a low-density polystyrene foam is used and only the "highlights" are in contact with the other material, the greater filling property of "Polytak" 860 will be preferred.

Although two-coat systems are preferable, "Polytak" 200 is not strictly a contact adhesive and it is often possible to make a good bond with only one coat which should generally be to the foam.

"Polytak" 200 is thermoplastic and will begin to soften at a temperature of 174°F. (80°C.).

"Bitutherm" 840 Adhesive

"Bitutherm" 840 adhesive has been formulated for fixing "Flamingo" foam expanded polystyrene to wood, concrete, plaster, brickwork, asbestos-cement sheeting and metal. The adhesive possesses an excellent "grab" and there is no need to use a mechanical means of support when fixing to ceilings.

The adhesive should be applied with a deep notched trowel at the rate of 1 to 2 lb. per sq. yd. on porous surfaces and ¾ lb. per sq. yd. on smooth non-porous surfaces such as metal. The foam should then be placed in position and pressed firmly home.

"Bitutherm" Hot-Dip

A bitumen-wax compound applied hot, it has been formulated for fixing "Flamingo" foam expanded polystyrene to itself and to non-porous surfaces. The surface must be clean, dry and free from grease, oil, dust and loose material.

The compound should be broken up into small pieces and heated in a tray to a temperature of 70-80°C. (158-176°F.). The temperature must be carefully controlled. If it is too hot it will damage the foam, and if it is not hot enough the compound will be too viscous for application.

The "Flamingo" foam should be dipped into the melted compound, allowing the excess to drain off, and placed into position and pressed firmly home. It is not necessary to dip the material deeply into the compound, as a good even coating over the face to be bonded is sufficient.

When fixing to ceilings a mechanical means of support should be used in accordance with "British Standard Code of Practice". When fixing two thicknesses of foam, the two layers should be skewered together in the usual manner.

"Uni-bond" Adhesive

The surface that is to be covered with polystyrene foam must be thoroughly cleaned, free of all dust, loose matter, grime and mould oil etc.

A solution of 5 parts water to 1 part "Uni-Bond" should be applied with a brush to the surface which is to receive the foam. This coating must be allowed to dry. One part of "Uni-Bond" should be mixed with one part water and siraphite or plaster added until a thick, creamy consistency is obtained. This mix can be applied to the surface of the board using a notched trowel, or applied in daubs and the foam pressed into position by hand ensuring even pressure overall. Complete set is usually in from 8–12 hours. 1 gallon "Uni-Bond" diluted with 5 gallons of water gives a coverage of 250 sq. yd. as a priming solution. One gallon "Uni-Bond" diluted with 1 gallon of water and thickened with siraphite or plaster, covers approximately 30–45 sq. yd.

"E-P-A" Adhesive

The method of application is to apply in daubs, using a notched trowel or knife. The surface of the foam should be coated and pressed into position by hand ensuring even pressure overall. "E-P-A" has instant contact but allows time for material alignment into correct position before setting. Complete set is usually in from 10–15 hours. The coverage is 10–12 sq. yd. per gallon. The material is not suitable for fixing to surfaces that have no porosity. "E-P-A" is unaffected by extreme changes of temperature.

"Tretobond" 740

This compound bonds "Poron", "Flamingo" foam, "Jablite", "Isocolor", "Polyzote", "Spandoplast", "Corblanit", "Airlite", "Marleycel", "Lustraplas", "Thermalon", "Warmafoam", "Lorlite", "Buxspan" and other materials to wood, metal, plastic, concrete, plaster, hardboard, plasterboard, asbestos-cement panels, glass, painted surfaces and to expanded polystyrene.

When used on expanded polystyrene in sheet or block form to wood, concrete, hardboard, brick, plaster, asbestos and plasterboard, apply the adhesive with a notched trowel or scraper only to the sheet or block in a uniform thin coat overall leaving no dry spots. Present the boards to the background surface immediately and with uniform pressure slide into position and bed well home to ensure intimate contact with the background. Make sure that the edges are closely butt-joined together.

When applying the same material to metal, plastic, glass and painted surfaces, apply the adhesive with a notched trowel or scraper to *both* surfaces. Wait 20–30 minutes for the solvents to evaporate and bond into position as already described.

When bonding expanded polystyrene tiles to wood, metal, plaster, concrete, hardboard, brick, plastic, glass and painted surfaces, apply the adhesive with a pallet knife or similar tool in a series of dabs (each dab not less than 1 in. in diameter) to the back of the tile only. With 12 in. × 12 in. tiles one dab near each corner and with larger tiles also apply 4 dabs per sq. ft. Immediately present the tile to the background surface and with uniform pressure slide into position.

To seal the join between one sheet and another, a thin coat of adhesive should be applied by brush along each edge, leaving no dry spots, and when bonding the sheets into position ensure that the edges are closely butt-joined leaving no gap. The application of adhesive to the edges should be carried out when the adhesive is being applied to the surface of the sheets.

With all these applications, immediate bond strength is adequate and maximum bond strength develops within 1–3 days, though this may take longer when bonding to non-porous surfaces. The adhesive must be allowed seven days to dry out if plastering or wallpapering on top of the expanded polystyrene is subsequently to be carried out.

Do not attempt to bond to corrugated materials as there is not sufficient surface area on the corrugation to permit an effective bond being made.

Covering capacity is 50–80 sq. ft. per gal. coating two surfaces and 100–160 sq. ft. per gal. coating one surface and 120–160 sq. ft. per gal. dab method, all figures being approximate.

Expandite Adhesive L.210

This is a blend of synthetic resins in solution for fixing insulating tiles of glass-fibre, fibre board, and expanded polystyrene etc. to walls and ceilings. L.210 is light cream in colour, is ready for use, has immediate tack and possesses gap-filling properties.

8.4.3 Bonding Laminated Plastics

"Evo-stik" Impact Adhesive 528

A one-part synthetic cement developed for attaching large panels of veneered hardboard or laminated plastic sheeting to vertical surfaces, i.e. plaster walls, chip-board, Plimberite or Weyroc panels etc. An immediate strong bond ensures quick and easy installation of wall panelling without the need of strutting. Optimum strength attained after four days. It is water, oil and petrol proof and resistant to high temperatures. Coverage according to porosity of surface, with an average figure of 16 sq. yd. per gal. of veneered surface.

Hard wall plaster must be trued up free of bumps and hollows and hard brushed to remove loose paint or distemper. Surface should be free of alkalinity and dry. New plaster walls must not be veneered until at least 28 days have elapsed to allow them to dry. Laminated plastic sheeting should be wiped free of grease and other foreign matter.

Application is by brush or serrated trowel to wall surface and to back of the wall panel. A spreader made from scrap board or plastic sheeting and finely notched to gauge the thickness of the cement will quickly prove an efficient method to adopt for this operation. Allow to dry for approximately 15–20 minutes. As this "impact" adhesive will bond immediately, it is essential that care be exercised in offering up the panel to its exact seating position, lining up one edge first and using hand press-ure over the panel as the joint is made. To ensure overall contact, use a rubber roller of a type similar to a washing machine wringer, particularly along butting edges.

An alternative method of application is for the adhesive to be applied to the wall surface, also by spreader, and allowed to dry thoroughly, up to 24 hours. The wall panel is then coated and after 5 minutes is carefully offered up into position. This method, called the "wetting back system", has the advantage that the whole wall surface can be treated in one operation some hours before final assembly, showing subsequent lower labour costs.

Extra-porous wall board surfaces may need two coats of the adhesive, but as a general rule one application by the spreader method is sufficient.

"Evo-Stik" Cement 528

This cement has been developed for use where 6 ft. $\times$ 3 ft. or 8 ft. $\times$ 4 ft. panels have to be bonded to vertical surfaces. The open-tack time (drying time), has been extended to answer this problem, and the operator can now easily spread the cement to both surfaces without the danger of the adhesive films becoming too dry before the bonding operation takes place.

It is also being used with great success for edge veneering by fabricators of small components, such as table tops and counters, as after 20–30 minutes of the "impact" bond being made, the edge veneer can be planed or filed to the surface dimensions, and the horizontal veneering proceeded with immediately. The use of pressure jigs is unnecessary. "Evo-stik" Cleaner No. 191 should be used to remove surplus adhesive from tools, etc.

"Tretobond" 404

The material bonds "Formica", "Arborite", "Warerite", "Evergleam", "Perstorp", "Decorplast", "Panax", "Coronet", "Lustrex", "Respatex", "Panelyte", "Consalac", "Polypanel", "Laconite", "Fablonite", and other types to wood, plywood, metal, plastic, plaster, smooth concrete and other surfaces. The approximate covering capacity is 140–160 sq. ft. per gal. bonded area, or 280–320 sq. ft. per gal. coating one surface.

During application, allow the adhesive to dry until, when touched lightly with the knuckles, it feels tacky but adhesive does not come away. This may take from 10–20 minutes, depending on local temperature and conditions. Position the coated materials accurately and bond firmly together using a roller or similar appliance to exclude air pockets and to ensure intimate contact between the 2 surfaces overall. Hand pressure is sufficient but a few minutes in a cold press will produce a more powerful bond. Maximum bond strength develops in 24 hours and the final bond is claimed to be permanent, waterproof, and resistant to heat, oils, mild acids, alkalis and petrol.

Expandite Adhesive S. 92

The material is especially recommended for bonding plastic veneers to walls, table tops etc. It possesses useful "open" time and provides a weatherproof joint of high tensile strength and elasticity.

"Bostik" 3

"Bostik" 3 permanent contact adhesive for "Formica" and all laminated plastics is specially formulated to give a powerful and permanent bond between "Formica", other laminated plastics, "Warerite" wallboard, other plastic-faced hardboards, edging strip and table tops, draining boards, cupboard doors and shelves, kitchen units, vanity tables, dressing tables, bathroom units and so on. It is proof against heat, petrol, grease, steam, oil, water, household acids etc.; in this respect it holds the Good Housekeeping Institute Seal of Guarantee. Since it is smooth and free flowing, it is quick and easy to spread and gives an even film of adhesive over both surfaces to be joined, which is essential for a permanent bond.

Directions for Use

(1) Make sure the surfaces to be joined are clean, dry, level and rigid.
(2) Spread a thin, even film of "Bostik" 3 on both surfaces to be joined (starting with the panel), using a piece of plywood, stiff card, a brush or a trowel.
(3) Take special care to spread the adhesive right up to the edges.
(4) Leave the two surfaces to dry for approximately 20 minutes.
(5) Make sure that the sheet is positioned exactly and then, starting from one end first, ease it down into position, pressing firmly from the centre outwards over all the panel to ensure that no air is trapped underneath.

Note: Once the two surfaces have been joined, adhesion is immediate and permanent. It is therefore important to place the sheet in correct position first time. In order to ensure that one gets this exact positioning, stick a few drawing pins into the vertical edge at one end of the table or draining board or whatever is being treated, so that the rounded heads of the pins project above the horizontal surface. Rest corresponding edge of plastic sheeting against these pinheads and then gradually press the panel down from this end to the other, rubbing the surface down with the hands. This will help to ensure an exact fit. Always replace cap of container after use.

LP Laminated Plastics

Easy-to-use, brushable contact adhesive for decorative laminates: excellent as a general purpose adhesive.

8.4.4 Bonding Boards

Many boards have to be dampened before use and manufacturers should be consulted for recommendations.

"Evo-stik" Impact Adhesive 528 and Evotex Adhesives SL.820

For the application of these see Sections 8.4.3 and 8.4.7 respectively.

"Tretobond" 425

A powerful synthetic rubber contact adhesive designed for bonding even the heaviest of insulation boards and acoustic tiles to walls and ceilings. It produces an immediate powerful bond which eliminates the need for any mechanical support. Drying before use may take from 10–30 minutes, depending on temperature and conditions. Position the boards or tiles accurately and bond into position with uniform pressure ensuring overall contact between the two adhesive-coated surfaces. A powerful immediate bond is obtained and maximum bond strength develops within from 24–48 hours.

8.4.5 Bonding Acoustic Tiles

"Tretobond" AT/79 (Light tiles)

This adhesive is used for fixing "Perfonit", "Perfonit Extra", "Treetex", "Celotex", "Huntonit", "Tentest", "Sundeala", "Kilnoise", "Gyptone", "Travertone", "Celotone" and all light-weight acoustic and ceiling tiles measuring 12 in. × 12 in., 16 in. × 16 in., 18 in. × 18 in., and 12 in. × 24 in. Suitable background surfaces include walls and ceilings of plaster, concrete, brick, wood, metal, hardboard, glass, plastic, asbestos, and sound painted surfaces. The adhesive should be stored in a dry place at a temperature between 50°–80°F.

Preparation of Surfaces: Background surfaces must be clean, dry, sound, level and free from high spots or protrusions. New plaster takes from 6 to 8 weeks to dry and new concrete should be about 6 months old. In new buildings, the heat should have been on for at least two weeks prior to installation or the installation preceded by two weeks of dry, warm weather. If efflorescence and dust cannot be removed, the surface must be treated with a thin, brush-applied coat of "Tretobond" A.T. primer at the rate of 300 sq. ft. per gal. This dries within 4–8 hours, depending on local temperature and humidity, after which the tiles may be fixed in the usual way.

The acoustical contractor is responsible for the examination and acceptance of all surfaces and conditions affecting the proper installation of the tiles. Technical advice is available on request.

Application: Apply the adhesive with a pallet knife, trowel or similar tool in a series of dabs, not more than 2 in. in diameter and up to $\frac{1}{4}$ in. thick, to the back of the tile only (with a 12 in.×12 in. tile, one dab near each corner). Present the tile to the background surface in its approximate final location and with uniform pressure slide it back and forth until the tile is felt to grip firmly. Immediate bond strength is adequate and a powerful bond develops within three days which is highly resistant to heat and moisture and is permanent.

Gap-filling: Where part of the ceiling is unlevel, gap-filling may be achieved by raising the thickness of the dab at the appropriate corner, but do not pull the tile down at one corner to level it as this may break the adhesive dab. Remove the tile, add more adhesive as necessary and re-apply. The maximum depth of gap-filling should not be more than ¼ in. to compensate for uneven backgrounds as the adhesive strength is reduced as the thickness of the dabs increase.

Covering Capacity: Approximately 80–100 sq. ft. per gal.

"Tretobond" 425 (Heavy tiles)
See Section 8.4.4.

Dunlop Chemical Products Division
AT acoustic tile—Mastic—for tiles up to 12 in. × 24 in., only 4–5 blobs needed; Adhesive—contact-type for larger tiles and panels.

8.4.6   Bonding Flooring Products
The adhesives employed may vary according to the sub-floor or the floor to be laid. This point should be kept in mind when examining the information here given.

The different types of adhesives for flooring are given in "British Standard Code of Practice 203:1961" for sheet and tile flooring. The Table which follows is a reproduction of Table 1 of this specification.

"Evo-Stik" Adhesive 873
A specialized synthetic rubber-resin emulsion adhesive for permanently bonding pvc and rubber floor tiles and sheeting, linoleum, "Hypalon", and any felt or hessian-backed floor covering material to concrete, cement screeds, timber hard-board and other porous sub-floors. The adhesive has extremely good water resistance, can withstand high temperatures and is, therefore, suitable for use where under-floor heating systems have been installed.

The adhesive should be applied by brush, roller or serrated trowel to the floor surface only. The flooring material should then be placed immediately in position and pressed firmly down to ensure overall contact. In the case of asphalt floors, however, it is essential to apply one coat of adhesive to the asphalt and one coat to the floor covering material, allowing them both to dry before assembly. One gallon of "Evo-Stik" Adhesive 873 is sufficient to cover approximately 25 sq. yd., depending on the porosity of the surface.

"Evo-Stik" Impact Adhesive S.H.100 and S.H.25
A one-part synthetic cement which develops strong initial "tack" within five minutes of application. Easy to apply, it possesses similar qualities to that of the pvc floor tile, being waterproof, oil and petrol proof, resistant to high temperatures and dilute acids. Adheres strongly to non-porous surfaces, reaching its optimum strength after four days, but floor surfaces can be used immediately after assembly, as its immediate bond holds tile firmly in its position.

Coverage approximately 12 sq. yd. per gal. Supplied in one-gallon containers.

It has been particularly developed for attaching pvc (plastic) tiles and sheeting to all floor surfaces, and because of its strong initial tack, is claimed to be eminently suitable for covings, and treads and risers in staircase work.

It is applied by brush or serrated trowel to the floor surface, and to the back of tile, working quickly and evenly in one direction only. Allow to dry, until the adhesive film can be touched without lifting, before final assembly. Press the two surfaces together over the whole area to ensure overall contact. Alternatively, apply by brush

Group	Type of adhesive	Thermoplastic flooring tile	PVC (vinyl) asbestos tile	Flexible PVC* Unbacked	Flexible PVC* Fabric backed	Linoleum and cork carpet	Cork	Rubber
Water-based adhesives	Starch	NS	NS	NS	S	S For 2 mm gauge or less	NS	P
	Casein	NS	NS	NS	S	S	P	NS
	Lignin (Sulphite-lye)	NS	NS	NS	S	S	S	NS
Emulsion adhesives	Rubber-Bitumen emulsion	S	S	NS	P	S	P	NS
	Bitumen emulsion	S	S	NS	S	S	P	NS
	Latex emulsion (natural or synthetic)	NS	S	S	S	S	P	NS
Solvent adhesives	Natural or synthetic rubber solutions	NS	P	NS	P	S	P	S
	Cutback bitumen	S	S	P	P	S	S	NS
	Gum-spirit	NS	NS	NS	S	S	S	P
Chemical setting	Rubber latex cement	P	P	NS	S	S	P	S

S = "suitable" and is used to indicate the most commonly used types of adhesives; NS = "unsuitable"; P = "possible", and indicates the use of certain adhesives for the fixing of particular flooring materials.
*Hessian-backed and some unbacked flexible pvc's are stained by anti-oxidants included in some rubber-based adhesives.

or serrated trowel a thin coat of the adhesive to back of floor tile, and allow to dry thoroughly. Tiles thus coated can be left for 24 hours if necessary. Apply adhesive to floor surface in a similar manner and after five minutes (approximately) lay pre-coated tile in position, pressing firmly home by hand. This will ensure immediate adhesion. "Evo-stik" Cleaner No. 185 should be used to remove surplus adhesive from tiles and tools.

"Evo-Stik" Cement 5080

This cement develops an exceedingly strong bond after final drying (approx-

19

imately 24 hours), but the initial tack will hold components in position after assembly within 30 minutes. Coverage is approximately 20 sq. yd. to one surface.

"Tretobond" T.658

Developed for cork-lino and felt-backed pvc.

"Cascoset" MT-3

A latex emulsion adhesive specially made for bonding a variety of floor tiles and sheet flooring including the high vinyls. The flooring includes: Vinyl (unbacked), vinyl (fabric backed), vinyl asbestos and cork bonded to wood, concrete, asphalt etc.

Vinyl tiles contain a certain amount of plasticizer in their composition. It is well known that this plasticizer has a tendency to migrate from the tile to the adhesive, causing the tile to shrink and the adhesive to soften. The adhesive can then rise through the gaps to result in an unsightly appearance.

This adhesive has been produced to combat this problem. By careful formulation "Cascoset" MT-3 is claimed to overcome the problem of plasticizer migration. Research shows that more flooring fails through shrinkage, lifting, curling, etc. than by fair wear and tear, so this problem of shrinkage must not be under-estimated, particularly when dealing with vinyl flooring. The adhesive is suitable for bonding all grades of flexible vinyls.

The coverage is 25–30 sq. yd. per gal. $(4 \cdot 5$–$5 \cdot 5$ m.^{2} per litre) of "Cascoset" MT-3 on reasonable screeds and floor bases. The adhesive is applied only to the floor and thus no time is wasted applying the adhesive to the tile as well. It spreads easily and has a good open assembly period (20 minutes at 70°F./21°C.).

The adhesive never completely hardens or becomes brittle but retains a degree of flexibility. Trowel lines will not show through when using thin vinyls. It withstands intermittent wetting and so can be washed at intervals. It withstands temperatures up to 120°F./50°C., making it suitable for use where underfloor heating is installed. Cascoset MT-3 is pale-tan in colour and will not stain the surfaces. Adhesive that accidentally gets on to the tile surface can be wiped off with a damp rag. The material is non-toxic and non-inflammable.

Armstrong Adhesive L.90

A bituminous adhesive for fixing "Accoflex" and "Accotile" thermoplastic tiles on direct-to-earth or suspended concrete sub-floors which have been screeded. Spreading capacity is 18–22 sq. yd. per gal.

Armstrong Adhesive L.128

This is for bonding lining felt to floor or hardboard, and linoleum, custom "Corlon", sheet "Corlon", "Linotile", Armstrong rubber tile and fibrous-backed pvc, to felt or floor. It is not recommended for direct-to-earth concrete sub-floors, or where excessive spillage of water is anticipated. Spreading capacity is 15–19 sq. yd. per gal.

Armstrong Adhesive L.510

This is a bitumen-latex emulsion for fixing "Accoflex" and "Accotile" thermoplastic tiles to asphalt saturated paper felt, or to suspended or direct-to-earth screeded concrete floors without the need for a primer except where the screed is dusty, but is not recommended where conditions of excessive dampness are suspected. It has a short setting-off time. Spreading capacity is approximately 15–18 sq. yd. per gal.

Armstrong Adhesive L.520

A spirit-based water-resisting adhesive for fixing cork tile, custom vinyl cork tile and linoleum sheet or tile to suspended or direct-to-earth sub-floors, and for coved skirting. Cork or linoleum should not be laid on a direct-to-earth sub-floor unless it is efficiently damp-proofed. L.520 has a relatively short open time and a good initial tack. It is also suitable for use with Armstrong wall tile. Covering capacity is approximately 12–14 sq. yd. per gal.

Dunlop Chemical Products Division

RF rubber flooring—Suitable for under-floor heating, permanently secures sheet or tiles to metal, wood or concrete sub-floors.

PT plastic floor/wall tile—Suitable for under-floor heating and all subfloor screeds, immune to plasticiser migration.

8.4.7   Bonding Flexible PVC
"Evotex" Adhesive SL.820

This is recommended for bonding all types of decorative and flexible pvc to wall surfaces and working tops such as plaster, hardboard, plywood etc.

A one-part adhesive ready for immediate use, which is non-toxic, non-inflammable and which can be applied by brush, roller-coat or spray. It is colourless when dry, and provides a strong immediate bond. The adhesive is unaffected by ageing or atmospheric changes or temperatures up to 70°C. It is also specially compounded to prevent mould growth. Approximate coverage 30–35 sq. yd. per gal. (one surface).

It is necessary that the surfaces to be covered should be thoroughly clean and dry. Where possible, hardboard and timber should be lightly sanded. Lining papers should only be used where it is necessary to hide mechanized surface flaws in the wall surface. Edges of the paper should be butt-joined. The lining paper must be allowed to dry completely before fixing the fabric, etc. and this also applies to new plaster walls. Painted walls should be wire brushed in order to remove all grease and foreign matter, or rubbed down with a coarse-grained glass paper to form a key.

For application, prepare the flexible decorative pvc by removing the selvedge and cutting required lengths, allowing a margin for final trimming. It is essential that the entire area of the pvc cloth be covered with adhesive, as any dry spots will tend to bubble after application. Apply the adhesive to the back of the pvc and while the adhesive is still wet, place it in position on the wall. At this stage it is possible to slide the panel into its final seating position. Use a clean paperhanger's brush or cloth pad to smooth out any irregularities, taking care not to use excessive pressure which might tend to distort or stretch the material. Edges should be butt-jointed, but can be overlapped if necessary. The most effective way to butt-joint is by overlapping and then cutting through both overlaps using a sharp linoleum knife and a straight edge. The severed edges should be removed and the fabric pressed into position. Air bubbles can be pricked and pressed flat. Any surplus adhesive on the face of the fabric can be removed, before it dries, with a clean damp cloth. Brushes are easily cleaned with water and detergent.

Part 9

STRUCTURAL WORK

CONTENTS

9.1 Introduction

9.2 Polyester/Glass Structures

9.3 Laminated Wood Structures
    9.3.1 Some of the Resins Employed
    9.3.2 Some General Principles
    9.3.3 Some Detailed Examples
    9.3.4 List of Designers and Suppliers

9.4 Other Structures
    9.4.1 Use of Inflated Hose
    9.4.2 Use of Polystyrene Foam
    9.4.3 Combined Use of PVC and Glass-fibre

Part 9

STRUCTURAL WORK

9.1 Introduction

It would be incorrect to suggest that plastics are used in structural work for, with exceptions to be mentioned, they are not normally employed as load-bearing members. Some semi-structural uses have already been described, including laminates for partitioning (Section 3.5.1) and cladding products (Section 4.2).

The main exception is the use of laminated beams for covering quite large spans. Some attractive and at the same time utilitarian buildings have been made in this way.

Polyester-glass structures have been used to a certain extent but as the materials are very strong and weather resistant there is no reason why their use should not be expanded considerably. Unfortunately, the cost is not low and it is probably this which holds back progress at the moment.

There are also a number of temporary structures based on plastics and allied materials and these will be discussed. The sections are therefore divided as follows:

9.2 Polyester-Glass Structures
9.3 Laminated Wood Structures
9.4 Other Structures

9.2 Polyester-Glass Structures

A detailed description of polyester-glass products has already been given in Section 5.7. From these it will be seen that some of the principal characteristics of the products are lightness, great strength, wide colour range, ease of manufacture into a wide variety of shapes, and chemical and weather resistance. These properties obviously recommend the materials as potential structural products.

It is not therefore proposed to deal with the manufacture of such products as the techniques already described can (and are) used for light buildings. In the event of damage, it may be noted, the laminates can readily be repaired.

Some examples of the products made may be given to illustrate the potentialities. It is well known that boat hulls and car bodies are made from "Fibreglass", a well-known example being a 38 ft. 6 in. boat hull made by Halmatic Ltd. In actual building work, curbs for roof domes, shower bath units and tanks have been made from the material.

An interesting structure was made for British Railways from "Fibreglass". This was a signalling relay station in an isolated position. It was a gleaming white structure of "futuristic" design employing many curves and was chosen because of its virtual indestructibility and its ease of installation.

Another example of structural use was a church spire. This was prefabricated away from the site (a most important point) and was so light that it could be lifted into position by a crane. Dormer windows, porches and other small projections could easily be made in the same way.

The relay station referred to above was made by Mickleover Transport Ltd. Its success prompted Bakelite Ltd. to employ the material for a new telephone exchange/office block. Such a building would, of course, demonstrate their resins and work of construction was undertaken by Mickleover Transport. Full testing of the building units was undertaken by this company.

The building was a double-storey type. The lower-floor walling was similar in some ways to a curtain-wall technique, but the upper storey was entirely self-supporting and only secured to a metal angle at first-floor level.

A conventional building of this size would have weighed 84 tons but the plastics building weighed about 15 tons, 7 tons of this being steel. Such a reduction in weight affords considerable saving in foundations and transport costs.

Filon (polyester) used by Hastings Corporation for a bus shelter. Filon translucent sheeting is made by BIP Reinforced Products Ltd (*British Industrial Plastics Ltd*)

As far as the structural panels were concerned, the stressed skin method was employed, where strength is obtained from a two-directional curve. The panels are composed of an outer and inner polyester/glass skin with a rigid phenolic foam core between. The materials used were a $4\frac{1}{2}$-oz. glass mat outside; a $\frac{3}{4}$ in. core of 2 lb./ft.^{3} density and a 3-oz. glass mat inside. Such a combination has a Class I surface spread of flame rating according to BS. 476: Part 1, 1953. The double curves do give an unconventional building as far as appearance is concerned, but the design also allows the minimum number of moulds to be employed.

As to costs, those for the above building were slightly more than for a conventional building. With large scale production, however, costs could be made at least equal, not counting the saving in speed of erection, etc.

The Royal Aircraft Establishment has had a glass-reinforced observation post made by W. and J. Tod Ltd. of Weymouth. It was a completely self-supporting glass-fibre structure 12 ft. 7 in. in diameter and 8 ft. 7 in. high. None of the prefabricated sections was so big that it could not be handled by two men. One of the sections contained a moulded door. The total weight of the structure was about 900 lb.

The Plastics Products Group of English Electric Aviation Ltd. has produced a 120 ft. high and 3 ft. internal diameter factory chimney in 6 ft. sections. The chimney is, of course, resistant to corrosive gaseous effluents and weathering.

"Indulex" cladding units made by Indulex Engineering Co. Ltd. have been used with steel frames to produce a 21-storey block. The units are composed of layers of embossed polyester/glass-fibre laminated to two layers of asbestos sheeting, separated by a core of glass or plastic foam. The units are 8 ft. 6 in. high by 9 ft. wide with continuous neoprene gaskets in all edges.

Fibreglass Reinforced Plastics Ltd. make "Spreglass", a permanent wall panelling for indoor or outdoor use. It has built-in thermal insulation.

Allan Blunn Ltd. also produce their Galt glass in a variety of coloured and textured finishes with built-in insulation.

It will be obvious that there is a definite place for glass-fibre structures in the building industry.

9.3 Laminated Wood Structures

It is not the object of this section to describe how laminated timber frames are made—this is the province of the manufacturer. It is necessary, however, to describe what can be made to assist the architect in designing structures.

The first point to note is that there are a number of synthetic glues based on resorcinol, phenol and urea-formaldehyde resins, and casein types and not every one is suitable for all conditions. Detailed information can be obtained from the Timber Development Association Ltd., and manufacturers of the resins, but the following will serve as a guide on the subject. Under wet conditions at temperatures above 100°F. glues based on resorcinol are satisfactory and under dry conditions at temperatures above 100°F. those based on resorcinol and casein are suitable.

At temperatures below 100°F. whether wet or dry, any of the resins may be used, but casein-based glues should not be used under wet conditions. Quite a a number of manufacturers make suitable adhesives for timber gluing and a list is given in Section 8.4. Two concerns specializing in these products are CIBA (A.R.L.), Ltd. and Leicester, Lovell and Co., Ltd.

9.3.1 Some of the Resins Employed
The following are some special resins available.

CIBA (A.R.L.) Ltd.
"Aerolite 300" (Urea type)
A liquid adhesive for assembly gluing, that is for constructional and joinery purposes, and primarily intended for use at ordinary shop temperature. It is widely

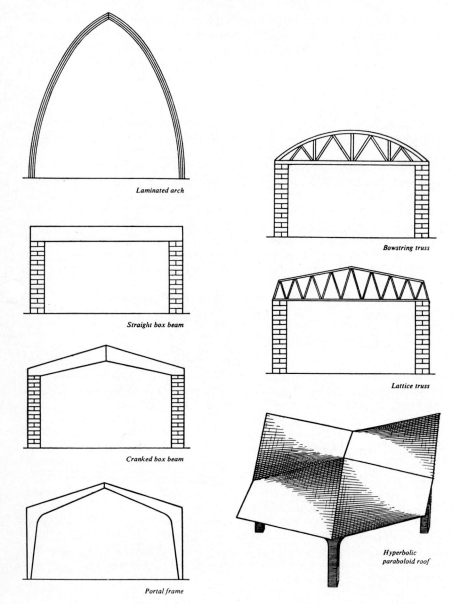

Laminated arch

Straight box beam

Cranked box beam

Portal frame

Bowstring truss

Lattice truss

Hyperbolic
paraboloid roof

Glued timber structures (*CIBA (A.R.L.) Ltd*)

used for building roof trusses and portal arches and for making laminated timber structures. Used with one of the GB hardeners it produces gap-filling glue lines which are free from subsequent crazing. In conjunction with Hardener GU.X, "Aerolite" 300 is used for the cold-bonding of laminated plastic sheet to wood.

"Aerolite" 311 (Urea type)

A new gap-filling resin specially suited for the making of large laminated timber structures. Used with one of the L.B.-range of hardeners it has a long closed assembly time, i.e. plenty of time is available in making up the structure for adjustments before full clamping pressure is applied.

"Aerodux" 185 (Resorcinol type)

This formulation has outstanding durability under severe conditions of exposure. It is gap-filling and has excellent resistance to moisture and bacterial attack. It conforms to the requirements of B.S.S.1203:1954/WBP and B.S.S.1204:1956/WBP (GF and CC). "Aerodux" 185 is tolerant of moisture content in the wood being glued. It cures at normal shop temperatures and is extensively used for the construction of laminated building structures, trusses and joinery. It is an excellent adhesive for many different materials, including cement-asbestos, brick, concrete, unglazed porcelain, rubber, cork and linoleum. The product is used with Hardener HRP 150, HRP 155 or HRP 300 as a mixed-application glue.

"Aerodux" 500 (Resorcinol type)

Similar uses to "Aerodux" 185. It is supplied in three grades—fast, medium and slow. All three are used in conjunction with Hardener 501, producing a system which will mix and spread easily. The mixture, when cured, conforms to the requirements of B.S.S. 1203: 1954/WBP and B.S.S. 1204: 1956/WBP (GF and CC).

Leicester, Lovell and Co. Ltd.

The following are some special resins made by this company.

Type	Grade	Specification	Weather Resistance
Casein	"Casco" Grade 1188 (powder)	B.S. 1444, Type A	Internal use only
	"Cascamite" "One Shot" (powder, incorporating hardener)	B.S. 1204, Type MR/GF	
Urea resin	"Casco"-Resin M.1195 (liquid) and separate application hardener M.1196	B.S. 1204, Type MR/GF	Semi-exposure
	"Cascamite" 6-D (powder and separate application Hardener M.1196	B.S. 1204, Type MR/GF	

Type	Grade	Specification	Weather Resistance
Resorcinol resin	"Cascophen" RS. 216–M* (liquid and hardener FM. 60–M (powder)	B.S. 1204, Type WBP/GF	Full exposure, including exposure to chemically polluted air
	"Cascophen" RS. 240–M* (liquid and hardener FM. 124 (powder)	BS. 1204, Type WBP/GF	

*Available for release to the requirements of the Aeronautical Inspection Directorate of the Ministry of Supply and approved by the Admiralty and the Surveyors of Lloyds Register of Shipping.

9.3.2   Some General Principles

Before considering the wide range of buildings which have employed laminated timber products, it is essential to give some of the general principles which have been formulated by Ciba (A.R.L.) Ltd.

The weakness of timber structures has always been in the joints. Modern glues, however, are capable of making joints which, when tested to destruction, break in the wood rather than in the glueline.

Glued timber structures can be conveniently classified thus: (1) laminated structures; (2) box beams; (3) portal frames; (4) lattice trusses and (5) shell roofs.

(1) Laminated Structures

The main advantages of lamination are that structures of almost any size and shape can be constructed. They can be made without the use of extensive tooling such as is necessary for steel structures, and the production in small quantities is therefore an economic proposition.

The surfaces to be glued require planing to fairly accurate dimensions, and scarfs are cut for the jointing of laminations in the same layer. In the finished structure such joints must be staggered. For small structures, glue can be applied by brush, but when large structures are being made it is usual to employ a mechanical glue spreader for the main surfaces, and to use a brush only on the scarf joints. In assembling, nails or dowels are used only to position the laminations and maintain contact while the glue sets. Where straight beams are being made, clamping arrangements can be comparatively simple. For example, the beam can be placed between rolled-steel joists, using a turn-buckle to apply pressure. For angular or curved members, special jigs of wood or steel are necessary. It is often convenient to clamp a number of components in the same jig. Waxed paper can be used to prevent adhesion between the components and the jig.

(2) Box Beams

Box beams can be made by gluing plywood webs to softwood flanges so that bending stresses are taken up in the plywood. Such beams can be straight or cranked.

(3) Portal Frames

For small halls, churches and schools, it is often convenient to provide a framework by means of portal arches, built in much the same manner as box beams with plywood webs and softwood flanges. The frames are generally made in two sections, each having a vertical part, the "leg", and a "rafter" running from the eave to the ridge of the building. The angle at the eave is generally referred to as the "knee". The legs and rafters are normally tapered from knee to base and from knee to ridge.

The portal frame has the advantage of providing an unobstructed floor space and when suitably constructed the structural weight is small. Portal frames built of timber have the advantage that purlins and walling members can be attached easily by ordinary joinery methods. The frames, when suitably designed, form an interior feature of great beauty, and they are easily decorated. Being of hollow construction they can accommodate electric wiring or other services. The separate halves are convenient to handle both in manufacture and transit. At the site, a frame requires mechanical handling only of the most simple kind—such as a block and tackle. The foot is generally bolted to a metal shoe embedded in concrete, and the join at the ridge is often made with a "secret" bolt.

(4) Lattice-type Trusses

For wider spans, lattice-type trusses are often adopted. These can be of the bowstring type, that is with the upper or compression member curved, or all the members can be straight.

A form of construction developed in Germany consists of a lattice beam with top and bottom chords machined from the solid with mortices along the length. Struts are made with tenons at both ends and are glued into the mortices with "Aerodux" 185 adhesive. This is known in Germany as the Dreieck-Streben-Bau (D.S.B.) system and in Britain as warren girder construction. It is used in roof structures for purlins as well as rafters.

(5) Shell Roofs

A shell roof consists of a sheet of material which is generally thin and therefore light in weight, and rigid as a result of curvature. Such roofs can be made at low costs without specially skilled labour, and with materials having good thermal insulation. Glued laminations of timber provide an outstanding way of obtaining these advantages.

Shell roofs can conform to simple geometric shapes such as a spherical dome. Recently a number of other geometric shapes have been analyzed and used to form roof structures.

One of these is the hyperbolic paraboloid, which can be described as a square sheet lifted at diagonally opposite corners and depressed at the other two corners. Thus the sheet is concave across one diagonal and convex across the other. Roofs of this kind have been erected in various parts of the country for schools, halls, factories and agricultural buildings.

The glues recommended for the building of laminated structures, box beams, portal frames, lattice beams and shell roofs are "Aerolite" 300, "Aerolite" 311 and "Aerodux" 185.

9.3.3 Some Detailed Examples

The first three structures to be described were designed by T.C.D. Services Ltd. using materials made by Ciba (A.R.L.) Ltd. The fourth was made with the use of glues produced by Leicester, Lovell and Co. Ltd.

(1) Glued plywood portal arches are now widely used as a framework for buildings such as churches, assembly halls, libraries and gymnasiums. They are generally adopted when the span is up to about 60 ft. Of great interest therefore is the construction of a set of arches of far greater span.

The contract in question was for the erection of a sports hall at Hylton Red House Comprehensive School, Sunderland. The building was to be 110-ft. square with sufficient height to allow for ball games such as tennis, badminton and netball. It would also be used for general assembly purposes, and the internal appearance had, therefore, to be suitable for formal occasions. The use of steel was discounted because of the higher capital expenditure and maintenance costs, and it was decided to build the framework in wood.

A further feature of interest was that the site had a known line of possible subsidence cleavage and this had to be taken into account.

The designs provided for four portal units (half frames) of 62-ft. span stretching from the corners of the building towards the centre; eight units of 44-ft. span set at right angles to the walls of the building and joining the 62-ft. frames near the centre of the building; and eight units of 22-ft. span also at right angles to the walls of the building and joining the 62-ft. frames half-way along their length. The system of arches does not reach fully to the centre of the building. The frames are, however, joined to four box beams which form a central square of 22 ft.

As a result, the whole structure is light at its centre and each quadrant is self-supporting. Thus, if any movement were to take place in the site, this would be accommodated without threat to the safety of the building.

For plywood frames of this size an entirely novel mode of construction was adopted. First, a simple box core of suitable profile was constructed consisting of 7 in. × 2 in. softwood members with $\frac{3}{8}$ in. plywood both sides. To the top and bottom of this core prelaminated chords were glued. The sides of the structure were then planed down and completely covered with a further skin of $\frac{3}{8}$ in. plywood glued on.

All gluing operations were performed with "Aerodux" 500 resorcinol adhesive.

The roof covering of the building consists of corrugated asbestos-cement sheets laid on 10 in. × 3 in. purlins, the surface of the roof following the profile of the frames. The central square is covered by a glass-fibre dome 22-ft. sq. with a maximum thickness of $\frac{3}{8}$ in. This dome, which provides ample lighting to the centre of the building, is one of the biggest of its kind ever made.

On the sides of the building the glazing panels are parallel with the internal slope of the portal frames so that the curved asbestos-cement sheets overhang the wall cladding, providing an open soffit which gives ample ventilation. At the same time there is full weather protection and draughts, which would be a big disadvantage for certain ball games, are eliminated. The building is unheated. All the internal woodwork is coated with a polyurethane foam system.

It is claimed that by the use of glued timber construction this large area has been covered at a cost lower than could be attained with any other material. Furthermore, the building is aesthetically attractive and maintenance costs will be low.

(2) Another example is the assembly hall in Bede Hall at Billingham Campus Schools, Billingham, Co. Durham. This assembly hall is one of three on this campus project, which forms a school of about 2,500 places.

It is 80 ft. long and has a timber framework made by Laminated Wood Ltd. of Bideford, Devon, using "Aerodux" 500. There are five portal frames with a span of 42 ft. and set at 20-ft. centres, supporting purlins at approximately 6-ft. centres. The overall height of the frames is 21½ ft. The roof covering is of channel-reinforced wood-wool slabs exposed on the underside, overlaid with a concrete screed about 3 in. thick in which electrical services are carried. The total roof cladding is such that the weight on each stanchion is 21½ tons.

The framework was completed by connecting the stanchion at a height of about 13 ft. with 30-in. perimeter beams, these being 3½ in. wide along the lengths of the hall and 7½ in. wide along the ends where they have to span a greater distance.

The purlins are supported in metal saddles which are not exposed, so that looking up in the finished building one sees only the beauty of the timber structure consisting of laminated purlins at right angles to the arches.

The whole of the laminated structure, after one coating of copal varnish, was erected in two weeks. Thereafter, it was exposed for several months before the cladding of the building could be completed. During this time the structure suffered no deterioration, and on completion the arches only had to be wiped down to make them entirely satisfactory.

(3) Another structure is a footbridge erected at Harlow New Town for the Harlow Urban District Council. With a clear span of 50 ft. the bridge consists of two laminated beams 66 ft. long, supported on laminated arches which compensate for the difference in site levels, one arch being 2 ft. 9 in. and the other 6 ft. 9 in. All the laminated components were prefabricated and delivered to the site ready for erection. The timber used was Douglas fir glued with "Aerodux" 185.

(4) Laminated timber was used to form an unusual vertical feature set astride a small chapel erected on the Stainer Wood Estate in Selby, Yorkshire. The chapel was built to provide church facilities for the elderly and others who were finding it difficult to travel the one-and-a-half miles or so to Selby's famous 12th century Abbey.

The existence of the Abbey makes this relatively small parish of Selby somewhat "overchurched" and, for this reason, the new chapel had to be made quite small to avoid any tendency for it to form the nucleus of a new

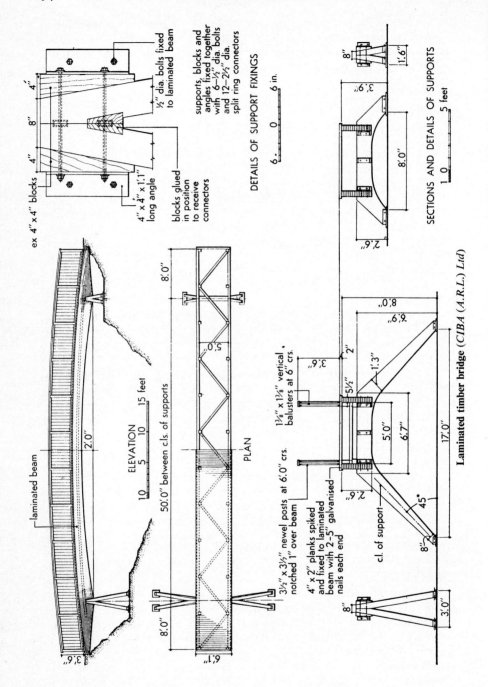

ex 4″ × 4″ blocks

½″ dia. bolts fixed to laminated beam

supports, blocks and angles fixed together with 6–½″ dia. bolts and 12–2½″ dia. split ring connectors

blocks glued in position to receive connectors

4″ × 4″ × 1.1″ long angle

DETAILS OF SUPPORT FIXINGS

6   0   6 in.

SECTIONS AND DETAILS OF SUPPORTS

1   0   5 feet

laminated beam

2.0″

ELEVATION

10   5   10   15 feet

50.0″ between c.ls. of supports

8.0″

PLAN

5.0″

3.6″

6.1″

1⅜″ × 1⅛″ vertical, balusters at 6″ crs.

3½″ × 3½″ newel posts at 6.0″ crs. notched 1″ over beam

4″ × 2″ planks spiked and fixed to laminated beam with 2–5″ galvanised nails each end

c.l. of support

8″

45°

17.0″

6.7″

5.0″

2.6″

5½″

1.3″

2″

3.6″

8.0″

6.9″

3.0″

8″

8″

8.0″

3.9″

11.6″

Laminated timber bridge (*CIBA (A.R.L.) Ltd*)

parish. At the same time, it was felt important that the new chapel, forming as it does a side chapel of the Abbey, should be seen to be a church and should be of such a design that there was no danger of it becoming overshadowed later when the other buildings for the Church Group (Vestry, Hall and Committee Rooms) were built. A vertical feature surmounted by a cross was found to meet these requirements best, and the architect selected laminated timber both for its aesthetic appeal and for its functional suitability in terms of the design.

The vertical feature takes the form of an open pyramidal structure bounded by four 60-ft. long tapered raking struts inclined to and joined at the apex. The struts were fabricated from clear Western Hemlock laminate bonded with "Cascophen" resorcinol resin glue by Kingston (Architectural Craftsmen) Ltd. They taper in section from $8\frac{1}{4}$ in. $\times$ $24\frac{1}{4}$ in. at the base to $8\frac{1}{4}$ in. $\times$ $5\frac{1}{4}$ in. at the apex and carry an 8 ft.-high Eroko cross, 4 in. $\times$ 4 in. in section, edged in aluminium; this aluminium edging also serves as the air terminal to the lightning conductor which runs down the length of one of the 63-ft. raking struts. In view of the height of the structure it was important to minimize maintenance work in the years to come. Cuprinol Ltd., the well-known specialists in wood preservation, were consulted and on their recommendation the struts were treated with six coats of their clear grade water repellent wood preserver. Apart from preventing attack by wood-boring beetles and wet rot, this product also reduces the absorption of water into timber.

Horizontal diagonal tie beams, also laminated from Hemlock, are bolted to the vertical struts and carry two inclined edge beams and a ridge beam. The edge beams support the roof of the chapel and carry the inclined timber side walls; they are positioned inside the quadruped formed by the vertical feature and are set at the same level as the tie beams to which they are fixed. The ridge beam which runs the length of the chapel is positioned above the tie beams and it is this difference in the level of the ridge and edge beams that provides the difference in level for the roof slope. The roof is simply supported with rafters which run from the ridge beam down over the top of the edge beams. The rafters support T and G timber decking and aluminium "Alstrip" roofing.

The angled gable walls are a feature of the chapel and are made up of stone reclaimed from a tithe barn originally associated with the Abbey. The 9-ft. high timber walls consist of Utile vertical members at 6 ft. centres with diagonal boarding felt and 1-in. shiplap cedar weather-boarding above which and reaching to the underside of the timber edge beams are unusual, abstractly patterned windows. These windows have externally projecting vertical fins which contrast with internal horizontal flat boards.

9.3.4   List of Designers and Suppliers

A list of some designers, manufacturers and contractors concerned with arches, beams and other structures in laminated timber is as follows:—

T.C.D. Services Ltd.,
Walter Holme and Sons Ltd.,
Laminated Wood Ltd.,

Coventry Timber Bending Co. Ltd.,
Gabriel Wade and English Ltd.,
Terrapin Ltd.,

20

Tysons (Contractors) Ltd.,
Beves and Co. (Structures) Ltd.,
H. Newsum and Sons and Co. Ltd.,
Kingston (Architectural Craftsmen) Ltd.,
Vic Hallam Ltd.,

William Kay (Bolton) Ltd.,
Knowles Woodworking Ltd.,
F. and H. Sutcliffe Ltd.,
W. Broadbent and Sons Ltd.,
Rainham Timber Engineering Co. Ltd.

9.4 Other Structures

Some unusual types of structures may be mentioned. The first is based on the use of inflated hose for the supporting members and can be temporary or permanent. The second item is based on a temporary structure from polystyrene foam. The third structure is a combination of pvc and glass-reinforced polyester resin.

9.4.1 Use of Inflated Hose

BTR Industries Ltd. produce "Plastidry" hose as high-pressure inflatable frameworks for the support of temporary or permanent structures. It was developed in co-operation with The Walter Kidde Co. Ltd. The application involves the use of individually sealed lengths of inflated "Plastidry" tubing as support members, bolted together to form a framework of the desired configuration. The framework is covered with pvc-proofed nylon, but other materials may be used to suit special requirements and conditions.

These structures, which are suitable for use in any climate, are extremely rugged and can be easily and quickly erected using either a portable air cylinder, a manual- or power-operated compressor, or a small foot pump. The "Plastidry" struts, manufactured from a nylon or Terylene woven reinforced fabric to which is fused a cover and lining of pvc compound, will maintain the working pressure for a period of 12 months or more without attention. Should any section be damaged the design is such that individual struts can be withdrawn for repair or replacement without dismantling the structure. When deflated and dismantled the whole structure can be packed quickly and compactly for easy transport.

9.4.2 Use of Polystyrene Foam

Monsanto Chemicals Ltd. have developed a new type of product called the "Geospace" dome shelter, a new light-weight easy-to-assemble dome-shaped structure suitable for a wide variety of storage purposes. The structure is formed from prefabricated triangular panels of half-inch expanded polystyrene board laminated between waterproofed kraft paper. The units are bent and bolted together in a simple geodesic design, which has the greatest strength-to-weight ratio of any type of construction. The panels are coated with a resin to give maximum protection from the effects of the weather.

The triangular panels weigh only 3 lb. each and are extremely strong, as well as having excellent insulation properties. Panels which are damaged can easily be removed and replaced. The structure, which is $12\frac{1}{2}$ ft. tall, weighs 450 lb. and contains 352 sq. ft. of usable storage space, is equipped with a hinged double door, window openings and ceiling vents.

The dome can be erected in less than a day by two unskilled men. No foundation or special site preparation is necessary. The dome bolts to a wooden base ring, which is then staked to the ground for permanence. After unstaking, it can be lifted and carried by four men, or quickly dismantled for longer moves or complete storage.

A smaller version of the "Geospace" dome, known as the "Domette" is also available. The "Domette" is nearly 7 ft. tall, 9 ft. in diameter and weighs less than 100 lb. Two people can assemble it in two hours with ordinary hand tools. The complete "Domette" "package" measures $6\frac{1}{2}$ ft. long, 3 ft. wide and $7\frac{1}{2}$ in. deep.

9.4.3 Combined Use of PVC and Glass-fibre

A. C. Plastics Ltd. of Croydon have made an interesting structure. This is a 70-ft. high stack with a steel frame filled with a combination of pvc and glass-reinforced polyester resin. The stack was made for Fisons Ltd. and the steel itself (as distinct from the outer laminate) was protected with a coating of pvc.

NEW WAYS TO BUILD WITH
BAKELITE PLASTICS

New age...new methods...new materials. And BAKELITE plastics are playing an increasingly important part in the new techniques in building and construction. For BAKELITE plastics have structural, decorative and protective properties—essential ingredients of good building materials.

All-plastics office building of sandwich construction using phenolic foam core and polyester/glass fibre skins. It is one-fifth the weight of a traditional construction. Phenolic foam has a high insulation value and can be used with plastics, metal or plywood skins.

LEFT: **Damp Proof Course** manufactured by British Cellophane Ltd, inert and rot proof—one of the many uses of **BAKELITE** Polyethylene. Film of this material is also widely used to protect men and materials on site and for concrete underlays.

RIGHT: **WARERITE** Veneered panels of Manhattan pattern are used for this entrance to Ilford Baths. Exteriors and interiors are made colourful, attractive and easy-to-clean with **WARERITE** wallboards and veneers.

Bakelite Limited

A BAKELITE XYLONITE COMPANY

12-18 Grosvenor Gardens London SW1 SLOane 0898 Birmingham (Central 5011) Manchester (Blackfriars 2861) Glasgow (City 6825)

 The trefoil symbol and the words BAKELITE and WARERITE are registered trade marks of Bakelite Limited

GB58A

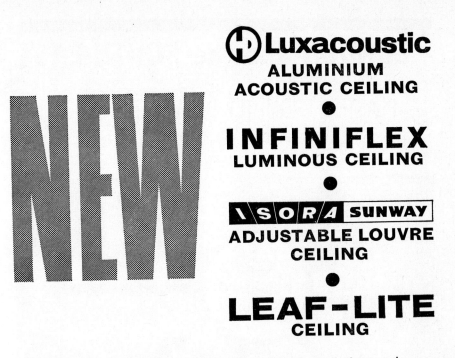

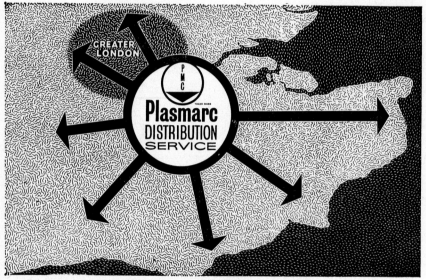
302

this
wallcovering
will stay fresh
for years

More durable than traditional wallcoverings, quicker and easier to hang, Stormur has a tough vinyl surface with a fabric backing. It has a life expectation of 10 years given normal treatment and occasional cleaning in the recommended manner. It is available in a wide range of embossed finishes in plain colours and printed effects based on British Standard colours to simplify the planning of decorative schemes.

Stormur

VINYL WALLCOVERING

IS EASILY CLEANED—CAN BE WASHED—EVEN SCRUBBED

A *Storey* PRODUCT

Write for samples and full details today to Dept. **6G**

GORCO BUREAU FILE NO. 38/10

STOREY BROTHERS AND COMPANY LIMITED, WHITE CROSS, LANCASTER. TEL: LANCASTER 3232. TELEX NO. 6587 ● BARBOUR INDEX FILE NO. 311

CIBA products from roof

CIBA resins and adhesives are used throughout the building industry for—(a) assembly and general purpose gluing of wood, (b) constructional gluing of wood to withstand extreme conditions and (c) for bonding metals, repairing concrete and for constructing wear-resisting floors etc.

AEROLITE wood glues are gap-filling and with stand wide variations in weather and temperature. They are used for making laminated beams and other glued structures, also for general assembly work involving wood-to-wood and wood-to-laminated-plastics gluing.

AERODUX resorcinol glues, which are suitable for wood, asbestos cement etc. are employed where extreme durability and resistance to exposure are required. For interior work, they find application where conditions of high humidity exist.

ARALDITE epoxy resins have remarkable properties of adhesion to metals and many other materials. Aluminium roofs and other sheet metal work can be bonded with Araldite to form immensely strong, weather-resistant structures. Monolithic floors and floor surfaces are made from Araldite and sand. They set overnight and are tough, hard wearing and resistant to many chemicals. Araldite is also invaluable for repair to concrete and other building materials.

May we add your name to the mailing list for our monthly publication 'CIBA Technical Notes'?

Aerolite, Aerodux and Araldite are registered trademarks.

CIBA (A.R.L.) LIMITED DUXFORD CAMBRIDGE
Telephone: Sawston 2121

to floor

AP781B

305

Building Plastics

BXP plastics provide the builder with a proved range of materials specially developed for applications covering every stage of building—from foundation to roof.

COBEX* Rigid Vinyl—light, light-giving and corrosion-resistant

COBEX is tough, stable, light, self-extinguishing and highly resistant to corrosion—easy to handle and to install. In tubes and extruded sections, it forms ducting, gutters, rainwater pipes, etc. that never need painting. As corrugated translucent roofing sheets, it brings glare-free light to dark places. As a cladding, COBEX opaque vinyl sheeting and fittings lend colour and modernity to buildings old and new—weathering corrosive atmosphere without maintenance.

VELBEX* Flexible Vinyl for attractive walls and panels

A tough, rotproof, waterproof and corrosion resistant sheeting in a wide range of colours, textures and designs. Bonded to aluminium, steel, hardboard, chipboard, asbestos and other materials, it makes attractive panels and partitions for interior or exterior use. VELBEX is colourfast, waterproof and maintenance-free.

BEXTHENE* Polythene Sheet for protective covers and concrete curing

A highly versatile on-site material. Provides temporary covers for men, materials and plant against rain, wind and frost. As a protective canopy it allows work to proceed on schedule in all weathers. Over or under concrete it provides a damp-proof membrane to keep out frost and moisture.

BEXPAND† Expandable Polystyrene for thermal insulation

A light, rigid material for thermal and impact sound insulation with a closed cell structure and densities as low as one pound per cubic foot. It is also used for concrete cavity forming and shuttering. Send for a comprehensive list of technical literature on the properties, applications and fabrication of these materials.

BX PLASTICS LTD

A Bakelite Xylonite Company

MANNINGTREE · ESSEX · MANNINGTREE 2401

TA 9391

308

RIGID POLYURETHANE FOAM - a new building material

With the accent on speed and economy, the increased use of prefabricated construction panels and on-site insulation methods is a feature of modern building.
®MOLTOPREN H—rigid polyurethane foam—is the ideal material for both applications. Produced from the liquid reaction components ®DESMODUR and ®DESMOPHEN, MOLTOPREN H is light in weight yet structurally strong, has excellent insulating properties and can be tailored to individual requirements.
For on-site insulation special mixing and dispensing equipment is available. Prefabricated building panels of sandwich construction type for curtain-walling, roofs, doors, are readily produced in the factory by special techniques—described in our booklet "Construction Parts with a Supporting Foam Core", available on request. For information about the raw materials DESMODUR/DESMOPHEN, the foaming equipment, and technical service—ask the pioneers of polyurethane foam.   ® Registered Trademark

Section of a MOLTOPREN sandwich structure

J.M. STEEL & CO. LTD.

Kern House, 36/38 Kingsway, London, W.C. 2, Telephone: HOLborn 2532/5
73/79 King Street, Manchester 2 · Telephone: Deansgate 6077/9
45 Newhall Street, Birmingham 3 · Telephone: Central 6342/3
144 St. Vincent Street, Glasgow C. 2 · Telephone: Central 3262/3

2562

DIRECTORY OF MANUFACTURERS AND SUPPLIERS

DIRECTORY OF MANUFACTURERS AND SUPPLIERS

AB Plastics Ltd., Cray Avenue, St. Mary Cray, Orpington, Kent.

Acalor (1948) Ltd., Kelvin Way, Crawley, Sussex.

Acrylic Industries Ltd.

Adamite Co. Ltd., 94/98 Petty France, London S.W.1.

Adhesive & Allied Products, 2/4 High Bridge Road, Barking, Essex.

Adie Manufacturing Co. Ltd.

Aerograph-Devilbiss Co. Ltd., The, Ringwood Road, West Howe, Bournemouth, Hants.

Aeroplastics Ltd., Carlyle Avenue, Hillington, Glasgow S.W.2.

Airscrew-Weyroc Ltd., Weybridge, Surrey.

Allied Iron Founders Ltd., 28 Brook Street, London W.1.

Allied Structural Plastics Ltd., Tolpits, Watford, Herts.

Arborite Co. (U.K.) Ltd., Bilton House, 54/58 Uxbridge Road, Ealing, London W.5.

Arlington Plastics Development Ltd., Arlinghide Works, Harlow, Essex.

Armabord Ltd., 24/27 Orchard Street, London W.1.

Armoride (Sales) Ltd., Armoride House, 24/27 Orchard Street, London W.1.

Armstrong Cork Co., Honeypot Lane, Kingsbury, London N.W.9.

Arnold, J., & Son, 124 Tottenham Court Road, London W.1.

Arnoplast Ltd., Queen Elizabeth Avenue, Hillington Industrial Estate, Glasgow S.W.2.

Arrow Plastics Ltd., Arrow Works, Hampden Road, Kingston-Upon-Thames, Surrey.

Artrite Resins Ltd., Stanhope Road, Camberley, Surrey.

Ashley Accessories Ltd., Ulverston, Lancs.

Associated Building Products Ltd., North Mills, Frog Island, Leicester.

Associated Electrical Industries Ltd., 33 Grosvenor Place, London S.W.1.

Atlas Lighting Ltd., Thorn House, Upper St. Martins Lane, London W.C.2.

Audio Ltd., Newport, Shropshire.

Austins of East Ham Ltd., Barking Road, London E.6.

Averill, C. R., Ltd., Alyn Mills, Gaergwile, Wrexham.

Avery Airflex Ltd., Garden Works, Eden Street, London N.W.1.

Avery, J., & Co. (Est. 1834) Ltd., 81 Great Portland Street, London W.1.

Avery, J., & Co. Ltd., 82/90 Queensland Road, Holloway, N.7.

Ayrshire Metal Products Ltd., Irvine, Ayrshire, Scotland.

Bakelite Ltd., Grosvenor Gardens, London S.W.1.

Barclay, Alan (Plastics) Ltd., 13b Grove Road South, Portsmouth, Hants.

Bardens (Bury) Ltd., Hollins Vale Works, Bury, Lancs.

Bardex (Plastics) Ltd., 119 Guildford Street, Chertsey, Surrey.

Baxenden Chemical Co. Ltd., The, Clifton House, 83 Euston Road N.W.1.

Beck, Koller & Co. (England) Ltd., Beckocite House, Edwards Lane, Speke, Liverpool.

21*

Bennett, J. & H., (Flooring) Ltd., 25 St. Barnabas Street, London S.W.1.
Berry Wiggins & Co. Ltd., Field House, Breams Buildings, Fetter Lane, London E.C.4.
Beves & Co. (Structures) Ltd., Shoreham-by-Sea, Sussex.
Binns, A. J., Ltd., Harvest Works, 99/107 St. Paul's Road, London N.1.
BIP Chemicals Ltd., Oldbury, Birmingham.
BIP Reinforced Products Ltd., Streetly Works, Sutton Coldfield.
Birkbys Ltd., Liversedge, Yorks.
Birmingham Guild Ltd., The, Grosvenor Street West, Birmingham 16.
Blue Gate Products Ltd., Faringdon Avenue, Harold Hill, Romford, Essex.
Blunn, Allan, Ltd., 29 Craven Street, London W.C.2.
Bolton Gate Co. Ltd., Tuton Street, Bolton, Lancs.
Bostik Ltd., Ulverscroft Road, Leicester.
Brand, R. A., & Co. Ltd., Works Road, Letchworth, Herts.
Brifix Ltd., Ashtead, Surrey.
Briggs, William, & Sons Ltd., Vauxhall Grove, London S.W.8.
British Bitumen Emulsions Ltd., Trading Estate, Slough, Bucks.
British Celanese Ltd., Celanese House, Hanover Square, London W.1.
British Cellophane Ltd., Henrietta House, 9 Henrietta Place, London W.1.
British Geon Ltd., Devonshire House, Piccadilly, London W.1.
British Insulated Callender's Cables Ltd., P.O. Box No. 5, 21 Bloomsbury Street, London W.C.1.
British Paints Ltd., Portland Road, Newcastle-on-Tyne 2.
British Resin Products Ltd., Devonshire House, Piccadilly, London W.1.
British Ropes Ltd., Carr Hill, Doncaster, Yorks.
British Visqueen Ltd., Six Hills Way, Stevenage, Herts.
British Werno Ltd., 79 Portland Place, London W.1.
British Xylonite Group of Companies, Highams Park, London E.4.
Broadbent, W., & Sons Ltd.
Bryce, White & Co., Deseronto Wharf, Langley, Bucks.
BTR Industries Ltd., Herga House, Vincent Square, London S.W.1.
Bulgomme-Silence, 11 Mount Park Crescent, London W.5.
Bull, The John, Rubber Co. Ltd., Evington Valley Mills, Leicester.
BX Plastics Ltd., Brantham, nr. Manningtree, Essex.

Cabot Signs Ltd.
Canopy Design Ltd., Marsh Lane, Ware, Herts.
Cape Asbestos Co. Ltd., The, 114/116 Park Street, London W.1.
Carborundum Co. Ltd., The, Trafford Park, Manchester 17.
Carson, Walter, & Sons Ltd, Holman Road, Battersea, London S.W.11.
Cascelloid (Division of British Xylonite Co. Ltd.), Britannia Works, Abbey Lane, Leicester.
Cementex (U.K.) Co., 157 High Street, Orpington, Kent.
Charlesworth Mouldings Ltd., Northcote Road, Stechford, Birmingham 33.
Chemidus Plastics Ltd., Brunswick Road, Cobbs Wood, Ashford, Kent.
Chiltern Hunt Ltd., Nash Mills, Belswains Lane, Hemel Hempstead, Herts.
Christensen, P. I., & Co. Ltd., 26/28 Bedford Row, London W.C.1.

Chubb & Sons Ltd., Wednesfield Road, Wolverhampton.

Ciba (A.R.L.) Ltd., Duxford, Cambridge.

Cisterns Ltd., Cross Bank, Balby, Doncaster, Yorks.

Clark & Chapman & Co. Ltd., Victoria Works, Gateshead, Co. Durham.

Clearex Products Ltd., Spring Works, Heather Park Drive, Stonebridge Park, Wembley, Middx.

Coates Bros. Paints Ltd., Imacula Works, Sidcup By-Pass, Sidcup, Kent.

Colodense Ltd., West Street, Bristol 3.

Commercial Plastics (Sales) Ltd., Berkeley Square House, London W.1.

Conex-Terna Limited, Whitehall Road, Great Bridge, Tipton, Staffs.

Cordor Ltd., 36 Dean Street, Newcastle-Upon-Tyne.

Corrosion Technical Services Ltd., Sunleys Island, Great West Road, Brentford, Middx.

County Furniture (London) Ltd., 1 First Avenue, Bletchley, Bucks.

Courtney Pope (Electrical) Ltd., Amhurst Park Works, Tottenham, London N.15.

Coventry Timber Bending Co. Ltd., Bodmin Road, Walsgrave, Coventry.

Cox, W. J., (Sales) Ltd., The Bothy, Tring, Herts.

Craig & Rose Ltd., 172 Leith Walk, Edinburgh 6.

Crane Ltd., 1277 Coventry Road, South Yardley, Birmingham.

Crater Products Ltd., Knaphill, Woking, Surrey.

Croid Ltd., Berkshire House, 168/173 High Holborn, London W.C.1.

Crompton Parkinson Ltd., Crompton House, Aldwych, London W.C.2.

Cromwell, E. M., & Co. Ltd., Galloway Road, Bishop's Stortford, Herts.

Crosland, R. A. & G., Ltd., Astley Mill, Bolton, Lancs.

Crossley Packings, Henry, Ltd., Astley Mill, Bolton, Lancs.

Cuprinol Ltd., 9 Upper Belgrave Street, London S.W.1.

Dahl Brothers Ltd., 21 Morley Street, London S.E.1.

Daleman, Richard, Ltd., 325 Latimer Road, London W.10.

Dalmas Ltd., 215 Charles Street, Leicester.

Dennis & Robinson Ltd., Bestwood Works, Drove Road, Old Portslade, Sussex.

Denny, R., & Co. Ltd., 15 Netherwood Road, London W.14.

Dermide Ltd., Valley Mills, Meanwood Road, Leeds 7.

Dickens, Stuart B., Ltd., Manor Way, Boreham Wood, Herts.

Dixon, Peter, & Son Ltd., 11 New Fetter Lane, London E.C.4.

Dorman Long (Steel) Ltd., Aycliffe, Co. Durham.

Dunlop Rubber Co. Ltd., 19 Berners Street, London W.1.

Duplus Domes Ltd., 58 Chatham Street, Leicester.

Du Pont (U.K.) Ltd., 76 Jermyn Street, London S.W.1.

Duraflex Housecrafts Ltd., Union Works, Carpenter Street, Manchester 1.

Durapipe and Fittings Ltd., Durapipe Works, West Drayton, Middx.

Duratube & Hire Ltd., Faggs Road, Feltham, Middx.

Dussek Bitumen & Taroleum Ltd., Louchers Lane, Wilderspool, Warrington, Lancs.

Easiclene Porcelain Enamel (1938) Ltd., Lord Street, Wolverhampton.
Eastham Thomas & Co., Holmes Road, Thornton, Blackpool.
Ekco Plastics Ltd., Ekco Works, Southend-on-Sea, Essex.
Elco Plastics Ltd., Desborough Park Road, High Wycombe, Bucks.
Ellis, J. T., & Co. Ltd., Crown Works, Wakefield Road, Huddersfield.
Elsy & Gibbons Ltd., Simonside, South Shields, Co. Durham.
English Rose Kitchens Ltd., Warwick.
Errington, S. C.,(Hanwell) Ltd., 132a Uxbridge Road, Hanwell, London W.7.
Ever-Tidy Kitchen Cabinets Ltd., Lower Stafford Street, Wolverhampton.
Evered & Co. Ltd., Surrey Works, Smethwick 50, Staffs.
Evode Ltd., Common Road, Stafford.
Expandite Adhesives Ltd., St. Helens, Lancs.
Extrudex Ltd., Western Road, Bracknell, Berks.

Fablon Ltd., Berkeley Square House, Berkeley Square, London W.1.
Falk Stadelmann & Co. Ltd., 91 Farringdon Road, London E.C.1.
Farmiloe Sealants Ltd., Nine Elms Lane, London S.W.8.
Federated Foundries Ltd., 4 Stratford Place, London W.1.
Fenton Bym & Co. Ltd., Armfield Close, West Molesey, Surrey.
Ferguson Ltd., Prince Georges Road, Merton Abbey S.W.19.
Ferro Enamels Ltd., Wombourn, Wolverhampton.
Fibreglass Ltd., Ravenhead, St. Helens, Lancs.
Folkard (Plastics) Ltd., Capital House, Broadway, Mill Hill, London N.W.7.
Fordham Pressings Ltd., Melbourne Works, Dudley Road, Wolverhampton, Staffs.
Foster Bros. (Plastics) Ltd., Leabrook Works, Wednesbury, Staffs.
Fothergill & Harvey Ltd., 37 Peter Street, Manchester 2.
Freer, W., Ltd., 68 Chatham Street, Leicester.
Fulford Brown Bros. Ltd., 6 Regent Parade, Birmingham.

G.E.C. Lighting Equipment Ltd., Witton, Birmingham 6.
General Plastics Ltd., Marden Works, Pattenden Lane, Marden, Kent.
Gerland Ltd., 90 Crawford Street, London W.1.
Getalit Ltd., Harts Lane, Barking, Essex.
Glass Fibre Developments Ltd., 25/27 Kelvin Way, Crawley, Sussex.
Goodall, R. A., & Co. Ltd., Albert Street, Redditch, Worcs.
Goodyear Tyre & Rubber Co. Ltd., Wolverhampton, Staffs.
Graceline Units Ltd., Leybourne Wharf, Norton Bridge Road, West Drayton, Middx.
Green, Albert, (Plastics) Ltd., New Normanton Mills, Charlotte Street, Derby.
Greengate & Irwell Rubber Co. Ltd., P.O. Box 62, Greengate Works, Manchester 3.
Greenwich Plastics Ltd., St. Mary's Cray, Kent.
Guest Industrials Ltd., 81 Gracechurch Street, London E.C.3.
Guest, Keen and Nettlefold Ltd., G.K.N. House, Kingsway, London W.C.2.

H.V.E (Electric) Ltd., Viaduct Works, Kirkstall Road, Leeds 4.
Hall-Thermotank Ltd., Regina House, 1/5 Queen Street, London E.C.4.
Hallam, Vic, Ltd., Langley Mill, Nottingham.
Halstead, James, Ltd., P.O. Box 3, Crow Oak Works, Whitefield, Manchester.
Harefield Rubber Co. Ltd., The, Bell Works, Harefield, Middx.
Harris & Sheldon (Display) Ltd., Bilston Road, Willenhall, Staffs.
Harrison (Birmingham) Brass Foundry Ltd., Bradford Street Works, Birmingham 12.
Harrison & Sons Ltd., Hanley, Stoke-on-Trent.
Hartington Conway & Co. Ltd., The Old Mill, Brigstock, Northants.
Haworth, V. & N., (A.R.C.) Ltd., 40 Buckingham Palace Road, London S.W.1.
Healey Mouldings Ltd., Wolverhampton Road, Oldbury, Birmingham.
Heating Investments Ltd., 12a Lodge Road, Brent Street, London N.W.4.
Hills, F., and Sons Ltd., Norton Road, Stockton-on-Tees.
Hinchliffe, E. D., & Sons Ltd., Hall Street South, West Bromwich.
Hinkleys Silica Sands Ltd., Sandiron House, Sheffield 7.
Holme, Walter, & Sons Ltd., Beach Road, Litherland, Liverpool 21.
Holmsund Flooring Ltd., 26 Calthorpe Street, London W.C.1.
Holoplast Ltd., New Hythe, nr. Maidstone, Kent.
Home Fittings (G.B.) Ltd., Victoria Works, Hill Top, West Bromwich.
Home Woodworkers Ltd., 16 Regent Place, Birmingham.
Hope, Henry, & Sons Ltd., Smethwick, Birmingham 2.
Howson, George, & Sons Ltd., P.O. Box No. 6, Eastwood Sanitary Works, Hanley.
Hughes Brushes Ltd., 32 Ajax Avenue, Slough, Bucks.
Humasco Ltd., 23 Old Bailey, London E.C.4.
H.V.E. (Electric) Ltd., Viaduct Works, Kirkstall Road, Leeds 4.
Hygene Ltd., Kirby, Liverpool.

I.C.I. Ltd., Paints Division, Rexham Road, Slough, Bucks.
I.C.I. Ltd., Plastics Division, Welwyn Garden City, Herts.
Ide, T. & W. Ltd., Glasshouse Fields, London E.1.
Indulex Engineering Co. Ltd., 27 Albemarle Street, London W.1.
Industrial Adhesives Ltd., Chesham, Bucks.
Industrial Floors & Treatments Ltd., 11 Upper Park Road, Bromley, Kent.
International Paints Ltd., Grosvenor Gardens House, London S.W.1.
Ionlite Ltd., 91 Farringdon Road, London E.C.1.
Isora Illuminating Ceilings Ltd., Bedford Avenue, Slough, Bucks.

Jablo Plastics Industries Ltd., Jablo Works, Waddon, Croydon, Surrey.
Jackson, Henry, (Liverpool) Ltd., Admiral Street, Liverpool 8.
Jayanbee Joinery Ltd., 88 High Street, Uxbridge, Middx.
Jenson & Nicholson Ltd., Jenson House, Stratford, London E.15.
Johnson, H. & R., Ltd., Stoke-on-Trent.

Kautex Ltd., Elstree Way, Elstree, Herts.
Kay & Co. (Engineers) Ltd., Bolton Brass Works, Blackhouse Street, Bolton.

Kelscreen Co. Ltd., Ringwood Works, Ringwood, Hampshire.

Kenyon, William, Ltd., Chaple Field Works, Railway Street, Dukinfield, Cheshire.

K.G. (Plastics) Ltd., Adcroft Street, Stockport, Cheshire.

Kings Plastics Ltd., Redeness Street, Layerthorpe, York.

Kingston (Architectural Craftsman) Ltd., Minster Works, Clough Road, Hull, Yorks.

Knight Electrics (Neon) Ltd., 54 Alsen Road, London N.7.

Knightshades Ltd., Silver Hill Works, Theaklen Drive, St. Leonards-on-Sea, Sussex.

La Breque Engineering Co. Ltd., 116 Canbury Park Road, Kingston, Surrey.

Laconite Ltd., Halfway Green, Walton-on-Thames, Surrey.

Laminated Wood Ltd., Bideford, Devon.

Lawrie, J. & T., Ltd., Clydebank, Glasgow.

Leicester, Lovell & Co. Ltd., North Baddesley, Southampton.

Leon Ellis Manufacturing Co. Ltd., Holland Road, Haverhill, Suffolk.

Lester, A. S., Ltd., 127 Oxford Street, London W.1.

Leyland & Birmingham Rubber Co. Ltd., nr. Preston, Lancs.

Limmer & Trinidad Group of Companies, The, Trinidad Lake House, 232 Vauxhall Bridge Road, London S.W.1.

Linolite Ltd., 118 Baker Street, London W.1., and Malmesbury, Wilts.

Liquid Metal Applicators, Ltd., 24/25 Conduit Street, London W.1.

Liquitile Supply Co. Ltd., The, Kings Ride, Camberley, Surrey.

Liverpool Borax Ltd., Maxwell House, St. Paul's Square, Liverpool 3.

London Sand Blast Decorative Glass Works Ltd., The, Seager Place, Burdett Road, London E.3.

L. & P. Plastics Ltd., Suffolk House, Hawthorn Grove, London S.E.20.

Lumenated Ceilings Ltd., Alliance House, Caxton Street, London S.W.1.

Lusty, W., & Sons Ltd., Empson Street, Bromley-by-Bow, London E.3.

Maison Fittings, 3/5 Washington Street, Liverpool 1.

ManMil Plastics Ltd., Castle Street, Stalybridge, Cheshire.

Marbourn Ltd., Roslyn Works, Roslyn Road, South Tottenham, London N.15.

Marley Tile Co. Ltd., Sevenoaks, Kent.

Marshall, C. & C., Ltd., Ponswood Industrial Estate, St. Leonards, Sussex.

Masonite Ltd., Bevis Marks House, London E.C.3.

Maul, F. W., & Son Ltd., 240 Eastwood Road, Rayleigh, Essex.

Mellowhide Products Ltd., 26/28 Great Portland Street, London W.1.

Melwood Thermoplastics Ltd., Willoughby Road, Harpenden, Herts.

Mentmore Manufacturing Co. Ltd., Six Hills Way, Stevenage, Herts.

Merchant Adventurers Ltd., Hampton Road West, Feltham, Middx.

Metal Box Co. Ltd., The, 37 Baker Street, London W.1.

Microcell Ltd., Jugersoll House, 9 Kingsway House, London W.C.2.

Midland Silicones Ltd., 68 Knightsbridge, London S.W.1.
Milton Engineering Co. Ltd., 126 Clarendon Road, Hyde, Cheshire.
Mitchell, W. A., & Smith Ltd., Mitcham, Surrey.
M.M. Electric Ltd., Wakefield Street, Edmonton, London N.18.
Mobil Chemicals Ltd., West Halkin House, West Halkin Street, London S.W.1.
Monogram Electric, Gatwick Road, Crawley, Sussex.
Monsanto Chemical Co. Ltd., Monsanto House, 10/18 Victoria Street, London S.W.1.
Moon Aircraft Ltd., Clift Works, Box, Wiltshire.
Moore, Harold, & Son Ltd., Bailey Works, Bailey Street, Sheffield 1.
Moseley, David, & Sons Ltd., Chaplefield Works, Ardwick, Manchester 12.
Moto Plastics Ltd., Ponteland, nr. Newcastle-Upon-Tyne.
Muntz & Barwell Ltd., Alexandra Works, West Bromwich, Staffs.

Nairn-Williamson Ltd., Kirkcaldy, Scotland.
National Adhesives Ltd., Slough, Bucks.
Newalls Insulation Co. Ltd., Washington, Co. Durham.
Newdome Ltd., 17 George Street, St. Helens, Lancs.
Newsum, H., & Sons & Co. Ltd., Gainsborough, Lincs.
Nicholls & Clarke Ltd., Niclar House, 3/10 Shoreditch High Street, E.1.
North British Plastics Ltd., Patterson Street, Blaydon-on-Tyne.
North British Rubber Co. Ltd., Castle Mills, Edinburgh 3, also 62 Horsferry Road, London S.W.1.
Northern Plastics Ltd., 86a Manchester Road, Hyde, Cheshire.

Orbex Ltd., Phoenix Mills, Failsworth, nr. Manchester.
Osma Plastics Ltd., Rigby Lane, Dawley Road, Hayes, Middx.

Paniquil (Sales) Ltd., 21 West Ferry Road, London E.14.
Paragon Plastics Ltd., Cross Bank, Balby, Doncaster, Yorks.
Paul, W. H., Ltd., Breaston, Derby,
Peak Displays Ltd., Salisbury Road, Rye Park, Hoddesdon, Herts.
Pearce Signs Ltd., New Cross Road, London S.E.14.
Pechin, F. H. & H. S., Ltd., Spinney Hill Road, Leicester.
Peglers Ltd., Belmont Works, Doncaster.
Perstorp Products (Great Britain) Ltd., 157 High Street, Orpington, Kent.
Petmar Industries Ltd., Greenhill Mills, Batley, Yorks.
Pfizer Ltd., Chemicals Division, Sandwich, Kent.
Phipps Plastics Products Ltd., Dome Works, 244 Bromford Lane, West Bromwich, Staffs.
Phoenix Rubber Co. Ltd., 2K Buckingham Avenue, Trading Estate, Slough.
Phoenix Timber Co. Ltd., The, Froy Island, New Road, Rainham, Essex.
Pickles, Robert, Ltd., Cairo Mill, Burnley, Lancs.
Pilkington's Tiles Ltd., Clifton Junction, nr. Manchester.
Pinchin Johnson & Associates Co. Ltd., 4 Carlton Gardens, London S.W.1.

Plastic Designers Ltd., Cree House, Annexe, 18/20 Creechurch Lane, London E.C.3.

Plastics Marketing Co. Ltd., Buckhurst Avenue, Sevenoaks, Kent.

Plastics & Resins Ltd., The Municipal Airport, Wolverhampton, Staffs.

Plus Lighting Ltd., 79 Wigmore Street, London W.1.

Plycol Ltd., Dundee Road, Trading Estate, Slough, Bucks.

Plysu Sales Ltd., Woburn Sansa, Bletchley, Bucks.

Prestige Furniture Ltd., Harvey Road, Crosley Green, Rickmansworth, Herts.

Prodorite Ltd., Eagle Works, Central Avenue, West Molesey, Surrey.

P. & S. Plastics Ltd., Love Lane Estate, Cirencester, Glos.

Rainham Timber Engineering Co. Ltd., Ferry Lane, Rainham, Essex.

Ranmore Ltd., 104 Maybury Road, Woking, Surrey.

Ranton & Co. Ltd., Rock Works, Commerce Road, Brentford, Middx.

Raydex Ltd., Edward Street, The Parade, Birmingham 1.

Redfern's Rubber Works Ltd., Hyde, Cheshire.

Rediweld Ltd., 25/27 Kelvin Way, Crawley, Sussex.

Redland Tiles Ltd., Castle Gate, Reigate, Surrey.

Reeves & Sons Ltd., Lincoln Road, Enfield, Middx.

Reinforced Plastic Developments, Middle Street, Shere, Surrey.

Revo Electric Co. Ltd., Tipton, Staffs.

Robbins Linoleum Ltd., 490/2 Wallisdown Road, Bournemouth.

Robin Plastics Ltd., Meadowfield, Ponteland, Newcastle-Upon-Tyne.

Robinson (Fibres) Ltd., Henry, Stewkins Foundry, Stewkins Road, nr. Stourbridge, Worcs.

Rollene Plastics Ltd., Holmer Road, Hereford.

Rubberoid Co. Ltd., The, 1/19 New Oxford Street, London W.C.1.

Rylands Brothers Ltd., Warrington.

Safety Tread Ltd., The, Dace Road, London E.3.

St. Albans Rubber Co. Ltd., The Camp, St. Albans, Herts.

Scholes, G. H., & Co. Ltd., Wylex Works, Wythenshaw, Manchester.

Scott Bader Co. Ltd., Wollaston, Wellingborough, Northants.

Sealocrete Products Ltd., Atlantic Works, Hythe Road, London N.W.10.

Secomatic Ltd., Western Road, Bracknell, Berks.

Shanks & Co. Ltd., Barrhead, Renfrewshire.

Sharplin, W. J. Ltd., Middle Lane Works, Hornsey, London N.8.

Shaw Glazed Brick Co. Ltd., Hoddlesdon, nr. Darwin, Lancs.

Shell Chemical Co. Ltd., 170 Piccadilly, London W.1.

Shires & Co. (London) Ltd., Guiseley, Yorks.

Silver Knight Industries Ltd., Barkworth Street, Manchester.

Sissons W. & G., Ltd., St. Mary's Road, Sheffield 2.

Smith & Sons (England) Ltd., Otterspool Way, Watford By-Pass, Watford, Herts.

Smith Meters Ltd., Rowan Road, Streatham Vale, London S.W.16.

Smith & Nephew Ltd., Welwyn Garden City, Herts.

Smith & Walton Ltd., Haltwhistle, Northumberland.
Solignum Ltd., Dagenham Dock, Essex.
Somerfields Ltd., 167 Victoria Street, London S.W.1.
Spicers Ltd., 19 New Bridge Street, London E.C.4.
Splintex Ltd., Nightingale Lane, Hanwell, London W.1.
Stanley Smith & Co. Ltd., Worple Road, Isleworth, Middx.
Statter, J. S., & Co. Ltd., Amersham Common, Bucks.
Steel, J. M., & Co. Ltd., Kern House, 36/38 Kingsway, London W.C.2.
Stewarts & Lloyds Plastics Ltd., St. Peters Road, Huntingdon.
Storey Witty & Co. Ltd., Chesham, Bucks.
Structoplast Ltd., 97 East Street, Epsom, Surrey.
Styrene Products Ltd., Devonshire House, Mayfair Place, Piccadilly, London W.1.
Summers, John, & Son Ltd., Shotton, Chester.
Suntex Safety Glass Industries Ltd., Thorney Lane, Ivor, Bucks.
Surfex Flooring Co. Ltd., Glebeland Road, Camberley, Surrey.
Sutcliffe Ltd., Wood Top, Hebdon Bridge, Yorks.

Tanks & Linings Ltd., Town Wharf, Droitwich, Worcs.
T.C.D. Services Ltd., Black Road, Litherland, Liverpool 21.
Technical Applications Ltd., Valley Works, Monton Road, Eccles, Manchester.
Temec Ltd., Maylands Avenue, Hemel Hempstead.
Tenaplas Ltd., Upper Basildon, nr. Pangbourne, Berks.
Tensile Products Ltd., Willoughby Road, Harpenden, Herts.
Tentest & Co. Ltd., Fiboars House, Oakleigh Gardens, London N.20.
Terrapin Ltd., Bletchley, Bucks.
Thames Plywood Manufacturers Ltd., Harts Lane, Barking, Essex.
Thermo Plastics Ltd., Luton Road Works, Dunstable, Beds.
Thermodare Ltd., 94/98 Petty France, London S.W.1.
Thermotank Plastics Ltd., New House Industrial Estate, Lanarkshire.
Thorn Electrical Industries Ltd., 105 Judd Street, London W.C.1.
Tinsley Wire Industries Ltd., Sheffield Road, Sheffield.
Tough Plastics Ltd., Common Lane, Culcheth, nr. Warrington, Lancs.
Tragacine Adhesives, Kirkstall Road, Leeds 3.
Tretol Ltd., Tretol House, The Hyde, London N.W.9.
Tretol-Servicised Ltd., 2 Caxton Street, London S.W.1.
Troman Bros. Ltd., Highlands Road, Shirley, Solihull, Warwick.
Troughton & Young (Lighting) Ltd., Wansdown Place, London S.W.6.
Turner Brothers Asbestos Co. Ltd., Rochdale, Lancs.
Tyrad Electric Ltd., 452 Fulham Road, London S.W.6.
Tysons (Contractors) Ltd., Liverpool.

U.A.M. Group of Companies, The, Tolpits, Watford, Herts.
Union Glue & Gelatine Co. Ltd., Cransley Works, Garrett Street, London E.C.1.

United Coke & Chemicals Co. Ltd., Orgreave Works, P.O. Box 136, Handsworth, Sheffield 13.
United Ebonite & Lorival Ltd., Little Lever, Bolton, Lancs.
Uni-Tubes Ltd., 197 Knightsbridge, London S.W.7.
Universal Laminated Plastics Ltd., 184 Royal College Street, London N.W.1.

Vacform Plastics Ltd., Pelsall Road, Brownhills, Walsall, Staffs.
V.C. Panels Ltd., Leybourne Wharf, Horton Bridge Road, West Drayton, Middx.
Venesta Manufacturing Ltd., West Street, Erith, Kent.
Venus Packaging Ltd., Lower Middleton Street, Ilkeston, Derby.

Wade, Gabriel & English Ltd., Southampton.
Walker, James, & Co. Ltd., Woking, Surrey.
Wallington, Weston & Co. Ltd., Vallis Mills, Frome, Somerset.
Walsh, S. &. J., (Plastics) Ltd., St. Lawrence Hill, Great Harwood, Blackburn, Lancs.
Walters, Austin, & Sons Ltd., Agnes Road, Old Trafford, Manchester 16.
Ward & Co. (Lathes) Ltd.
Wardle, Bernard, (Everflex) Ltd., Peblig Mill, Caernarvon, N. Wales.
Watson, H. A., & Co. Ltd., 448 Derby House, Exchange Buildings, Liverpool 2.
Wednesbury Tube Co. Ltd., The, Bilston, Staffs.
Wellington Tube Works Ltd., Great Bridge, Tipton, Staffs.
Welwyn Plastics (1955) Ltd., Wellite Works, Woodside Road, Welwyn North, Herts.
Wembley Fibreglass & Plastics Ltd., Manor Farm Road, Alperton, Wembley.
Williamson, James, & Sons Ltd., Lune Mills, Lancaster, Lancs.
Willmotts Ltd., Swan Lane, Evesham, Worcs.
Witter, Thos., & Co. Ltd., Chorley, Lancs.
Wokingham Plastics Ltd., Denton Road, Wokingham, Berks.
Wragby Plastics Ltd., Wragby, nr. Lincoln.
Wraithe Bros. Ltd., 76 Nuttall Street, Ewood Park, Blackburn, Lancs.
Wundabath Products Ltd., Ashfield Works, Monsall Street, Manchester 9.

Yale & Towne Ltd., Willenhall, Staffs.
Yorkshire Imperial Plastics Ltd., P.O. Box 166, Leeds.
Young, S. G., No. 1 Factory, Byrford Road, Byrford.

SUBJECT INDEX

ABS Pipes 161
"Accoflex" tiles 26
"Accotile" tiles 26
Acoustic ceiling tiles 133
— pyramids 134
— tiles, bonding of 277
— — "Melinex" covered 135
Acoustic tile suppliers 134
"Aerolite" 287
Adhesives 268
"Alkafloats" 199
"Altro" hessian-backed flooring 33
"Amtico" tiles 27
"Arborite" laminates 89
"Arlon" tiles 26
"Aspect" profile pvc 118, 154

Ball valves 197
"Barclay" rainwater goods 154
Bathroom furniture 232
Baths, fitting of 207
— "Perspex" 207
— "Tufolene" 200
Bending, pipes 168
Blinds, Venetian, plastic 108
Boards, bonding of 277
— plastic faced 96
— plastic faced, fixing 98
"Bostik" 276
Bottle traps 177
Box beams 290
Buildings, "Fibreglass" 285
"Bulgomme Silence" floors 32

"Cascalite", polyester roof lights 117
"Casco" glues 289
"Cascoset" 280
Ceilings, acoustic tiles 133
— finishes 133
— finishes, hardboard 133
— polystyrene louvres 132
— translucent, polystyrene 132
— translucent, pvc 130
— translucent, suppliers 130
Ceiling tiles, foamed 121
Cementing 171
Certite 264
"Chequerplast" floors 53
Cisterns 197
Cladding, plastic-coated aluminium 101
— pvc-coated steel 103
— roofs 119
— wall, polyester 101
— wall, pvc 101
Coating, plastic, pipes 179
Coil sizes, pipes 185
Concrete, additives 246
— curing 245
Conduit, pvc 231
"Corlon", pvc sheet 79

Corolux, pvc profile 118
"Corroplast" laminated 119
"Coxdomes", pvc 114
"Crestaflex" pvc tiles 26

"Decopon" laminates 89
Dimensions, polythene pipes 183
— pvc pipes 190
Dome lights 113
Door furniture 231
Doors, plastic 102
Drainers, "Perspex" 206
Ducting, coated 16

Eave filler blocks 125
"Epoweld" epoxy floors 60
Epoxies, chemical resistance 255
Epoxy floors 53
— paints 61, 252
— pipes 182
— protection 224
— resins, general 8
"Evokote" epoxy floors 61
"Evostik" adhesives 271, 275, 278
— sealing compound 261
Expansion, rainwater goods 146

"Farmiloe" sealants 261
Fence, plastic-covered, suppliers 108
Fencing, metal, coated 16, 107
"Fibreglass" buildings 285
— chemical properties 222
— products, general 8
"Filon" polyester roof lights 116
Filtration, with foams 212
Fittings, electrical 231
— pipes 174
— rainwater goods 148
"Flomaster" siphons 199
Floor heating, electric 66
— sealants 264
Flooring, metal, coated 16
— products, bonding of 277
Floors, abrasion resistance 39, 66
— alkalinity test for 52
— antistatic 34, 37
— chemical resistance 41
— composition of 36, 55, 63
— epoxy 53
— epoxy, application 58
— fire resistance 38
— foam insulation of 68
— Hypalon 43
— jointless 53, 62
— laying 29, 58
— low temperature properties 39
— maintenance 260
— piggery insulation 70
— polyester 62
— polyester, spraying 64

22

Floors, pvc, manufacturers' details   25
—   pvc-tiled   23
—   rubber   42
—   sheet   31
—   stiletto heel resistance   40
—   synthetic rubber   43
—   technical aspects   35
—   textile-backed   32
—   vinyl cork   31
Flow, in pipes   159
Foam, bonding of   270
Foaming "in situ"   126
"Foamflex" insulation   214
Foam—"Plastylon" pvc flooring   33
Foams, forms   14
—   for plumbing   211
—   general   9
—   insulation of floors   68
—   insulation of roofs   120
—   insulation of walls   107
—   polystyrene   10
—   polyurethanes   10
—   suppliers of   10, 12
"Formica" laminates   90

"Galt" glass   115
"Getalit" laminates   88
Glazing, plastic   103

Handrails, pvc   234
Hardec, melamine-faced board   98
"Holoplast" walls   78, 99
Hose   247
"Houseproud" tiles   25

Illuminated ceilings   130
"Interclad", polyester roofing   116
"Isora" illuminated ceilings   130

Jointing   172
Jointing with ptfe   225
Joints, expansion   173

Kitchen furniture   232

"Laconite", wall boards   97
Lagging with foams   211
—   sets for tanks   201, 213
Laminated buildings, designers   295
—   wood structures   287
Laminates, bonding   275
—   chemical resistance   93
—   for walls   76, 87
—   heat resistance   93
—   machining   94
—   polyester   95
—   technical properties   91
Lavatory basins, "Perspex"   207
—   seats   197
Laying floors   29
Lock mechanisms   232

"Marleycel", ceiling tiles   121
"Marleyclad"   101
"Marleyglaze", pvc roof lights   117

"Marley" floors   32
"Marley", acoustic pyramids   135
—   boards   89
"Marley" laminates   89
—   rainwater goods   151
—   tiles   27
—   wall tiles   85
"Melinex" covered tiles   135
Metals, plastic-coated   16
Mural Florestin, pvc wall covering   81
Mole ploughing   166

Nosing, stair   35
Nylon, coating with   182
—   general   15

Odour exclusion   212
"Oroglas"   6, 202
"Osma" rainwater goods   149

Paints, epoxy   252
Panels, plastic   102
"Pegufelt" floors   32
"Penton", coating with   182
"Perspex", cementing   210
—   general   6, 202
—   machining   209
—   roof lights   112
—   sinks and drainers   206
—   urinals   208
—   wash basins   208
"Perstorp" laminates   91, 101
Phenol glues   287
Phenolics, general   7
Pipes, ABS   163
—   bending   168
—   cementing   171
—   epoxy   182
—   fabrication   168
—   flow in   159
—   installations   164, 167
—   jointing   172
—   jointing with ptfe   225
—   lagging of   213
—   plastic coating   179
—   plastic, general   155
—   pressures in   191, 195
—   pvc, rigid   192
—   screwed joints   192
—   suppliers   188
—   welding   170
Polyester floors   62
—   plumbing products   223
Polyesters, chemical properties   222
—   general   8, 216
"Polyorc" pipes   189
"Polypanol" faced board   96
Polypropylene pipes   160
Polystyrene, general   7
Polythene, coating with   181
—   chemical properties   186
—   general   6
—   pipes   157, 162, 183, 187
"Polyzote" insulation   214
—   roof foam   125

"Poron" insulation   213
Portal frames   291
Pressures, pipes   184
PTFCE, coating with   181
PTFE, general   15, 225
PVC, adhesive type sheets   76
PVC, flexible, bonding of   281
PVC, general   5
PVC glazing products   104
PVC pipes   160, 163, 190
PVC, rigid, chemical resistance of 192, 238
PVC roof lights   117
PVC tiles   25
PVC translucent ceilings   130
PVC wall coverings   79
PVC, wire reinforced   114, 118

Rainwater goods   141
—   —   fittings   148
—   —   fittings   154
—   —   installation   154
—   —   suppliers   155
"Raplag" pipe insulation   215
Resorcinol glues   287
Ridge filler blocks   125
Riser covering   35
Roof lights, "Perspex"   112
—   —   "Perspex" suppliers   113
—   —   polyester   114
—   —   pvc   117
Roofs, "Bitumetal"   119
—   foam insulated   120
"Rymway", rainwater goods   152

Sealants, floor   265
Sealing compounds   260
"Secoseal"   262
"Semflex" tiles   27
Shuttering, plastic   245
Signs, "Perspex"   230
Silicone, water repellants   255
Sinks, "Perspex"   206
—   polypropylene   202
Siphons   197
Skirting, pvc   84
"Stelvetite", plastic-coated steel   103
"Stormur" fabric-backed pvc   81
"Structoplast"   265
"Styrocell" foam for roofs   122
"Styroglue"   271
Suppliers, acoustic tiles   134, 135
—   adhesives   268
—   anti-static floors   33
—   ceiling boards   133
—   continuous pvc floors   31
—   curtain walling   99
—   decorative laminates   88
—   door furniture   231
—   doors   102
—   ducting   240
—   electrical fittings   231
—   electric floor heating   66
—   epoxy floors   59
—   epoxy paints   253

Suppliers, fibreglass/polyester
       products   223
—   flexible pvc coverings   79
—   foam filtration   212
—   foams   12
—   glazing products   105
—   kitchen and bathroom
       furniture   232
—   lighting fittings   229
—   lock mechanisms   232
—   metal panelling   102
—   nosings   35
—   odour sealing products   212
—   "Perspex" baths   206
—   "Perspex" fittings   205
—   "Perspex" roofing   113
—   "Perspex" signs   230
—   "Perspex" sinks and
       drainers   205
—   "Perspex" urinals   205
—   pipe fittings   149, 174, 179
—   pipe lagging   214
—   plastic coatings   182
—   plastic-faced boards   96
—   plumbing fittings   197
—   polyester floors   65
—   polyester laminates   95
—   polythene film   243
—   polythene pipes   188
—   ptfe tapes   225
—   pvc-coated fabrics   81
—   pvc-coated wallpaper   83
—   pvc handrails   234
—   pvc pipes   194
—   pvc tiles   25
—   pvc translucent ceilings   130
—   pvc wire laminates   118
—   quilted pvc   81
—   rainwater goods   155
—   rigid pvc sheets   82
—   risers   35
—   rubber floors   42
—   screens   102
—   sealing compounds   260
—   shuttering   245
—   silicones   256, 257
—   soil goods   155
—   tank lagging sets   213
—   tank liners   225
—   telephone kiosks   240
—   Venetian blinds   108
—   ventilation systems   240
—   ventilators   231
—   wallpaper backings   84
—   wall tiles   85
—   waterstops   265
—   wire fences   107
—   wood glues   287

Tank linings   223
Tanks, foam lagging of   213
Taper plug valves   182
Telephone kiosks   240
"Terrain" ventilation systems   236
"Terrazzite" polyester floors   65

"Tesamoll" adhesive foams 215
Tiles, ceiling, foamed 121
— wall, polystyrene 87
— wall, pvc 85
Traps, bottle 177
"Tretobond" 274, 277

Underlays, polythene 245
"Unilex", polyester roof lights 117
Urea-formaldehyde glues 287
Urinals, "Perspex" 208

Ventilation systems 236
Ventilators, "Perspex" 231
"Verplex" polyester, roof lights 116
"Vertiseal" 263
"Viking" cisterns 197
"Viking Johnson" couplings 172
"Vinylex" floor tiles 26
"Vynide" pvc wall covering 77
"Vynoleum" flooring 33

Wall cladding, polyester 101
— — vinyl 101

Wallpaper, foam-backed 83
— pvc-coated 83
Wall tiles, polystyrene 87
— — pvc 85
— — pvc, fixing 86
Walls, curtain 99
— flexible pvc covering 79
— foam insulation for 107
— laminates for 76, 87
— plastic-faced boards 96
— pvc-coated steel 103
— pvc, fabric backed 80
— pvc stick-on decoration 76
— quilted pvc 81
— rigid pvc covering 81
— sandwich construction 100
— sprayed in types 77, 82
"Warerite" laminates 88
Washbasins, "Perspex" 207
Water repellents 255
Waterstops 265
Weather protection 244
Welding 170
Window frames, plastic, suppliers 106
— — pvc 104

INDEX TO ADVERTISERS

Bakelite Ltd. 300
Beck, Koller & Co. (England) Ltd. 304
Bostik Ltd. 310
B.X. Plastics Ltd. 308

Ciba (A.R.L.) Ltd. 305

Duratube & Wire Ltd. 306

Hartley, V. & N. Ltd. 310
Isora Illuminating Ceilings Ltd. 301
Perstorp Products (Gt. Britain) Ltd. 299
Plastics Marketing Company Ltd. 302
Semtex Ltd. 307
Steel, J.M. & Co., Ltd. 309
Storey, Brothers & Co., Ltd. 303